SURVIVAL

DAVID & CHARLES
Newton Abbot   London

CONTENTS

Editor: Len Cacutt
Designer: John Fitzmaurice

First published 1988
Second impression 1989
Third impression 1990

© Aerospace Publishing Ltd 1988
This edition © Marshall Cavendish Limited 1988

British Library Cataloguing in Publication Data

Survival.
    1. Survival – Manuals
    I. Cacutt, Len
    613.6'9

ISBN 0 7153 9282 4

Printed and bound in Italy
for David & Charles Publishers plc
Brunel House
Newton Abbot, Devon

8 Introduction

10 CHAPTER ONE
THE PROTECTION RACKET

12 Body Armour

16 Special Forces Personal Protection

20 Personal Camouflage and Concealment

24 Camouflaging Your Vehicle

28 Surviving Killer Fires

32 CHAPTER TWO
THE BATTLEGROUND

34 Contaminated Battlefield

38 Surviving a Nuclear Strike: 1

42 Surviving a Nuclear Strike: 2

46 CHAPTER THREE
HUMPING IT ALL ABOUT

48 Fighting Footwear

52 Personal Load Carrying

56 Combat Jacket and Webbing

60 Equipped for Battle

64 Preparing Your Load

68 Marching Order

72 CHAPTER FOUR
IF . . . .

74 Evasion and Capture

78 Under Interrogation

82 P.O.W.

86 Escape, Rescue and Release

90 Escape and Evasion

   in Hostile Territory

94 Escape and Evasion Kit

98 Urban Evasion

102 Jungle Evasion

106 Surviving the Dogs of War

110 Snakes, Crocs and Other Varmints

114 Crossing a River

118 CHAPTER FIVE
THE ART OF SURVIVING

120 Shelter for Survival

124 Combating the Climate

128 Travel in the Arctic

132 Jungle Survival

136 Making Fire: 1

140 Making Fire: 2

144 Beware the Unseen Enemy

148 CHAPTER SIX
THE INNER SOLDIER

150 Scoff That Ratpack!

154 The Search for Water

158 Purifying Water

162 Flint Tools

166 Alternatives to Stone

170 Hunting With Spears

174 Choosing Your Survival Knife

178 Using Your Survival Knife

182 Trapping Animals for Food

186 Index

INTRODUCTION

Survival – it is one of man's strongest instincts and one that he shares with the rest of the animal kingdom. When faced with the alternatives of survival or probable extinction a person can be capable of the most extreme actions, things he or she would not dream of doing in normal circumstances, and there are innumerable true stories of this to be found as far back in history as one can investigate. No doubt, even before the period of written history began early man had exactly the same sense of self-preservation, and if Charles Darwin's evolutionary theory is to be understood it explains why man has lasted this long!

Just a single example from a host of possibles will make the point about what a determined person can do when survival or extinction faces him. The story of Captain William Bligh, RN, of HMS *Bounty* is well known, and he was absolutely not the tyrant some fictional accounts have accused him of being. His ship was on a peaceful botanical mission to the South Seas in 1789 and whatever the reason for his being put in that 'open boat' and set adrift with a few shipmates in the wastes of the Pacific he was up to that awful challenge.

Bligh was in the classic survival situation; to save his life and the lives of his few shipmates, he had no option but to get that small craft across hundreds of miles of the Pacific Ocean – and he did. He navigated his small boat 3618 miles across the open sea to Timor, a Javanese island, taking three long, desperate months in the process.

The soldier or civilian of today can be faced with the problem of survival, although perhaps not on such a monumental scale as Bligh. The fighting man now operates in some of the most inhospitable places to be found on this earth. Suitable battlefields cannot always be selected beforehand, for instance it is hardly likely that Britain would have chosen those bleak, far-off Falklands for their battle against the aggressive Argentinian forces, but they were there and there was no one else to establish her territorial rights and push the invaders back into the sea at considerable loss.

In SURVIVAL we treat the subject from the point of view of the serving man, and so the first subject is a straight throwback to the medieval times and those knights in shining armour. Their helmet, body and leg armour was a protection against sword-thrust, lance, arrow and mace. It was heavy and cumbersome and the warhorse had to have the strength and size of today's carthorse to cope with it all, but it was necessary in order to avoid being un-horsed and hacked to pieces while lying comparatively helpless on the ground. Chainmail was also an excellent defence against sword and arrow before the invention of gunpowder in the East gave projectiles enormous penetration power.

The 'tin-hat' of World War One makes the soldiers of the time immediately recognisable and those helmets saved many lives, but the body armour of today goes much further. It is able to stop rounds of some calibres although not all, but even without its penetrating the impact on armour of a large-calibre small-arms round will knock a man over, breathless, and put him out of useful action for a time.

Flak-jackets are a commonplace item of military clothing and equipment and they are very comforting in urban areas such as Northern Ireland where terrorist snipers can be active. One instance of this records how a British soldier while serving in that theatre had his life saved. His flak-jacket was hit from behind by a terrorist round. The high-velocity bullet, probably from an Armalite, struck the man's protective clothing at the rear and was stopped by the ceramic plate built into it. This soldier's life was spared at the expense of a badly bruised back and the discomfort of sleeping face-down for a few days.

Not all body armour is suitable for active battlefield use. The steel-nerved and extremely highly expert bomb-disposal teams, sometimes working in close proximity to large quantities of unstable, home-made and boobytrapped high-explosive, need as much protection as science and technology can provide for them and their armour is specially designed to deflect blast away from the head and body. It would be too cumbersome and not much use on the battlefield.

The Special Forces, too, require a wide range of complex protective body armour and – not simply because the cost of training one of these men is said to be £1 million – they employ their own specially designed armour, called the Integrated Personal Protective System and it is alleged to be the most effective yet produced.

While bodies need protection, both men and military vehicles need camouflage as well. One remembers the very distinctive zig-zag camouflage painted onto World War Two warships, which effectively broke up the ship's silhouette when seen broadside on and confused anyone trying to estimate her course, but the introduction of radar which was not fooled by such visual trickery soon took over from the crow's nest lookouts. Camouflage, however, is still important and it is a subject into which a great deal of thought has gone and in SURVIVAL it provides a useful and interesting feature.

The unimaginable threat of nuclear war has perhaps receded somewhat since the thankful signing of the treaties between the major Powers in late 1987, but battlefield weaponry is still capable of using limited range nuclear weapons and it is unlikely that agreement could be reached on the total disposal of all conventional weapons. For one reason, it would not solve the contentious matter of the severe numerical superiority of the Warsaw Pact armies in men and AFVs over those of the NATO countries.

It means, therefore, that the effect of a nuclear weapon strike on a battlefield must be part of the modern soldier's anticipation and he must be prepared for it and know how to take as much avoiding action as possible should that malevolent, lethal mushroom cloud be created. The effects and parameters of blast, light, heat and radiation damage are important enough to have two full articles devoted to the discussion of the possible actions he must take.

If there is one thing an infantryman learns very early on in his training as a soldier is that while the personnel carrier will transport him to the fighting zone, sooner or later he will be on his feet – and carrying everything he needs to live and fight for the next few hours or days, perhaps longer. And this is where the importance of top-class combat boots enters the arena, they are vital pieces of equipment and a great deal of thought has gone into the matter. That old, classic 'ammunition boot' both respected and hated by the soldier of World War One, has long gone, apart, perhaps, from the parade ground.

Those fighting men who 'humped' huge personal loads and their weapons and ammunition over morasse and bog all through an icy winter's long night in the Falklands to get to grips with the enemy did so because their self-discipline and long training had toughened them to a condition where they were capable of accomplishing the job. Those men could not have carried all that gear, though, had it not been for proper clothing and webbing designed to do the job and so the importance of webbing is stressed in these pages.

To a POW who has managed to get away from his captors survival is a very immediate problem. The odds stacked against him are considerable, for not only must he remain free, he must eat, get some kind of rest, keep a reasonable appearance, and do his best to make for friendly territory. To add to his problems the local population will probably speak a foreign language. A full article here illustrates and discusses the kind of difficulties an escapeé will face and how best he can surmount them.

Survival does not end there. The dangers and perils awaiting in jungle and arctic waste are legion and each is treated in turn, as are the living dangers to life, the animals that kill through hunger or in defence of their territory. In SURVIVAL one can understand why soldiering is truly a matter of the survival of the fittest.

CHAPTER ONE

THE PROTECTION RACKET

Today's soldiers have armoured clothing available to them which at first consideration seems to have bearings on the complicated medieval armour that was worn by knights in the days of chivalry. But whatever the connections with the past, the armour of today saves lives and gives the fighting man some confidence when bullets and shrapnel are flying about.

Whether he is in territory known to contain a population harbouring malevolent sections, manning a road block through which it is very possible armed terrorists might soon try to pass, or investigating a car thought to be boobytrapped with high-explosive, personal armour gives a soldier some measure of comfort. He does not feel quite so exposed. This chapter opens with a discussion of body armour and it contains some descriptions of the range of equipment available to members of the armed and security forces.

For members of the ultra-elite Special Forces the nature of the often dangerous operations requires that they have effective body protection. Ballistic helmets, for instance, protect their heads from various-calibre small-arms fire as well as carrying the means of communication between them and other members of the team, but from head to toe, including modular tactical armour, very special personal protective clothing gives these forces every chance of surviving a close-quarter fire fight.

A 'walking bush' might convey a comic impression in one of those TV slapstick comedies, but in bush country one could walk right up to a 'bush' without having the slightest indication that it harboured a heavily armed soldier, who could earily have taken you out long before you got anywhere near. Being able to merge into whichever kind of terrain you are in is an important facility for any clandestine operations behind enemy lines, and this chapter includes hints and tips about how to do it.

It is possible to make pretty well any vehicle virtually invisible from the air and from, say, 200 yards if a few basic elements of camouflage theory are followed. Netting is always included in every military vehicle's standard operational equipment but the local vegetation, into which the AFV must merge, is very important and must be used for the final touches. How to do this – and how not to – forms part of this interesting section of chapter one.

We deal next in this chapter with fire. Man needs it, it is a necessity of life in many parts of the world and without it industry could not survive to provide munitions and military equipment. But the fire kills as surely as the best-aimed bullet and one of its allies is panic. An article here discusses the reasons why fires start, which fires can be fought with water and, more importantly, which fire-fighting attempts act only to spread the flames. And there are chemicals which burst into flames when water comes into contact with them. This opening chapter in the book introduces the subject, but in the following chapters there are many more sides to survival.

Modern body armour is designed with different combat situations in mind.

Protect yourself with Body Armour

Like any clothing, body armour has to be chosen according to the nature of the threat. You wouldn't take a parka to the desert, or shorts to the Arctic; in the same way, body armour has been configured according to the climate of violence you will be operating in. Choose the wrong armour and you won't be hot or cold – you'll be dead.

Vital organs

In essence, armour is either 'soft' or 'hard' and comes in different lengths and sizes. A mix of soft and hard armour gives protection to vital organs like the heart against high-velocity rounds, while soft armour protects against fragments and low-velocity ammunition.

Bomb protection

At the extreme end of hard armour is the Explosive Ordnance Device suit (EOD), designed for bomb disposal teams. This consists of a helmet, and body, leg and arm protection in a mix of hard and soft armour. There is a breast plate in hard ceramic material which has a curve designed to deflect blast away from the wearer's face. A cooling system keeps the wearer comfortable and prevents the clear armoured visor from fogging. The major problem with this type of body armour is that the wearer must leave his hands unprotected so that he can handle the explosive to defuse it.

Bulletproof accessories

One of the lighter and more discreet forms of protection is a bullet-proof clip board, which will stop hits by weapons such as 9-mm .45 and .357 Magnum pistols and shotgun blasts. One of the problems is that the user's hands are exposed, and if a handle is fitted on the other side it looks like a shield and the value of concealment is lost. Bulletproof briefcases are also available.

The average body armour, however, is soft and is designed to cover the wearer from neck to hips, leaving his arms free to handle a weapon, and not weighing too much; three to five kilograms on average. It may include pockets at the back and front to take additional hard armour plating to upgrade the standard of protection.

Zip problems

Jackets dating back to the Vietnam War that have now come onto the commercial market offer protection against low-velocity ammunition, but not against 5.56-mm rounds. They have a zip and press stud closure, and British soldiers wearing similar jackets in Northern Ireland were instructed to use only the press studs – if the clothing caught fire the nylon in the jacket would melt and the zip would fuse solid.

The pattern of jacket adopted by the US Marines in Vietnam had a band of material at the bottom with eyelets from which equipment could be hung.

The US Forces have used body armour on a regular basis since World War II. Here US Air Force security troops watch an airstrike on VC positions outside the perimeter of Tan Son Nhut. They are wearing the old style flak jacket which can now be bought commercially and cheaply.

Above right: US Marines in action at Khe Sanh. Their flak jackets have a pad to stop the rifle butt slipping off the shoulder and attachment points for webbing along the bottom. These early armour vests were heavy and opened at the front with a zip and press studs.

Vital protection

Artillery remains the 'grim reaper' of the modern battlefield, causing more casualties than any other weapon. In the major conflicts since World War II roughly two-thirds of all combat casualties have been due to the steel fragments produced by exploding shells, bombs and mines. Body armour can offer considerable protection against otherwise lethal shell splinters and many armies now issue it as standard equipment.

Head protection
In Vietnam it was estimated that if troops had kept their helmets on more regularly admissions to the neurosurgical centre would have been reduced by a third. Moral: don't make a habit of taking your helmet off when you think it's quiet.

Searching an enemy position
Dying soldiers have often been known to lie in their position clutching a grenade with the pin removed, holding the fly off lever down with their body. Troops fighting through the position turn the body over and the grenade explodes, so watch out!

Booby trap
Here, members of a US squad have captured an enemy position only to suffer casualties from a grenade trap. If you see a grenade thrown or hear someone shout 'Grenade!' you should take cover immediately.

A BM21 multiple rocket launcher of the Iraqi army unleashes a storm of explosive and steel splinters on Iranian positions. These weapons are widely used by the Warsaw Pact, making the issue of flak jackets to NATO troops a very sound idea.

The result: wounded Iranian soldiers taken prisoner are suffering from multiple fragmentation wounds. Body armour can protect your chest cavity from otherwise fatal damage; wounds to this area are more likely to kill you than hits to peripheral areas.

Bullet wounds
The vest offers a high degree of protection against pistol and sub-machine gun bullets which travel at a much lower velocity than a rifle round. However, although the vest cannot guarantee to stop a rifle bullet, it can convert an otherwise fatal wound into a less serious injury.

US body armour
The current issue US Army flak vest seen here is a very solid piece of kit made from Kevlar ballistic cloth. It forms part of PASGT (Personal Armour System Ground Troops) together with the Kevlar helmets.

PASGT helmet
Laminated with 18 layers of Kevlar armour, the helmet is designed to stop or deflect shell fragments and low powered bullets. It is substantially stronger than the old steel helmet.

Flak jackets
Your flak jacket can mean the difference between life and death. The vest protects your vital organs from shell splinters, pistol and SMG rounds and, in this case, the blast and fragmentation produced by a grenade trap.

Grenade Immediate Action
If there is no cover available, hit the ground and roll away from the grenade. Do not try to run to cover: if it goes off while you are standing up you are more likely to be injured.

Layered armour
Fragments may penetrate the outer layers of ballistic fabric but are slowed down by multiple layers. Only a large chunk of shell or a very close range blast will have enough velocity left to injure you after it has penetrated the armour.

The Israelis in the 1982 invasion of Lebanon took this further by fitting ammunition and equipment pouches directly to their flak jackets. This scheme makes sure that ammunition and jacket are always together, and spreads the load evenly across the shoulders and back.

Modern jackets have a Velcro closure, normally under the arms. This makes alteration for different-sized wearers much easier, leaves no weak lines at the front of the jacket, and allows it to be removed quickly if the wearer needs medical treatment.

Neck protection has become a priority in body armour design – current US and Israeli jackets feature a high collar; when worn with a ballistic helmet this increases the protection for the very vulnerable head and neck. Future developments will certainly include eye protection.

Discreet protection

Body armour does not have to be obvious. Some patterns are designed to be worn under combat jackets: this has a number of advantages, because in a politically sensitive area 'flak jackets' worn by police or soldiers are inclined to raise the emotional temperature. Also, you will be able to get at the equipment stored in your combat jacket. The disadvantage of discreet protection is that it does not cover your neck or reach down to cover your kidneys and lower abdomen.

The ultimate in discreet body armour are jackets and vests designed for covert police wear or VIP protection. These can be worn under a shirt and are normally in white. Others are cut like a windbreaker or blouson and are in neutral colours, and so can be worn with casual clothes without attracting attention.

Non-standard wearers

Not all wearers are a standard size. Military protective clothing can be adjusted using the Velcro closures and comes in small, medium and large, but police or civilian clothing needs to be properly sized. One US company has a properly-cut vest to accommodate a bust for female police officers to wear under a shirt. In Northern Ireland an enterprising company produces a wide range of clothing including car coats, corduroy jackets, and even a quilted body warmer.

Bullet shock

There are mixed opinions about the trauma that the body suffers when it takes the shock from a bullet hitting body armour. Some people maintain that the function of body armour is to stop hits by small arms; others say that

An EOD engineer in full protection minus helmet looks on as a tertiary explosive (fertiliser and diesel oil) is shovelled out of the boot of a car bomb. The boot was blown open with a remote controlled tractor, Goliath. There are two types of body armour in the photo, two soldiers are wearing the current issue INIBA vest which is worn underneath your combat jacket.

Almost any article can be lined with bullet-proof material. Bullet-proof clip boards are in service with a number of police forces, but they do not protect your hands.

Combat experience often leads armies to adopt body armour; this is the Israeli system of load-carrying armour. Even the Soviets, not previously very concerned over the lives of their conscripts, are now issuing body armour to their units occupying Afghanistan.

this is not enough and that the shock and bruising from hits can cause internal damage to the wearer. They advocate a 'trauma pad' – in effect, padding inside the armour – which dissipates the shock. One soldier who took a hit from an Armalite while serving in Northern Ireland survived because the round hit the ceramic plate on the back of his armour, but the bruise was considerable and he was unable to sleep on his back for several days afterwards.

Foot armour

Armour can extend to the feet: US jungle boots in Vietnam had a plate in the sole to protect the wearer from punji stakes, the sharpened bamboos that would penetrate the foot of an unwary soldier. A modern commercially-marketed boot has Kevlar material in the uppers, though this is intended as protection against indus-

Left and inset: The forerunner of the INIBA vest was a simple flak vest intended to protect you from shell splinters rather than a sniper's bullet. Inset is the next in line, with added rubber shoulder pads to stop the butt slipping off your shoulder.

trial injury.

Nomex fire retardant fabric is not regarded as 'armour', but it is a valuable addition to a soldier's protection. Nomex clothing is now used in flying overalls, tank crew clothing and even in gloves. The Israelis issued large amounts of it to their soldiers in 1982 when they invaded Lebanon. Interestingly, it is one type of protection that can be bought second hand in surplus stores, or even unissued through mail order firms.

Protected flying

US Air Force flying jackets (but not the ones with reversible orange linings) are made from Nomex, and with gloves would give the wearer protection against fuel-generated fires such as those in helicopters or vehicles. Even leather gloves can save your hands in a flash fire, and as long as they do not prevent you from using a weapon they are a simple but sensible precaution.

Special Forces Personal Protection

It now costs around £1 million to train a Special Forces trooper, so any money spent on keeping him alive is money well spent. The trouble is that such personnel are prone to all types of attacks and aggressive or defensive counter-measures, so it is difficult to decide exactly what to protect an individual against.

The result has been a wide array of protective clothing with each item proof against something or other, and designed in isolation from anything

A positive-entry situation: in a hostage rescue you do not have a choice, you may have to go in. Faced with an increasingly sophisticated terrorist threat, Special Forces have developed a wide range of kit to meet this threat.

Helmet
The National Plastics AC 100/1 ballistic composite helmet provides an advanced head protection system for special forces. It is made up of layers of ballistic cloth and will protect the head from a variety of small arms fire as well as blows.

Headset
The Davies Communications CT 100 ear protection and communication harness has a body-worn microphone and switching unit with a large press-to-talk button, which can be operated by either hand.

Respirator
The Avon Industrial Polymers SF 10 respirator features high levels of protection against incapacitants and low breathing resistance. You can use two canisters or one canister and an air bottle.

Body armour
The Armourshield REV777/25 contoured front and back ceramic composite plates, layered Kevlar and blunt trauma shield will defeat high velocity rifle fire.

Heckler & Koch MP5 sub-machine gun
The closed bolt design is inherently more accurate than the more simple open bolt models.

Fire-retardant suit
This is the GD Specialist Supplies fire retardant body protection system.

Ballistic helmet

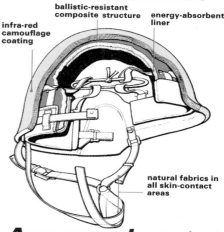

ballistic-resistant composite structure

infra-red camouflage coating

energy-absorbent liner

natural fabrics in all skin-contact areas

Armoured vest

The Armourshield GPV/25 armoured vest is capable of absorbing a bullet's energy so successfully that the wearer will be able to react. It is a combination of soft Kevlar and hard ceramic plates.

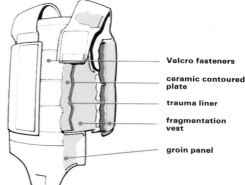

Velcro fasteners

ceramic contoured plate

trauma liner

fragmentation vest

groin panel

else. This often means that when all the various items are worn together they do not integrate: NBC respirator face seals may be broken when a helmet is put on, weapons cannot be sighted through respirator lenses, bulletproof garments interfere with movement, and so on.

This integration problem has been overcome by five British companies which have got together and developed a protective outfit that is proof against most threats to special forces personnel. It is known as the Integrated Personal Protection System (IPPS), and has been tested by Special Forces. The IPPS is not just a design venture: it has been developed using all manner of practical combat experience, and the result is a superb protective outfit.

Starting from the skin outwards, the basis of the IPPS is a set of carbonised viscose 'long john' underwear. The material is light and comfortable to

wear but is flame-retardant, as is the main overgarment, a one-piece assault suit also made from carbon fibre material, in this case Nomex 3. The suit incorporates flame retardant pads at the elbows and knees, allowing the wearer to crawl safely over hot surfaces such as aircraft engines during hijack hostage rescue missions.

Incidentally, the suits are very similar to those being worn by tanker crews currently operating in the Persian Gulf, but theirs are coloured bright orange; the IPPS is usually black.

Flame-retardant

Over the flame-retardant garments the IPPS features a bullet-proof waistcoat made of soft fragmentation armour and with a built-in trauma liner to absorb shock. Without this liner internal injuries could occur even if a bullet is stopped by the

Special Forces personnel prepare to storm through a doorway. Experience has shown that the third man to enter a building is in the greatest need of body armour because he stands the highest chance of being hit by enemy fire.

17

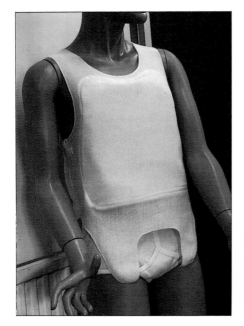

This Armourshield Ultra Light Undervest concealable body armour with blunt trauma shield weights just over a kilogram: little more than the weight of a bag of sugar.

Armourshield FW 25 TF: This is a dual-purpose body armour designed to stop both low velocity fragments and a high-velocity rifle round fired at three metres. The ceramic plates are specially held off the chest to allow unrestricted breathing.

armour. The soft armour protection is enhanced by inserting curved ceramic plates at the front and back; these can stop 0.357 Magnum bullets at a range of three metres. A groin panel can be added if required.

Further armoured protection is provided by a special helmet known as the AC 100/1, a National Plastics product made from layers of a Kevlar-type material. This can withstand the impact of a 9-mm bullet at close range, and to ensure the wearer's head is not knocked off by the impact, the helmet uses a bullet trauma lining.

An optional fire-retardant leather waistcoat can be worn over the suit and armour protection, and is used to carry special equipment such as an assault axe, stun grenades or rescue knife, all in specially-fitted pockets or leather loops.

These days some form of respirator is worn operationally by most special forces, so the IPPS uses a specially-developed respirator known as the SF10, a variant of the Avon S10 used by the British Army. The SF10 has an internal microphone, but its most prominent features are the outset darkened eyepieces. These have been incorporated to cut down the flash produced by stun grenades or other bright lights. The SF10 can also be fitted with its own air supply from an air bottle carried in the leather waistcoat or an extra filter canister can be worn.

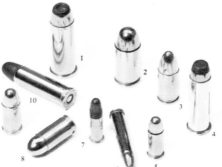

Above: The threat, (1) 44 Magnum; (2) .45 ACP; (3) 9-mm; (4) .357 magnum; (5) 6.35-mm; (6) .22 Magnum; (7) .22LR; (8) 9-mm Short; (9) 7.65-mm (10) .38 Special.

Left: This shows the effect of a .357 Magnum fired at Plasticine protected by a vest with and without a blunt trauma shield.

Assault team

The respirator microphone connects into an assault team communications harness known as the CT 100, which has a chest or respirator microphone and press-to-talk switches located on the wrist or anywhere handy. The communications system uses electronic earphones that are designed to cut out sound produced by grenades or gunfire (i.e. high air pressure) but which allow all other sounds to be heard normally. The earphones are connected into the communication harness to allow the wearer to listen in to a team command net.

The main feature of the IPPS is that all the components are designed to work together. For instance, the IPPS helmet does not interfere with the respirator seal, and the ear defenders fit under helmet ear lobes that have been

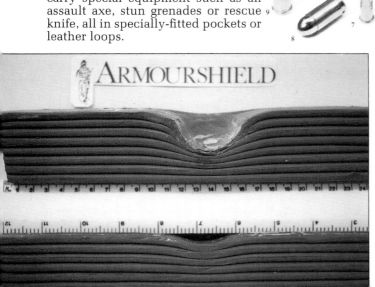

designed for just that purpose. The darkened eyepieces permit almost any weapon to be aimed and fired without difficulty, and even though the protective waistcoat can stop most fragments or bullets it still allows complete freedom of movement.

Belt kit

A belt carrying combat or other gear can be worn, and an abseiling harness has been developed for use with the IPPS, which provides an indication of the degree of movement available.

The IPPS is not cheap, but considering the cost of training special forces personnel and the fact that their operational missions are very often 'one-offs' where not everything can be anticipated, the costs involved appear to be well worth consideration. Perhaps its most important 'selling feature' is that it has been designed and developed by people who know only too well the problems involved with such equipment and the situations in which the IPPS is used.

Right: The US solution – high-risk modular tactical armour developed by Point Blank with LAPD SWAT units (Special Weapons And Tactics). The armour has a number of separate load-bearing removable pouches. Construction is of Kevlar with pockets for up-armour plates.

The Iranian Embassy Siege. In this situation you need a high level of protection whilst still being able to move fast and use your weapons; this requires an exceptional level of fitness.

Above and right: Ballistic protective shield. This will protect against bursts of sub-machine gun fire, high powered handguns, shotgun blasts and grenades.

Personal Camouflage and Concealment

Good camouflage and fieldcraft are almost as important as good marksmanship — in fact, a well-camouflaged man who is a poor shot will probably survive longer than the badly-concealed sniper. In an escape and evasion operation, camouflage and concealment are paramount. The hunted man will con-

Remember your legs when adding local vegetation to break up your shape, but don't add too much foliage here or you will trip up.

When you sort out your camouflage leave your rifle resting on your webbing, out of the mud. Make sure the foliage you use matches the area you will be moving through.

ceal himself and sleep by day, and move by night – and here even the cover of darkness will not negate the importance of camouflage.

Personal camouflage (PC) has certain simple rules that will defeat the most obvious sensor on the battlefield – the human eye.

Shape

Your helmet, web equipment, rifle and other kit such as manpack radios have a clear, often square shape – and there are no squares in nature. Break up straight lines by the addition of scrim – neutral-coloured strips of cloth in browns and greens. Camouflaged elasticated pack covers exist, and these can be stretched over packs and radios.

Rifles and LMG/GPMGs have a clear shape, and are often black. Though scrim can be used to break up their line, it is not advisable to fix it to the stock – it may slip when you are firing and by shifting your grip cause you to shoot inaccurately. It is better to cover the weapon with camouflaged tape, or

even green masking tape (tape is a useful aid to PC – see **'Sound'**)

A discarded vehicle camouflage net is a very useful source of camouflage for PC. It will have nylon 'scrim' that has been treated to give an infra-red reflection similar to vegetation. Fixed to the back of packs and webbing, or in the netting on a helmet, it breaks up shape very well and enhances the chlorophyll-based infra-red camouflage treatment. (see also **'Silhouette'**).

Shine

In the old days of brass buckles, soldiers were told these should be allowed to grow dull, or be covered with masking tape. However, most web equipment has plastic or alloy fittings that do not reflect – but there are still shiny surfaces even on a modern battlefield.

Binoculars and compass surfaces, even spectacles, can catch the light. There is little that can be done about spectacles, but when using binoculars or a compass make sure that you are well concealed: like radios, they are 'signature equipment' and attract attention. Stow binoculars inside your smock, and take care that your map is not opened up and flapping about – a drab map case with the map folded so that it gives the minimum

Use everything that comes to hand: in this case, a bit of discarded vehicle camouflage net which helps blur the shape of your kit.

Too much
The 'walking bush' looks effective at first sight, but he has so much foliage over his webbing he cannot get at his ammunition.

Too little
The white face and hands reflect the light and stand out horribly, and the lack of foliage reveals the obvious shape of the human figure.

Just right
Proper camouflage breaks up your shape and dulls the skin areas but does not restrict your access to your webbing or block your vision.

working area is all that is needed. Take care also that the clear cover to the map case does not catch the light.

Shine also includes skin. At night it will catch moonlight and flares, and even black soldiers need to use camouflage cream.

Silhouette

Similar in many respects to shape, silhouette includes the outline

By adding more vegetation to your shoulder straps you can hide the familiar 'head and shoulders' shape of the human figure.

of the human form and the equipment it is carrying. The shape of the head and shoulders of a man are unmistakable and an unscrimmed helmet attracts attention.

The use of vegetation as garnishing helps break up the silhouette. Thick handfuls of grass tucked into equipment can remove the shape of the shoulders, and garnishing on the helmet breaks the smooth curve of the

The man with too much camouflage must sit up in order to see through the jungle on his helmet but the soldier on the right blends in well.

top and the line of the brim.

Silhouette also includes fieldcraft – however well camouflaged you may be, it is little help if you 'sky line' by walking along the top of a hill, or stand against a background of one solid colour.

21

FACIAL CAMOUFLAGE

1 The first coat
First, get rid of all that white, shining skin. Mix a small quantity of camouflage cream with spit in your hand and rub it all over your face, neck and ears. This gives a full light coverage of camouflage. Then cover your hands with the cream.

2 Breaking up the shape
Now break up the outline and shape of the eyes, nose and mouth. Any pattern that breaks up this familiar format will do: use more if you're going on night patrol. Don't forget your neck and ears.

3 Finishing off
Fill in the rest of your face with earth, loam and green colours, then spit in your hands and rub them over your face to blur it all together. On the move you will probably sweat heavily, so you must top up your face cream as you go along.

Smell

Even the most urbanised man will develop a good sense of smell after a few days in the open. He will be able to detect engine smells, cooking, body odour and washing.

Some smells are hard to minimise. Soaps should be scent-free and activities such as cooking confined to daylight hours when other smells are stronger and the air warmer.

One of the greatest giveaways is smoking: its refuse has a unique smell. Rubbish produced by cooking as well as smoking should be carried out from the operational area and only buried as a second choice: buried objects are often dug up by animals and this can give a good indication of the strength and composition of your patrol or unit as well as its morale. The disciplines of refuse removal are important.

Sound

You can make a lot of noise while out on patrol. Your boots can squeak, your cleaning kit or magazines may rattle in your ammunition pouches. Even your webbing can creak if it is heavy. Fittings on your weapon may rattle. Radios can have background 'mush'. Coughing and talking can carry for long distances in the darkness of a clear night.

You must become familiar with a 'silent routine' in which field signals replace the spoken word, or conversations are conducted in a whisper.

Right: Personal camouflage must be secured so that it does not shift about when you are running.

Below: The familiar round shape of the helmet is broken up and the man's back and shoulders blend in well, but note how an uncamouflaged rifle stands out: there are no straight lines in nature.

Proper stowage of kit, taping of slings and other noisy equipment and a final shakedown before a patrol moves out will reduce noise. If a position is being dug, sentries should be positioned at the limit of noise so that they can see an enemy before he hears the digging.

Colour

Though most modern combat uniforms are now in a disruptive pattern camouflage, there may be times when this is less helpful. If you are evading

HELMET CAMOUFLAGE

1 Kevlar helmet
The new issue Kevlar helmet comes complete with a cover of DPM – standard military camouflage colours – and straps for local camouflage.

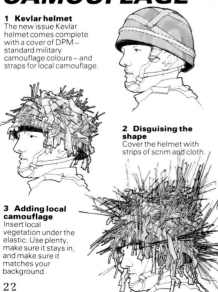

2 Disguising the shape
Cover the helmet with strips of scrim and cloth.

3 Adding local camouflage
Insert local vegetation under the elastic. Use plenty, make sure it stays in, and make sure it matches your background.

CAMOUFLAGING YOUR RIFLE

Camouflage the stock and butt with pieces of DPM material from an old pair of combat trousers. Make sure nothing gets in the way of the sights and check that you can load, make ready, and change the gas regulator setting easily. Secure the DPM material with tape and strips of cloth. Tie strips of cloth on the fore end and the barrel too, to disguise the overall shape and outline of the rifle. Green or camouflage tape on the magazine and top cover completes the job.

capture and are unarmed, drab civilian outdoor clothing will be less conspicuous if you encounter civilians.

The trouble with camouflage-type clothing is that in the wrong environment, like cities, it seems to do the opposite and say 'Hey, look at me!' In fighting in built-up areas a camouflage of greys, browns and dull reds would be better. The use of sacking and empty sand bags as scrim covers would help here.

Natural vegetation used to garnish helmets and equipment (see 'Silhouette') will fade and change colour. Leaves curl up and show their pale under-surfaces. You may have put grass into your helmet band and now find yourself in a dark wood; or be wearing dark green ferns when you are moving across a patch of pale, open grass land. Check and change your camouflage regularly.

The most obvious colour that needs camouflaging is that of human skin, and for that you need camouflage cream. As mentioned, even black or brown skin has a shine to it. A common mistake is to smear paint over the front of the face and to miss the neck, ears and back of the hands.

Camouflage cream needs to be renewed as you move and sweat. A simple pattern is to take stripes diagonally across the face – this cuts through the vertical and horizontal lines of the eyes, nose and mouth. Some camouflage creams have two colours, in which case you can use the dark colour to reduce the highlights formed by the bridge of the nose, cheek bones, chin and forehead. The lighter colour is used on areas of shadow.

Association

The enemy may not see you, but he might spot your equipment or refuse and associate that with a possible unit on the move. A cluster of radio antennas shows that a company HQ is on the move or dug in. The cans stacked near a vehicle park, perhaps with white tape around them, are likely to

Royal Marines prepare for the landings at San Carlos. Even at night your skin must be camouflaged because it will reflect moonlight.

be fuel. To a trained observer the unusual – a flash from a plastic map case, or the smell of cooking – will alert him and he will bring his own sensors to bear on the area.

CAMOUFLAGING YOUR BODY & EQUIPMENT

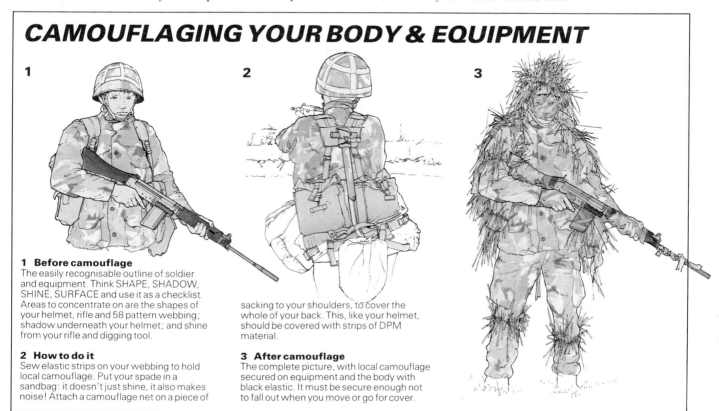

1 Before camouflage
The easily recognisable outline of soldier and equipment. Think SHAPE, SHADOW, SHINE, SURFACE and use it as a checklist. Areas to concentrate on are the shapes of your helmet, rifle and 58 pattern webbing; shadow underneath your helmet; and shine from your rifle and digging tool.

2 How to do it
Sew elastic strips on your webbing to hold local camouflage. Put your spade in a sandbag: it doesn't just shine, it also makes noise! Attach a camouflage net on a piece of sacking to your shoulders, to cover the whole of your back. This, like your helmet, should be covered with strips of DPM material.

3 After camouflage
The complete picture, with local camouflage secured on equipment and the body with black elastic. It must be secure enough not to fall out when you move or go for cover.

Camouflaging your Vehicle

Good camouflage and concealment is often a trade-off against good fields of fire or good positions for observing enemy movement. Radio communications work better with line-of-sight, but sitting on top of a hill is very public. And if you are trying to evade or escape you will need a vantage point for a sentry to observe likely enemy approaches, and may be observed yourself.

Assuming that you are part of a group of six to 12 men and that you have a light vehicle like a Land Rover or jeep, how would you conceal your position while evading capture?

Siting

Avoid the obvious. If the enemy are looking for you they will sweep the countryside, and if there are not many of them they will concentrate on rivers and woodland, farm houses, barns, known caves and natural cover. All are on maps, and the first move that an enemy search team will make is to do a map reconnaissance and look at likely locations.

Track plan

A track plan is essential if you are going to stay in the location for any length of time. Trodden grass and

A little camouflage can go a long way; these vehicles look like patches of gorse at a distance. Concealment on the move is dependent on using cover and dead ground.

Selecting a vehicle hide

1 Site selection
Left: Choose a harbour area away from the edge of the wood, away from tracks and with good cover overhead as well as at ground level. Try to pick a 'hull down' or 'dead ground' position. Remember to back the vehicle in; you may have to exit fast.

2 Hessian sacking
Above: All the principles of personal camouflage apply equally to your vehicle. Black hessian destroys the shine from windows, headlights and number plates, and disguises the general shape of the vehicle.

footprints will show clearly from the air, and large areas of normally lush undergrowth can be flattened in a way that attracts attention.

Vehicle tracks are even more dramatic from the air – bad drivers will carve a path across a field in a way that no farmer would dream of driving. Track planning means attempting to copy the normal routes adopted by animals, farmers or the locals. Thus vehicle tracks along the edge of a field and a footpath that might also be used by the inhabitants will pass unnoticed by the enemy.

IR signature

As with personal camouflage, the infra-red band is the most difficult to avoid. Thermal imaging will penetrate cover, and activities like running a vehicle engine to charge batteries or simple tasks like cooking become a major problem since both will show as a very strong hot point in an otherwise cool terrain.

Though a cave may not be ideal if it is on the local map, it will give good thermal screening. Parking the vehicle under cover will also reduce its IR signature – but again remember that barns and farmhouses are very obvious and may attract attention from the air or ground.

Concealing your vehicle

Any vehicle will be under suspicion. If you are moving in convoy, take care to avoid bunching. Vehicles close together are very recognisable from the air, and make easy targets for enemy aircraft. And remember the following points when finding somewhere to position your vehicle.

1 If you are near buildings, for instance on a farm, try to get the vehicle close to a wall or under cover in a barn. A camouflage net will attract the attention of a nearby enemy; use hessian and local materials to disguise the vehicle.
2 If you park in the country, try to find the shadow of a hedge to disguise the vehicle's hard shape. But remember that in northern and southern latitudes the sun moves, and the shadow of the morning can be the sunlit field of the afternoon.
3 Late evening can be particularly difficult, with low sunlight catching the glass fittings of

your vehicle. As a short-term precaution, cover the windscreen and lights when you stop, not forgetting the reflectors.
4 If your vehicle is military, it will have been painted with IR reflective paint and you should not cover this with hessian, which will produce a blue-grey colour on any infra-red device that the enemy might be using. You should cover the reflective surfaces and then deploy a camouflage net.
5 A camouflage net should stand clear of the vehicle, partly so that you can get in and out and also to disguise the vehicle's shape. It should also stretch far enough to contain any shadow that the vehicle might cast. Ideally, it should also have a 'mushroom' on the top: a frame of wire about the size of a domestic saucer. This gives a smooth line when the net is stretched over. Make sure that the net will not snag on the vehicle or underbrush or trees, preventing any quick exit you might need to make.

Camouflage net
Above: Use the surrounding trees as well as the poles. The ideal situation is to create a camouflage 'garage' you can drive into and out of without having to remove net, poles etc.

3 Net poles
Above: A good selection of net poles is essential to hold the camouflage net off the vehicle to disguise its shape. Chicken wire can also be used. You must not cut poles from trees around your position; the cut-off shoots will give you away. Harbouring two vehicles together with nets over both can be helpful in producing a more natural shape. Remember, you cannot afford to leave any equipment lying about; concealment is an ongoing task, as the threat of discovery is ever-present. Plastic bags and uncovered windscreens are asking for trouble.

Sound and smell

As with personal camouflage, sound and smell are important. If you run your engine to recharge batteries, you will make noise and exhaust fumes (and take care that fumes do not blow into the vehicle if the exhaust pipe is blocked by the camouflage). Use a flexible metal extension pipe to reduce the noise.

If you are in a convoy, the sound of your vehicles will attract attention, and so will your radio traffic.

Smell will come from cooking as you prepare your evening meal, and the smell of fuel is also distinctive. Spilled fuel and the wrappings from rations are a calling-card for an alert enemy.

Concealing your position

Don't make the mistake of thinking you're safe as long as you have dug your position. A good hide or bunker should be invisible even at close quarters; if you have dug it well and are careful in your movements, it may pass unnoticed. But the enemy can still spot you if you haven't been careful enough: keep the following in mind.

1 The colour of soil that has been dug from lower than about a metre is lighter than the topsoil, and a trench has a strong shadow at the bottom. Conceal earth by covering it with turfs; and put light-coloured straw at the bottom of a trench to reduce some of the shadow. This will also be more pleasant to walk on and live in.

2 In a tropical environment, cover can grow very quickly, so replace plants and creepers around your position and it will soon be concealed.

3 A simple basha made up with poncho or basha sheet can be square, shiny and noisy. Do not put it up until after last night — although you can position it flat on the ground before dark. Carry a length of old camouflage net; it will break up the shape and shine.

4 When you are cooking or brewing up, keep your opened kit to a minimum; you might need to make a quick getaway. Also, avoid littering tins and wrappers around the position that may catch the light and be seen from a distance.

5 It is commonly thought that a hand torch with a red filter does not show at night. It does; it's certainly less obvious than a white light, and it does not impair night vision, but it shows. Do not use a torch at all; by last light you should have set up your position so that your kit is packed and you can reach for your weapon, webbing and pack without needing one.

5 Two-sided net
Above: There are two sides to a camouflage net, with different colour combinations, so use the side that best matches your surroundings.

6 Shell scrapes and track plan
Right: As soon as the position is occupied, a route around the site must be marked by cord and cleared. By using this trackplan, disturbance of natural ground is minimised. Shell scrapes must be dug in 'stand to' positions.

Association is also important — radio antennas around a position or on a vehicle show that it is of significance. Antennas can also catch the light and show up as long, hard shadows in an otherwise concealed position. Most antennas can be situated away from the set, so put them on a reverse slope where they are not only invisible to the enemy, but also have some of their signal screened. Failing that, locate them against a building or tree.

Camouflage is a complex and sometimes contradictory skill. There is a reduced TI signature in a building under cover; but buildings attract attention. Hessian should be used on a vehicle among cold buildings; but not in warmer woodland. If you want to remember one rule to camouflage, it is that you should not give the enemy the signal that will make him look twice.

7 Thermal Imaging (TI)
Above and above left: A short-wheelbase Land Rover on the move, with heat radiating from the engine, transmission and wheel hubs. Each type of vehicle has its own TI signature. Note that the image does not go away when the vehicle's engine is switched off; only when it is cold.

How not to do it

Spot the mistakes in this picture; all of them invite an enemy attack.

1. The background deciduous trees are too open and light; it would be better to move right a few metres to the coniferous trees.

2. The position is far too close to the track.

3. Although the use of hessian is good, the absence of net poles means that the enemy will see a Land Rover and tent covered in a net.

4. Where is this man's rifle, helmet and webbing? He will be vulnerable in the event of a sudden attack.

Surviving Killer Fires

Man has always had a love/hate relationship with fire. It's one of the most fundamental building bricks of our society and civilisation, yet it's also a fearsome enemy. Whether it starts with a natural accident, like lightning or spontaneous combustion, simply gets out of hand or is deliberately used as a weapon, fire can kill more quickly and surely than a bullet. It is lethally dangerous everywhere, from the Poles to the Equator and from the top of the highest mountains to the bottom of the sea.

The fire triangle

Three things must come together before a fire can start: fuel, oxygen and heat. By the same reasoning, a fire can be put out by removing any one of the three components. Remember that. You can put out a fire by removing the fuel, by cutting off the air supply, or by removing the source of heat.

Perhaps the most common way to put out a fire is to pour water on it. This is very effective because it removes two of the three elements at once – it cuts off the oxygen and cools the heat source.

But in some circumstances – oil and gas fires especially, and that includes petroleum and paraffin – it is worse than useless. Water has little effect on gas – it can't contain it and cut off the oxygen, and it won't stay around long enough to cool the heat source – although a fine spray can reduce the gas to a safe concentration. Water sprayed or poured onto an oil fire will probably cause it to spread. Oil is lighter than water, so it will float on the surface and be carried wherever the water goes.

Water can start fires

In some exotic circumstances water can even start fires. Three metals – calcium, sodium and potassium – actually ignite and even explode in the presence of water. Water sprayed onto an electrical fire will cause more trouble than it will cure, too, by causing further short-circuits and sparks and possible electric shock.

And even when water puts a fire out, there are some times when it will flare up again as soon as the site dries out: this is known as spontaneous combustion. The phosphorus used in many types of grenade works in just this way.

2 Pull his right arm strongly over your left shoulder, then reach in and grab his belt with your right hand.

Rescue from a burning vehicle

1 Open the door and move the driver's feet clear of the pedals. Then take firm hold of his right arm.

Vehicles on fire

One of the greatest dangers from a burning vehicle is that the fuel tank will explode. Petrol is much more volatile than diesel, but all fuels have their flashpoint.

Many vehicle fires start with a short-circuit in the electric system. The first warning you'll get will be the smell of burning insulation. Another cause can be a build-up of petrol fumes under the bonnet ignited by a spark. Once again, your nose may give you some warning.

In a vehicle fire, if you have no extinguisher, there's not much you can do except to throw sand or soil on it. If you do carry one, make sure it's somewhere you can reach it immediately – that means in the car itself, not in the boot!

Don't panic. Try to get the vehicle into an open space, where it won't spread the fire to other cars or buildings.

If the vehicle catches fire when you're not in it, don't get in. Push it, steering through the open door or window if necessary.

If it's in a confined space such as a garage, toxic fumes will build up very quickly. Ensure that your escape is always possible.

In a crash, the doors of the car may jam closed. Get out through a window. If that's not possible, kick out the front or rear screen – there's enough give in the rubber sealing strip that secures the screen to allow almost anyone to do that, even if the glass doesn't shatter under the impact. Removal of the negative battery lead will substantially reduce the risk of fire as the result of a collision.

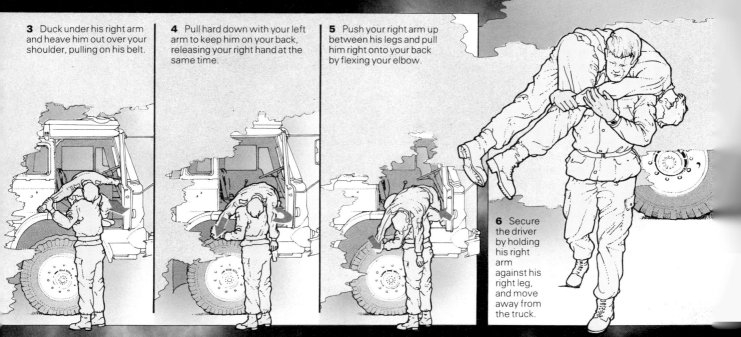

3 Duck under his right arm and heave him out over your shoulder, pulling on his belt.

4 Pull hard down with your left arm to keep him on your back, releasing your right hand at the same time.

5 Push your right arm up between his legs and pull him right onto your back by flexing your elbow.

6 Secure the driver by holding his right arm against his right leg, and move away from the truck.

You can see from these examples that putting out a fire isn't straightforward. And you may not even have the time to try. Under the most favourable circumstances (favourable to the fire, that is), a fire can spread faster than a man can run.

Keep calm

Whenever you're in danger, the most important thing is to stay calm and not panic. When you panic you stop thinking and start relying on brute force and ignorance to save your life. Chances are, it won't work.

Evaluate the situation. Where is the seat of the fire? How far can it spread? Can you limit it by removing fuel from around its site? Can you cut off – or cut down – the oxygen supply?

You must be looking for escape routes at the same time, of course, in case the fire already has too firm a hold to be beatable.

But no matter whether you are able to fight the fire, or you can only try to escape from it, your chances of surviving will be vastly increased by taking precautions in advance. You will probably find it impossible to fight a fire with things that are at hand at the time.

The right extinguisher

Always try to get hold of at least one fire extinguisher that is suitable for the type of fire, and put it where you can find it with your eyes closed. And be sure you know how to use it with your eyes closed, too. You won't have time to read the instructions, and anyway, the atmosphere may be full of smoke or it may be dark.

Where you can't get hold of an extinguisher, have blankets (preferably made of some fire-resistant material, but pure wool is quite effective), and buckets of sand, earth or water handy, once again where you can find them in the dark or smoke.

It's absolutely essential to take these precautions anywhere that you're using naked flames of any sort, whether it's a lantern or a candle to see by, a fire to cook on or a gas torch to weld with.

Remove the fuel

As well as providing yourself with something to extinguish the flames you should take care to remove anything that might become fuel to a fire that gets out of hand – before you light it. When you're dealing with fire, prevention of accidents is a great deal better than attempting to cure their effects.

The heat of the fire itself, if it gets out of control, is not the only enemy. First of all, the air will be depleted of oxygen. You need that oxygen just as

You may have a flak jacket, a personal weapon, the latest boots and helmet: but only your training and presence of mind will save you from an inferno.

The fireman's lift

1 Place the victim at 90° to a wall with his feet against it. Try to get his feet together.

2 Lift him to the kneeling position and support him with your right thigh.

3 Take his right wrist in your left hand and extend his in line with his shoulder.

4 Step back with your left leg and grab his upper right thigh with your right hand.

5 Use his right arm as a lever to pull him across your shoulders. Balance his body evenly.

Trapped by fire

Toxic fumes
Modern synthetic materials produce poisonous gases when they burn: this was a serious problem aboard HMS *Sheffield* when she caught fire after being hit by an Exocet missile in 1982. The fatal combination of poisonous fumes, dense black smoke and intense heat makes escape difficult but imperative.

Countdown to death
Smoke is often a bigger killer than the flames themselves: 2½ minutes after a fire begins, a typical interior room will be half-filled with smoke, and 30 seconds later it will be completely full. Without breathing apparatus you cannot last much longer.

Don't open doors
If you have to open a door for rescue purposes, put the back of your hand against the back of the door to check for heat, and look for signs of smoke. When you open a door on to a fire you give it a new supply of oxygen and can cause the flames to leap through the doorway; so if you must open a door, keep low and ensure that a means of extinction is available to back you up.

Death from above
Plastered ceilings provide the best resistance to the spread of the flames, but timber ceilings burn more readily and cause fires in rooms above. The fire can also run between floors unchecked and unnoticed, causing added danger.

Look before you leap
If you are stuck at an upper storey window, open or smash it and try to attract attention. Don't panic, and don't jump until you really have to: you may be rescued in time. If you do have to jump, reduce the height of the drop by lowering yourself to the full extent of your arms.

Beware the stairwell
Stairwells can act as channels for the fire, spreading the flames upwards to higher storeys. Use protected routes by following 'Fire Exit' signs.

Blocking a door
If you are cut off by the fire, try to block gaps around the doorway to stop smoke coming in. Most doors will hold back the flames for about 20 minutes.

A burning building

Whether it's under attack or has caught fire for some other reason, a burning building can be as big a killer as any weapon on the battlefield. Remember these points and you stand a better chance of coming out alive.

1 Smoke – or the smell of it – will probably be the first indication you'll get of a fire. Your first reaction will probably be to go to the door and open it. Don't. Feel the door first. If it's hot to the touch, that's a sure sign that the fire is right on the other side of it.

2 Even if you can't feel the heat of the flames through the door, you should still take precautions: put on clothing that covers as much of your body as possible. A pad for the nose and mouth and clothing to cover as much of your body as possible are the absolute minimum.

3 Now brace your foot against the door and open it just a crack. If there is fire right behind the door, the pressure of hot air and burning gases will try to blow it open. If it's reasonably clear, go through the door as close to the floor as possible, and close it behind you to delay the spread of the fire. Even a very ordinary door can be expected to delay a fire for 20 minutes or more.

4 If you have to evacuate, do so immediately. Close all doors behind you and make sure everyone is aware of the fire. Do not stop to collect personal belongings and, once you're out, stay out.

5 Fire travels upwards more quickly than downwards, though collapsing floors and staircases will carry the fire down with them. Never try to use a lift, no matter how many flights of stairs you'll have to descend – you never know when the cables will burn through or the electricity will cut out.

6 Never jump from a window. If you have to go out that way then drop, hanging from anything available to reduce the distance between you and the ground. If there are fire-fighters prepared for you, wait until they give you a direct order. Dropping from a window is an absolute last resort.

7 If you have no rope available, then try to make one from bedclothes, curtains or whatever is at hand. Even if it doesn't reach the ground, every foot you save yourself dropping may reduce the chances of a serious injury.

8 Throw out anything that might help to cushion your fall. If this is impossible, then try to land in the softest possible place. Lawns and flowerbeds are much softer than concrete or tarmac, and even a gravel path is softer. The roof of a car or van will give under the impact and give you a better chance of surviving the fall. Trees will help to break your fall, but you run the risk of impaling yourself on a branch. Avoid railings for the same reason.

9 Protect your head as much as possible. A helmet is ideal but, in an emergency, wrap towels or a sweater around your head. Remember – any protection is better than none.

10 If it does come to dropping out of the window, hang at arm's length, push off with one foot, turn away from the wall as you fall, and wrap your arms around your head. Bend your knees as you descend, and try to absorb as much of the impact as you can with your bent legs. Roll over to one side as you land, and carry the roll on, still with your arms wrapped around your head.

11 If you're able to escape by running through the flames and your clothes catch light, fall to the ground and roll over and over as soon as you're in the clear. Wrap yourself up if you can, to smother the fire and keep oxygen out.

much as the fire does, but it will grab it much quicker than you can: so you'll suffocate while it burns.

Secondly, the fire will produce smoke. Even if it's not poisonous, it will asphyxiate you very quickly. If the fire's fuel includes plastic or other synthetic products, the smoke coming off will almost certainly be loaded with poisons, cyanide very prominent amongst them.

Smoke protection

Breathing apparatus or a specially-designed smoke hood are the only sure protection.

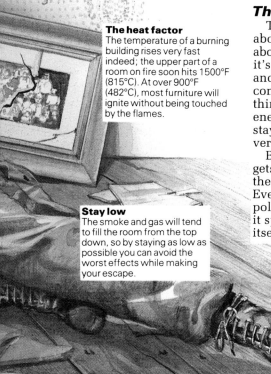

The heat factor
The temperature of a burning building rises very fast indeed; the upper part of a room on fire soon hits 1500°F (815°C). At over 900°F (482°C), most furniture will ignite without being touched by the flames.

Stay low
The smoke and gas will tend to fill the room from the top down, so by staying as low as possible you can avoid the worst effects while making your escape.

If you've reached the point where this sort of action is necessary, it's time to get out – and fast. Look for the clearest escape route and take it. Don't run blindly. Don't stop to collect anything along the way – your life is the most precious thing you have.

There's one exception to that, though – injured or incapacitated comrades. Not for nothing is the cross-shoulder carry called the Fireman's Lift. It's not absolutely straightforward, so practise it until you are confident. It won't take long, and once you've learned it, you won't forget how it's done.

Think in advance

Take precautions – learn something about firefighting techniques; learn about how fire acts and the directions it's likely to take; learn what to expect and what you can and can't do. This combined with common sense, clear thinking and a healthy respect for the enemy, will increase your chances of staying alive and uninjured in even very serious fires.

But make no mistake – once a fire gets hold of a major source of fuel, there will probably be no stopping it. Even the professionals don't try. Their policy is to contain the blaze and stop it spreading, then they can let it burn itself out in comparative safety.

The tactical man-carry

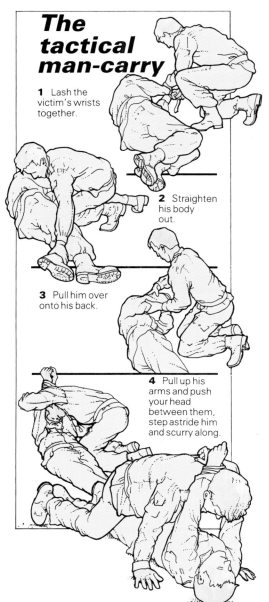

1 Lash the victim's wrists together.

2 Straighten his body out.

3 Pull him over onto his back.

4 Pull up his arms and push your head between them, step astride him and scurry along.

CHAPTER TWO

THE BATTLEGROUND

The traditional battlefield is the arena where two opposing armies plot and plan to eliminate each other and so long as the human race for one reason or another makes war the presence of the battlefield must be accepted. In the past, war was a brutal man-to-man slog with the strongest or perhaps best-armed walking away and leaving his defeated enemy prone. Today this elemental encounter can still occur when our complex or armies, corps, even brigades, becomes fragmented due to some successful enemy action and single units – soldiers – come face to face.

There is no avoiding the fact that there are – unfortunately – brutal new weapons available to all the major powers which can deal death and injury at a distance and, worse, in a form that is often invisible even when it has been released in one's immediate vicinity. and it is too late when the first effects become apparent. These weapons are the various battlefield contaminants such as types of poisonous gases, biological hazards, or one of the many toxic substances that 'progress' has brought. Some can incapacitate by the merest touch on the skin of an amount invisible to the eye.

Once any of these terrible weapons, under the collective description of Biological, Chemical and Toxinal agents, has been released on or over a battlefield the area wil be contaminated and the first article in this chapter deals with this formidable subject.

The NATO soldier is properly equipped with a set of NBC suits that will give him protection from battlefield contaminants, and of course it must be assumed that the Warsaw Pact soldier is similarly equipped. But careful training in their use is absolutely essential when it is pointed out that as soon as warning is given that an attack with a toxic agent has been made one has nine seconds to assume the necessary protective wear. And when one's life is in peril nine seconds is a very short period of time, hence the absolute necessity of thorough training – and there can be no substitute for that.

In the unlikely event of another major global war (because the stakes are too high), it is possible that small sub-kiloton tactical nuclear strikes would be made on military installations or concentrations of troops. The last two sections in this chapter take a long look at the possibility of purely military actions of this nature and the first describes the combination of threats from heat, light, blast and lethal radiation capable of various degrees of penetration.

During the course of some military exercises explosive devices are available that produce a horrifically realistic but harmless mushroom cloud simulating an atomic explosion. Considerable training takes place in their forbidding shadows. These exercises are designed to give soldiers adequate training on what to do so that they can respond properly.

The second article continues with the theme of nuclear strikes and discusses the chances of survival when the correct precautions are taken, including the use of meters indicating the presence of radiation and its strength. It must be hoped that use will never be made of nuclear weapons, either by the military on the battlefield or global use when one of those notorious Red Buttons is pressed deep in some underground bunker. But the weapons exist and will not go away until international agreements, such as those made towards the end of 1987, remove the threat. Until that time comes today's soldier must have all the protection science can give him and he must be properly trained in how to use it.

A U.S. Army soldier in action on contaminated ground.

The Contaminated Battlefield

A pair of MiG-27 aircraft streak over the battlefield. Each drops a pair of cluster bombs. Bomblets discharge from the main bomb units. When they're within 30 metres of the ground they explode, and hundreds of tiny puffs of smoke appear in the air above the troops.

'Gas! Gas! Gas!'

It may indeed be gas, a chemical vapour that will burn your skin and tear the lining from your lungs; or perhaps it's a biological agent such as Anthrax, Plague or even (humble but disabling) a specialised flu. Or maybe it's a deadly toxin produced from the most poisonous snakes or fungi on Earth.

Live practice

It is standard practice for the Warsaw Pact countries to use contaminants both in European exercises and in action: for example, in Afghanistan. US forces also have the potential for deployment. And remember, such weapons are very unselective, so you might have to content with Allied- or enemy-deployed hazards.

What can you do to survive these and the other apocalyptic hazard — nuclear contamination — and be in a fit state to fight on?

The first step in protection is the use of NBC (Nuclear Biological Chemical) IPE (Individual Protection Equipment), a set of protective overgarments and a respirator (sometimes known by its World War I name of 'gasmask').

The British Forces first started wearing NBC suits 20 years ago; before that, standard protection was limited to a rubberised gas cape and

Marking contaminated zones

These are the warning panels used by NATO and the Warsaw Pact to mark contaminated areas. On the Warsaw Pact signs the type of danger is marked in the box on the left, labelled as follows:

Nuclear	+ PB
Biological	+ b
Chemical	+ OB

An arrow on the sign indicates the direction of the contaminated zone; a set of lines means there is a decontaminated path through the area, and its width is marked on the right-hand side. The sign on the right means the path is 10 metres wide and 1000 metres long. If ЧЕРЕЗ is replaced by ОЬЬЕЗД (detour) the area cannot be contaminated and you must go around it.

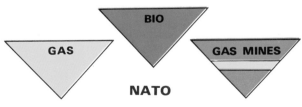

GAS   BIO   GAS MINES

NATO

ЗАРАЖЕНО ЧЕРЕЗ 500м   ЗАРАЖЕНО ЧЕРЕЗ 1000м   10

WARSAW PACT

Modern NBC suits offer a realistic chance of protection against some of the hazards of nuclear and chemical warfare. Chemical weapons have been widely used since World War II, and it is likely they would play a major role in a future world conflict.

respirator. The initial suit design called for an easily-produced, durable fabric that could be folded easily into a small packet. The suit would have a maximum operational wear-life of three days and a protection times of six hours. Six suits would be on issue to each soldier: one to wear, one to carry, one in close support and the rest in store.

Delivering the weapons

Biological, Chemical and Toxinal weapons, as the disease and poison-bearing hazards are known, are usually dispensed as a gas, smoke, mist or liquid. Radiological or nuclear contamination will take the form of radioactive-contaminated dust following a nuclear explosion.

A groundburst (an explosion where the fireball contacts the ground) can create high levels of blast pressure. A proportion of the energy of the explosion will be transmitted into the ground, producing a crater and an earthquake effect. The debris from the crater will be irradiated and thrown up into the atmosphere with the typical rolling dirty brown mushroom cloud associated with nuclear explosions. This will come to earth later as contaminated fallout.

An airburst, where the explosion takes place above ground, has less fallout but a more widespread blast effect. Subterranean explosions create the equivalent of an earthquake and often a massive crater with much fall-out.

Hotter than the sun

The nuclear explosion is immediately accompanied by an intense flash, and by the release of radiation. The flash generates intense heat, often hotter than the surface of the sun. Combustible material can spontaneously ignite, and firestorms will rage, causing death and injuries from burns, smoke inhalation and oxygen starvation.

Chemical weapons have been used with alarming frequency since World War II and are horrifically effective against unprotected personnel. The key to survival lies in preparation: without proper kit and thorough training there is no defence.

In the event of an attack by chemical weapons you have just nine seconds to get your respirator on. 'Be in time, mask in nine' as the British Army is taught, if you take much longer you are doomed to an agonising death.

Respirators are uncomfortable and tiring to wear. Just the threat of nuclear or chemical attack can reduce your efficiency by forcing you to put on your defensive equipment. The British Army will soon be receiving a new respirator that allows you to drink without taking it off.

The respirator protects your eyes, face, mouth, throat and lungs against chemical, biological and toxinal agents as well as radioactive dust. The filter canister contains activated charcoal and must be changed at intervals.

Suiting up for NBC

1 Individual Protection Equipment comes in sealed plastic bags that must be opened only when you need to put the suit on.

2 You put on the trousers first. These are very tightly folded, and must be opened out before you can get your legs in.

3 Bring the braces over your shoulders, cross them over your chest, and feed them through the waist loops before tying them in a bow.

4 Now put on the smock and use the Velcro fasteners on this and the trousers to tuck in the slack.

5 The rubber overboots come in one size only, designed to fit either foot.

Initial radiation will consist of alpha particles, beta particles and gamma rays. As with all contaminants, shielding is the only method of survival. The danger from alpha particles comes from inhalation, since they will not penetrate the skin and can be deflected by clothing or paper. Beta particles will not usually penetrate the skin, and can be deflected by a thin metal shield.

Gamma rays, however, will go right through a human being with devastating effect, but about half of them can be stopped by 20 cm of tightly-packed earth or 15 cm of concrete.

The nuclear explosion then produces a fireball and a blast wave radiating out from the centre. The fireball is fanned by air being sucked into the vacuum created by the blast. The blast will often be devastating: build-ings will collapse, trees will be uprooted and vehicles thrown like toys.

Vital protection

If you are exposed to the lethal effects of a nuke you will die. But your exposure is dependent on many factors: the size of the weapon, its point of detonation, the type of terrain and, most importantly, on how well you are protected. If you anticipate that nuclear weapons might be used, prepare protection shelters — which should be at least a foxhole with a covering — and wear your individual protection equipment.

In the shelter, keep all your equipment — rifle, pack etc — together to prevent its loss in the high winds. If you are caught unprepared, find an expedient shelter: use walls, hills, dips in the ground, drainage ditches, culverts or any feature that will give you some protection.

Biological contamination usually comes in the form of diseases with a successful track record in debilitating the human race, such as flu, typhoid, gastro-enteritis or cholera. Some ad-

During the Vietnam war the Americans sprayed the jungle with 'Agent Orange', a chemical defoliant that killed the vegetation used as cover by the Viet Cong.

6 Lace up the boots and fasten the trouser bottoms over the top so that no contaminants can enter through the top of the boots.

7 Put on the white inner gloves, then the large rubber protective overgloves.

8 Put on your gas mask and replace your webbing and helmet. If you are under gas attack, you must obviously put the respirator on first.

9 Wearing the Mk 3 NBC suit and ready for action. It is hot, sweaty and uncomfortable, but a lot better than dying of radiation sickness.

vance protection can be acquired through innoculations and a course of antibiotics, and basic field hygiene will reduce the effect of the weapons and the spread of the disease.

Chemical agents are of five types:

1 Incapacitants such as LSD, which induces hallucinations.

2 Blister agents such as sulphur mustard gas – as used in World War I.

3 Nerve agents such as Tabun, Sarin and Soman, which break down the nervous systems.

4 Choking agents such as phosgene or chlorine, which make your eyes and throat swell and make you vomit.

5 Blood agents such as hydrogen cyanide, which produce heart and muscle spasms.

In all cases, protection is your first priority, since once the agent has made contact it's too late. A drop of mustard gas on exposed skin will cause blistering, and a persistent agent such as thickened Soman carried on your clothing can evaporate to form a lethal gas. The tiniest amount of nerve agent on exposed flesh is enough to incapacitate and kill you.

The deadly toxins

Toxinal agents are toxins produced from living organisms such as fungus,

plants, marine life or snakes. Yellow Rain or T2 is produced by the *Fusarium* fungus. NATO specialists regard this as a product of a living organism and therefore biological, but the Soviets argue that, not being a living organism itself, such a toxin is chemical. Toxins can work instantaneously, causing paralysis and death, or can have the same graduated effect as a disease.

Be prepared

All in all, the NBC battlefield is an horrendous place in which to fight. Both sides have the weapons or potentially have the weapons, and only mutual respect may make the battle commanders think twice about using them.

In any case, you should be prepared, know what to expect and what to do if the worst happens. Your ability to survive and fight back will make the use of the weapons by enemy forces that much less likely.

Lacking any protective clothing, Iranian soldiers in the Gulf War have suffered badly from Iraq's use of blistering and nerve gases in artillery shells and in improvised canisters dropped from helicopters.

Surviving a Nuclear Strike
Part 1

Nuclear survival is like Arctic survival, but worse. There is plenty of theory, but practice is based on the two atomic bombs at the end of World War II and tests that have been conducted since 1945.

When a nuclear weapon explodes, three killers are released: **heat and light, blast,** and **radiation. Heat and light** from the flash reach temperatures higher than the sun, and include ultra-violet, infra-red and visible light rays which will burn human skin and also set fire to flammable materials such as timber. The good news about a nuclear flash is that it only lasts a few seconds.

Radios
Most systems will be damaged by the huge electro-magnetic pulse given out by a nuclear detonation; only 'hardened' systems will survive. Some measure of protection will be provided by wrapping electronic equipment in tinfoil and keeping it switched off.

NBC sentry
After the immediate effects have passed, the sentry takes a bearing of the cloud of a distant strike, estimates the range and size, and reports it so that supporting units can be given a fallout warning.

Decontamination cell

Morale
If your unit is subjected to nuclear attack and has to deal with fallout hazard, radiation sickness, mass casualties and an unprecedented level of destruction, battleshock and morale are going to be a problem. Junior commanders must maintain the will to survive, fight and win.

Blast comes in two forms: an initial shock wave, and then air that is sucked back into the vacuum that has been created by the blast. The initial blast will demolish buildings and the vacuum effect may bring down structures that have been weakened. There will be danger from flying glass and small objects as well as collapsing buildings.

Radiation killer

The third killer, and the most disturbing feature of nuclear weapons, is radiation. It comes in two forms – radiation released by the explosion,

Trenches
Your battle trench must have at least 45 cm of overhead protection and must be revetted and contoured to the ground to provide good protection.

Targets
Tactical weapons will be used against any large troop concentration detected by the enemy. Your defence lies in good camouflage and concealment and dispersion over a wide area, coming together only to put in an attack.

The nuclear battlefield

Your duty as a soldier does not end with learning how to survive a tactical nuclear strike; your aim is to survive to fight. Small sub-kiloton yield devices are likely to be used in any future large-scale conflict in Europe as tactical weapons in support of conventional operations on the battlefield. These strikes are surviveable; some weapons are designed to devastate only one square kilometre. If you are some distance from ground zero and dug in you are likely to survive the initial effects. How well you survive after that is a question of your discipline, training and preparation.

Recognition
You must be able to tell the difference between nuclear and conventional munitions: not easy as some FAE (Fuel Air Explosives) and HE devices look like nuclear air bursts. A strike report must be sent without delay so that troops can take cover from any downwind fallout.

Personal protective measures

1 Against immediate effects
Stay over cover as much as possible, and cover all exposed skin. If you are caught in the open, carry out the nuclear immediate-action drill: this must be instinctive. Plan patrol routes, making best use of natural cover as you move. Once you have received the warning, keep all kit and weapons under cover.

2 Against fallout contamination
a Wear your respirator and suit at all times.
b Do not touch anything you know is contaminated.
c Do not smoke.
d Make sure your food and water is not contaminated.
e Do not raise dust.
f Decontaminate yourself thoroughly.

Types of burst
You must be able to tell the difference between **air burst**, where the fireball does not reach the ground; **ground burst**, where the fireball touches the ground and the classic mushroom cloud is formed; and **sub-surface burst**, where the fireball cannot be seen.

NBC hazard warning
This sign is a radiological contamination warning, showing the dose rate of the area you are about to enter; when the survey took place; and the date and time of the strike that produced the radiation.

and residual radiation. In the explosion three types of radiation are released: Alpha, Beta and Gamma.

Alpha particles will not penetrate through overhead cover in a fire trench, but can be ingested or inhaled.

Beta particles can cause burns on unprotected skin and if ingested attack the gastro-intestinal tract, bones and thyroid gland. NBC clothing and respirator will give protection.

Gamma are highly penetrative and though they travel slower than alpha and beta they damage all body cells.

Symptoms of sickness

The symptoms of exposure to radiation are nausea, vomiting and weakness. The skin may appear grey and develop sores. The radiation that you will receive in the first blast will be greater than the residual radiation occurring during the rest of the week. And in the first few days you would receive a higher dose of radiation than if you were to stay in the area for the rest of your life. This is why it is critically important to keep under cover during the initial stages of a nuclear attack.

Types of burst

Nuclear weapons can be delivered in three ways: **airburst, ground burst** and **subsurface**.

Subsurface will produce a crater and some of the fireball will appear. Blast and radiation will vary according to the size of the weapon and the depth at which it is exploded. However, subsurface explosions are normally only used in nuclear tests.

A **ground burst** has an explosion where the fire ball touches the ground. Here it produces a crater and blast, heat and initial and residual radiation. The residual radiation is particularly heavy as the fire ball sucks debris upwards and then deposits it as fallout. Radiation affects the ground around the explosion and also makes equipment radioactive.

Military preference

In the chilling language of nuclear war, a surface burst is 'dirty' since there is a lot of fallout which can be blown away from the target area and contaminate areas downwind.

The attraction of an **air burst** is the electro magnetic pulse (EMP) that it causes, which will burn out radio and telephonic communications unless they are EMP hardened. In tactical

Above: If you are caught in the open during a nuclear detonation, carry the Nuclear Immediate Action Drill. Close your eyes and mouth; do not look at the flash; drop to the ground, feet together and face down, hands underneath your body, and your head pointing towards the detonation. If there is cover very close by, move into it. Stay down until all immediate effects have passed, then get under cover.

Left: A GPMG gunner emerges from his shelter ready to defend his position. If you take correct defensive measures it is possible to survive a tactical nuclear strike and continue the battle.

The tactical nuclear threat: methods of delivery

The Soviet army has a large number of nuclear-capable weapon systems, ranging from primitive ballistic missiles such as FROG to the very capable SS-21 and SS-23. All Soviet artillery of 152-mm calibre and above has nuclear ammunition. This diagram shows the respective ranges of Soviet nuclear weapon systems that could be used in a future conflict in north west Europe.

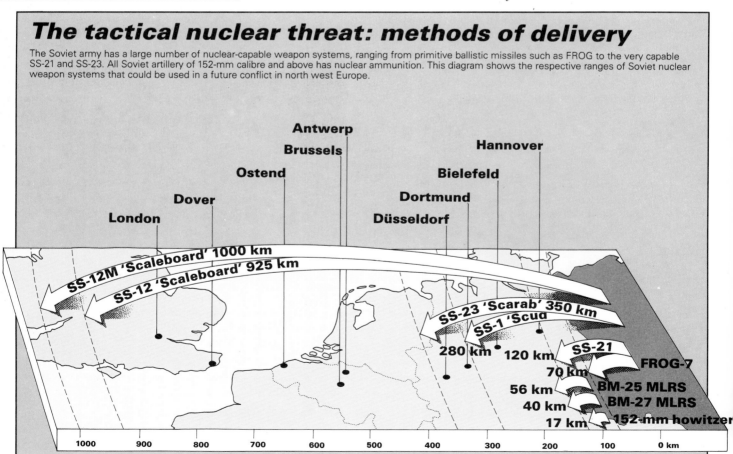

Above: Looking after casualties is greatly complicated by the danger from radioactivity. Wounds must be washed with clean water and covered to keep out radioactive dust.

terms this will destroy your enemy's communications, kill many of his men in the target area, but leave the battlefield reasonably 'clean' for your own troops.

Protection

To survive, you must take defensive measures before, during and after an explosion. Before the explosion dig deeper and get overhead cover in place; even a poncho will give some protection, but one metre of soil will be better. Brickwork 0.60 metres thick or concrete 0.66 metres thick will reduce radiation by 50 per cent. Wear your NBC clothing and respirator.

During the explosion get under cover. If you are in the open, do not try to take cover if it is more than a few metres away. Lie down on your stomach with your feet to the explosion. Do not look at the explosion; it is 'brighter than a thousand suns', as a Japanese survivor described one of World War II's atomic bombs. It will blind you temporarily or even permanently. Stay where you are until the blast and vacuum effects have passed.

Careful decontamination

After the explosion, keep under cover until the fallout has stopped. Decontaminate your clothing and equipment. Scrape out dirt that has fallen into your slit trench and pile it up away from your trench.

All wounds should be covered to prevent alpha and beta particles entering. Burns caused by the fire ball, flash or radiation should be washed with clean water and covered. Radiation reduces resistance to infection, so simple precautions should be taken against respiratory infections.

Sealed rations such as Composition, MRE or T Rations will be proof against most of the contamination caused by radiation: fresh dairy products and foods with a high salt or preservative content are more prone to contamination. Water from underground wells and springs is likely to be the least contaminated. Avoid unprotected water for at least 48 hours after a detonation.

Arguably, nuclear survival depends on how far the war develops. An

'SCUD' missiles are one of the many delivery systems used by the Soviets to drop tactical nuclear warheads on enemy positions. With a yield of up to 100 kilotons, they do not need to be precision weapons.

exchange of tactical weapons may be survivable, but if strategic weapons are employed the possibility of a 'nuclear winter' caused by dust from several large explosions blocking out the sun makes survival more questionable.

Surviving a Nuclear Strike Part 2

The face of nuclear battle: the large arsenals of tactical nuclear weapons fielded by **NATO** and the **Warsaw Pact** make combat in an irradiated zone a realistic possibility. Unless you are well prepared you will not survive, let alone continue to fight.

If you find yourself in a battle involving tactical nuclear weapons this is the view you must get used to: the world through the lenses of the S6 respirator.

After a tactical nuclear weapon has been deployed you could be a casualty from blast, flash or injuries from flying debris. You may have received a massive dose of radiation which will kill you in a few hours, or if you are on the fringes you may get a lighter dose: perhaps as little as those received during a routine hospital X-ray.

There will be the problem of radioactive contamination of food, water and equipment. You may also have to cope with civilians who have become casualties within your area of operations or are hurrying through as they attempt to escape from potential target areas.

Remember, a nuclear weapon may be detonated by friendly forces as well as enemy. You may have slightly more warning of a 'friendly nuclear attack', but operational secrecy will mean that this warning is given at very short notice.

Tactical nukes

Nuclear weapons will be employed as part of an attack or counter-attack plan. If you are on the defensive and it is an enemy attack, you must be prepared for subsequent conventional bombardments and also enemy ground forces. With a 'friendly' attack you must also be prepared to react fast, since your unit may be part of the counter-attack force – particularly if it has taken low casualties.

Means of delivery

1 Aircraft
These are flexible and can have a good operational range, but the weather and enemy air defence can be a problem.
2 Artillery
Although range is limited (40 km), this delivery method is excellent for rapid response and can be very accurate with laser-guided munitions.
3 Guided missiles
These are reasonably accurate, with long range but slow response.
4 Rockets
These are fast and reasonably accurate, e.g. Lance and Honest John.
5 Atomic demolition munitions
Nuclear mines etc are usually deployed in advance in an area the enemy is likely to occupy or move through. Excellent for route blocking and key point demolition.

Detecting radiation

Infantry units are issued with the RSM 2 Radiac survey meter, which will detect beta radiation and measure levels of gamma radiation.

The personal dosimeter above works in the same way by detecting the degree of ionisation in the air, but unlike the RSM 2 it records the total amount of radiation absorbed by the wearer. Pen-type as well as watch-type meters are on issue. The dose received cannot be read by the individual but only by the unit commander, with a specially-issued kit.

Individuals who have received a lethal dose will usually be able to carry out tasks for two or three days after the attack. Duties in contaminated areas should be carefully divided and personal dosimeters monitored so that individual radiation dosages are kept below danger level.

Radiation will be measured in two ways in your unit. **Dose rate meters** are used to locate radiological contamination and to measure the rate at which nuclear radiation is being absorbed; **dosimeters** are used to measure the total nuclear radiation dose received by an individual. A dosimeter is worn by all personnel, and can look like a fountain pen or a digital wristwatch. Dosages are measured in rads. Under some cir-

This GPMG is mounted on a tripod for sustained fire in a trench with proper overhead cover.

After a tactical nuclear strike you must be able to emerge from your shelter to repel the attack that will follow.

US troops man their .50 cal anti-aircraft machine-gun to defend a vehicle column against air attack in NBC conditions.

The old and the new: (left) the S10 respirator, which allows you to drink without taking it off, (right) the old S6.

cumstances some men may build up a greater number of rads than others and it is important to check dosimeters regularly.

Decontamination

These procedures assume that you have a chance to come out of the line and clean up in a secure location.

Vehicles and large pieces of equipment can be decontaminated with truck-mounted high-pressure water systems. Individuals can go to a mobile decontamination unit with a series of sealed shelters in which each man can remove his clothing and shower.

If these units are not available, you should try to find a source of uncontaminated water. Take off all your clothes – they will have trapped dust. Shake and brush them. Then wash and rinse them and either set them aside or have them sent to a laundry unit. Decontaminate your weapon by brushing and wiping. Then wash yourself thoroughly with soap and water – in the form of a shower if pos-

sible – to remove dust and irradiated matter.

While washing, pay special attention to hairy parts, body openings and creases. Scrub your hands and nails thoroughly. After washing you should be checked with a dose rate meter. If you are still contaminated, wash again. When you are free from contamination, put on fresh clothing.

A more likely scenario is that the chaos following tactical nuclear strikes will prevent all but the most rudimentary decontamination. If this happens, then your mission becomes the priority and the health of your men and their radioactive dosage has to be considered. Men with a higher dosage have to be used more carefully, and exposure has to be monitored.

Living dead

The firemen at Chernobyl were a good example of men working under 'war' conditions. Many knew that they had received almost lethal dosages, and with this in mind they accepted that they were already 'dead'

Surviving the blast

You must not be caught standing; if there is no cover within a few metres, dive face down away from the explosion. Overhead protection or foxholes are preferable, but a ditch or any piece of ground that shields you from the blast is worth using. Do not use a poncho for protection – it could melt and cause burns.

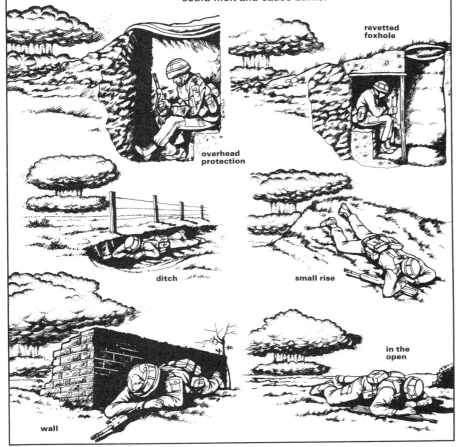

overhead protection

revetted foxhole

ditch

small rise

wall

in the open

Right: Contaminated areas are wired off and marked. The top line is the dose rate per hour in cGy (a unit of measurement equivalent to a rad); the middle line shows the time and date of the survey, 1st June at 11.00 Zulu (GMT); and the bottom line the date of the nuclear strike, 09.30 Zulu on 30th May.

ATOM
300 cGy/hr
011100 Z JUN
300930 Z MAY

Soviet T-62 Main Battle Tanks are decontaminated after passing through a contaminated area. The Soviets use real chemical weapons to add flavour to their NBC exercises and accept a number of casualties every year as the price of realistic training.

Effects of a nuclear explosion

1 Flash
This causes flash blindness. The severity depends on proximity to the burst, direction, time of day, level of cloud base, and the weather.

2 Fireball
The size of this sphere of hot gas indicates the yield (size) of the device.

3 Heat
Massive heat radiation in straight lines causes two types of fire: **primary**, started directly by the heat radiation, and **secondary**, caused by the blast rupturing gas mains.

4 Blast and shock
This is caused by pressure differential. The blast has both a positive and negative phase, i.e. a push-and-pull effect.

5 Radiation
There are three types:
a Initial, very high levels, released during the first minute; mainly gamma
b Residual, or fallout, radioactive dust emitting alpha, beta, and gamma
c Neutron-induced activity; objects in the path of the initial radiation will themselves become radioactive.

6 TREE
Transient Radiation Effect on Equipment accompanies the initial radiation and will temporarily make communications unworkable.

7 EMP
Electro-Magnetic Phenomena, ionisation of the air, causes wide-ranging damage to electronic equipment.

8 Cloud
Note the characteristic shape, and be aware that an airburst may not produce a mushroom cloud at all.

and kept on with firefighting. This spirit of self-sacrifice may be hard to understand in anything but an emergency of continental proportions.

With Chernobyl in mind, it is worth remembering that nuclear power stations have been built throughout the world and even a conventional war could become 'dirty' with radiation released by battle damage to a nuclear power station. Fires and winds could produce a complex downwind hazard, so it is important to be able to mark a contaminated area.

Detailed marking

A triangular marker is attached to a fence around the area. The marker is white, with the word ATOM on the front facing away from the contami-

Nuclear strike will cause a large number of injuries and fallout will be an ongoing threat. Also, battle shock will be greater than with conventional warfare. Casualty care and evacuation systems are unlikely to be able to cope in the initial stages of the attack.

The first live nuclear artillery shell lands with devastating impact in 1953, fired from a US Army 280-mm gun. Modern NATO and Soviet heavy artillery now possess a devastating range of nuclear shells which would be temptingly effective.

nated area. The dose rate, date and time of the dose rate reading and date and time of the detonation that produced the contamination will be put on the back. The markers should be placed close enough together so that they cannot be missed.

If you have to pass through a contaminated area you should wear full NBC protection. APCs and AFVs will be protected, but if you are in a soft-skinned vehicle move as quickly as you can, avoiding the dust clouds that may be kicked up. Avoid contact with objects in the contaminated area.

After you have moved through the area, use decontamination equipment on your vehicle and person. You may have to use allied or even enemy equipment, so a familiarity with different types is important. The Warsaw Pact has a wide range of equipment; some systems are vehicle-mounted, but others, like the RDP-4V, is a man pack system rather like a plant-spraying kit. Others fit on 20-litre jerry cans or are specifically designed for use on weapons such as machine-guns or mortars.

After the bomb

In a post-nuclear strike environment at home, survival and the maintenance of order will become a priority. Even a small group of civilian men or women will offer a core around which order can be rebuilt. Government is not the business of soldiers, so you should make your group available to a representative of government, however lowly they may be, and advise and assist him or her in the restoration of order.

WARNING	METHOD	MEANING
Attack Warning (RED)	**By siren (rising and falling note) and by BBC broadcast**	**Imminent danger of air attack**
Fallout Warning (BLACK)	**By maroon, gong or whistle (three bangs or blasts in quick succession)**	**Imminent danger of fallout**
All Clear (WHITE)	**By siren (steady note)**	**No further danger**

CHAPTER THREE

HUMPING IT ALL ABOUT

Footwear worn in combat today bears little resemblance to those gleaming black boots which make the ground shake as a regiment of the Queen's Guards crashes to attention during the ceremony of Trooping the Colour in London, so it is no news to an infantryman to be told that one of the most important items of his equipment is his boots. They have to be very reliable and well fitting, for any soldier incapacitated because his boots were in some way faulty can literally be a dead loss to his unit.

At the same time, a soldier is responsible for keeping his feet as healthy as possible and to the best of his ability. If a serving man reports sick with foot problems that might have been avoided had the correct remedial treatment been given early enough, he can usually expect to be before his Commanding Officer and on the receiving end of disciplinary action.

The extreme terrain experienced in the Falklands campaign highlighted serious deficiencies in the British Army's pattern of combat boots. Unlike the footwear worn by the Argentinian forces, whose boots were ideal, the British boot came in for a great deal of criticism from the infantry. This chapter begins with an article about this the most important subject of footwear as used by a number of different armies, including those worn by soldiers in Russia's Red Army with their very distinctive sole pattern. It is safe to say that the last word in the design of military fighting boots has not been written.

From boots to webbing and the next two articles describe how best to carry bedding, clothing, ammunition, food and water, field-dressings and first aid supplies, knife, compass, entrenching tool, NCB gear – and still be able to make a long forced march across rough terrain and then go into action when you get there.

From HQ down to the individual soldier, the secret of most aspects of warfare is mobility and logistics – the organisation of equipment and how safely to transport it where and when it is needed. In the case of the infantryman well-fitted webbing is the answer and that old saying 'A place for everything and everything in its place' is engraved indelibly on every soldier's memory.

In some circumstances, carrying it is the only way and the third and fourth articles in this chapter of SURVIVAL describe the system in detail, including fascinating (and totally unbelievable) photographic breakdowns of each item, culminating in the Complete Equipment Fighting Order based on the 58 Pattern webbing, which is soon, we are informed, to be replaced.

The new boot, the Improved Boot Combat High Mark II, is supple and reliable and has a special sock to improve waterproofing.

This mass of essential combat equipment must be carried – no one will do it for you, for in an army every man and every rank has his own problems, and in article five there is an incredible account of what one British paratrooper carried into battle in the Falklands, how he coped with severe equipment problems – and what he had left when the fighting was over.

'Marching Order', a time-worn phrase familiar to everyone who has ever served as a soldier. It is now known as CEMO, short for Complete Equipment Marching Order, and the awesome extent of it is the subject of the last feature in this chapter. One look at those photographs should be enough to put any man off contemplating joining an infantry regiment.

In the field and on the move, a soldier must carry all the necessities for fighting as well as first aid, food and drink.

Fighting Footwear

Sound boots, correctly chosen for the terrain and the role you undertake, are as important as your pack, waterproofs or belt order. Men have become casualties and even had their feet amputated through cold, wet conditions that have produced what was called 'trench foot' in World War I.

It is essential to keep your feet in good condition before you even consider the boots and socks that you are going to use in the field. Athlete's foot and other fungal disorders can become crippling if they go untreated and feet stay damp for long periods. Toenails need to be kept trimmed. One veteran of the Vietnam War used to change into 'flip flop' shower sandals whenever he could to allow air to circulate, and during three tours in Vietnam he had no trouble. When you change your socks, use the dry top half to clean and dry between your toes.

Reducing blisters

Use your issue Foot and Body Powder on your toes and soles and, particularly in hot wet environments, in your groin and armpits. Powder will not only combat fungal disorders but reduce sweat and thus the potential for blisters.

Blisters afflict everyone, but with boots that have been broken in and moulded to your feet there is far less chance that they will occur. On the market there are some proprietary kits for blisters – Spenco, a US firm, makes a very good range of products that not only allow you to repair the damage caused by blisters but also to anticipate them by padding areas where they may develop.

Socks for absorption

Socks are the next layer. Padded sole socks which are produced for sportsmen and outdoor activities absorb sweat and protect the sole. The Swiss army has an excellent sock with pure wool soles, heels and toes, but a stretch nylon upper. The upper gives some support to your calves and will never slide down, even under the most strenuous activity. Civilian cotton socks for tennis or squash players are excellent in tropical areas. Avoid thin civilian nylon socks – they will almost certainly give blisters and trap sweat.

Most of this advice could have been given to you by an officer in World War I. Nowadays, Gore-Tex, a breathable fabric originating in the United States but now widely used in Europe, has revolutionised waterproofing. In essence, it has minute pores that allow condensation to escape without permitting larger water droplets to penetrate. When used in the construction of boots it saves weight as well as making them waterproof; as socks (a French concept) or boot liners (a US and British concept) Gore-Tex has

The Gore-Tex sock is a tremendous breakthrough for the infantryman and it would be possible for the British Army to issue them as standard.

The boot on a dead Argentine soldier. They had excellent boots: full length, with leather upper and sole plus storm welt.

In the Falklands the British Army Issue Boots DMS (Direct Moulded Sole) were simply not up to the job. They were light ankle boots, they tended to stay wet and easily led to trench foot. Many troops used their NBC overboots to keep their feet dry and many Royal Marines wore privately-purchased boots.

u must look after your feet: a good tip is to keep a plastic bag full of foot wder which you can dip your feet in. Change your socks as often as ssible, drying wet ones in your armpits, and use insulating insoles.

The new Boots Combat High introduced into the British Army after the Falklands have a full-length tongue and are waterproof. But the leather softens quickly, destroying the waterproofing.

solved a nagging problem: if a boot is totally waterproof (like a Wellington boot) your foot will slop about in sweat, but if it can breathe, as with leather, this will allow water to penetrate and socks and feet will become wet and cold.

Breathing liners

Gore-Tex boot liners have to be correctly sized, and the socks, which use a lighter-weight fabric, have to be treated with care when they are put on: if the breathable membrane is broken they cease to be waterproof.

Inner soles are another area where improvements have recently been made. These used to be either a nylon mesh or a cork inner. Today's foam rubber, though, has a nasty way of becoming sweat-soaked, but the Norwegian army has a practical idea: it uses newspaper as inner soles. By changing it each day you will keep your boots dry and it also gives some insulation. The trick is to be able to tear the layers of paper to make a neat fit inside the boot.

Sorbothane rubber – developed for sports shoe inners – is also used in service footwear. It is a tough rubber that absorbs the shock either of walking or running and so does not transfer it through your feet to the rest of your body. You will be glad of the investment after a cross-country yomp!

Boots for the job

Though some servicemen will assert that their temperate issue combat boots are fine wherever they go, there are better boots for climatic extremes.

The US Army jungle boot developed for the Vietnam War is now very widely used in hot and wet environments. It has a canvas, leather and nylon upper with air holes at the instep and is a tough and comfortable boot to wear. The soles have changed since the Vietnam War; the non-clogging Panama sole gives good traction, but does not have sharp angles that used to collect mud and so slow the soldier down. There are versions of the boot in black and desert tan as well as the conventional olive drab.

Combat boots for temperate climates have a number of interesting features. The US Army introduced a boot at the end of World War II that had a double buckle wrap over the anklet, attached to the upper of the boot. This means you can quickly put the boot on even if there is no opportunity to lace it up, and it also reduces the need for laces right up the ankle. It has been adopted as the basis for the French 'Ranger' combat boot as well

Rhodesian Light Infantry boots had a stipple pattern instead of a tread, and no heel, to make them harder to track.

West German boots are extremely tough, a good airborne boot, and have a speed lacing system using tubular eyes.

Like the French boots, these Czech officer's boots copy the US Army style of the 1950s with the double buckle wrap.

French Ranger boots have a double buckle wrap, which allows you to put them on in a hurry without tying the laces.

Rugged and comfortable, British desert boots are made of suede with a sorbothane inner.

The US firm Rocky produces these top quality High Combat Boots, which are far superior to any government issue kit.

as the Czechoslovakian army boot and other Eastern Bloc footwear.

The USSR has retained the short 'jack boot'. The West Germans produced an excellent speed-lacing system that does not use conventional hook and eyes, but small tube-like eyes. With the laces in a criss-cross pattern, the soldier can quickly tighten them up by pulling as they slide effortlessly through the 'tube eyes'. The boot also has a padded tongue, and second-hand boots have been popular in the British Army. The speed-lacing system will soon be adopted by the US Army.

The Norwegians use a mix of hook and eyes; a hook at the top, and eyes

around the foot area to ensure a good fit. Also, the sole has a groove to take skis.

Some excellent commercial combat boots have been produced, notably in the United States, and the firms of Timberland and Rocky have taken the 'high boot' to a quality well beyond that found in mass-produced government contract footwear.

The 'British Boot, High Combat' has received a mixed press. Many people are quite happy but some soldiers have suffered problems with their tendons; others have found that their boots wear out and collapse easily.

Lacing for boots has been the subject of some interest. Dismissing fancy 'parade' patterns found in the US and France, a lacing pattern should allow, in an emergency, a surgeon to run a knife down the front and pull the laces apart. A criss-cross pattern does not allow this, but a neat and effective method is a single length knotted at the top, taken down to the front and then brought through the eyes in a spiral configuration, to be wrapped around the ankle and tucked away at the top.

Arctic footwear

Insulated Arctic footwear will keep you very warm when you are standing as a sentry or engaged in light work. However, violent action will produce sweating – though confined inside the boot this will not present the cold hazard it would in ordinary footwear – and the boots are very bulky and clumsy to move about in.

The Royal Marines recommend reflective Dr Scholl thermal inner soles in combat boots.

Boots Ski March – a Royal Marine issue – let you wear skis or move conventionally on foot.

British desert boots are not the flimsy 'brothel creepers' that you can buy in the High Street, but father of that old friend Boot, DMS – in suede with a yellow-brown sole. They are tough and cool and, with a sorbothane inner, immensely comfortable.

Look out for this print! This is the left-hand boot print produced by the standard Soviet army combat boot.

Footprints are distinctive, and in a CRW (Counter Revolutionary Warfare) campaign this can be a valuable aid to tracking. The Rhodesian and British forces looked at soles with a slightly stippled tread so that there was no pattern. Also, slip-on overshoes were developed with no toe or heel shapes so that the direction of movement would not show on the track. If issue footwear was to be worn, everyone had to wear the same: a random pattern would alert trackers to the presence of an intruder.

Improvised boots

You can improvise boots from a variety of materials; canvas, cardboard, wood, vehicle tyres, webbing and even parachute nylon can all be pressed into service. If you don't have any socks, wind strips of old cloth around your foot and leg. The Russians still do this, and veterans speak of its comfort and effectiveness!

Left: Your foot can be wrecked by the simplest trap, in this case a Viet Cong punji stick pit: sharpened bamboo smeared with excrement to infect the wound.

Left and below: The late pattern US Army jungle boot with panama soles which don't trap as much mud as more angular treads. Walking across a paddy dyke your feet receive an inevitable soaking, but the drainage holes in the boot let the water out again.

A regular soldier of the North Vietnamese Army clutches his Ho Chi Minh sandals cut from old truck tyres: simple but effective footwear commonly used by both NVA and VC troops.

Personal Load Carrying

'**There are two things you need in your equipment: ammunition, food and more ammunition,' so said a Royal Marines Captain after the 1982 campaign in the Falklands.** These priorities, as well as a few others, have to be fitted either onto your back, or in the pouches around your belt. It is an old axiom that you live with the load on your back, fight with the load on your belt and survive with the contents of your combat jacket pockets.

Webbing

All armies issue their soldiers with load-carrying equipment widely known in the English-speaking world as 'webbing', though now it is often made of nylon. Some armies and units insist that their soldiers use only issue equipment and allow no freedom for alteration or adjustment.

However, when you can adjust your webbing, the popular 'belt order' is often favoured. Basically, this is a belt, generally without the load-carrying yoke across the shoulders. The belt order should have an adjustable buckle – aircraft cargo straps were very popular, though now 'Fastex' plastic buckles can be quickly adjusted or opened.

The belt should be wide enough to take the range of issue pouches and water-bottle carriers you may have access to. Nylon has become widely available from US All-Purpose Lightweight Individual Carrying Equipment (ALICE), though webbing has some advantages. Nylon is lighter, less prone to saturation by water and very strong; however, webbing will not burn and so stick to the wearer. The same fire considerations apply to metal and plastic fittings, but are also compounded by the tendency of plastic to become brittle in very cold temperatures.

Individual loads for operations must be a compromise between two principles: maximum self-reliance and minimum weight. Here a paratrooper struggles away from the drop zone, still carrying his reserve on his chest and main chute stacked on his Bergen.

Leather is still used for some items on a belt order – scabbards for knives and pouches for clasp knives are common examples. However, leather has the disadvantage that it rots in the damp of the jungle, and can become saturated in wet weather.

The load

The first consideration is: is there an NBC threat? If the enemy are likely to use chemical weapons, then your kit must include a respirator and NBC clothing. This latter item is bulky, but must be accommodated. The respirator should be positioned on the left, so that your right hand with the rifle or SMG is free while your left hand reaches for the respirator. The respirator case should also contain the relevant cleaning, decontamination and repair kits for your NBC clothing.

The next priority on your belt is ammunition. The choice of pouches depends on the size of magazines your rifle takes, as well as grenades. Like the respirator, the magazines on the left will be easier to reach when a rifle is in the right hand. The Rhodesian forces in the 1960s and 1970s adopted the terrorists' ammunition stowage methods by putting their magazines in chest webbing – this puts a row of magazines in a separate harness, but also allows the wearer to carry more on his belt.

Carrying grenades

Grenades can be carried on the ALICE pouches, but care should be taken if they are stowed externally. If the handles are tucked into loops, the grenades – with the pin in place – have a nasty way of dropping off if the wearer takes any violent action. This not only gives a grenade to anyone in the area, but also deprives you of one when you need it. It is better to stow them inside a pouch.

Other ammunition such as M60 or GPMG link can be carried, and a 66LAW can be attached with bungees to the rear of the webbing. Machine-gun link can catch the light, and must be stowed inside a pouch or bandolier.

Knives and bayonets

A bayonet or knife will also be part of your belt order. Modern bayonets are more likely to be a combat knife design, with saw edge and wire cutters. Do not dismiss the clasp knife: the Swiss Army Knife with its multi-function blades will give better service than a spectacular sheath knife, and a 'survival' knife will either be taken from you if you are captured,

The ALICE system

ALICE, the All Purpose Lightweight Individual Carrying Equipment used by the US Army and popular worldwide, is basically designed for troops who are operating from APCs. It can be expanded from this basic layout to the equivalent of the British Fighting Order. Made of nylon, it is stronger, lighter and easier to de-contaminate than British webbing, and it does not shrink. On the other hand, it melts in a fire and in very low temperatures it cracks.

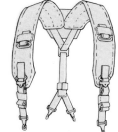

Harness/yoke
Adjust the straps so the V-shape is at the nape of your neck and the belt is positioned correctly on the waist. Then tape them down so that they don't move.

Water bottle
As with all plastic water bottles, keep it away from your burner and any other heat source. It holds less than the British water bottle but is easier to get at while wearing NBC gloves. The side pocket holds sterilizing tablets.

Magazine pouch
This takes 3×30-round M16 magazines and is therefore also suitable for the SA80. The side pouches are for L2 hand grenades. The clip closure makes it easier to use than British kit, and because it exactly fits the magazines you are not tempted to squeeze extra kit in as well!

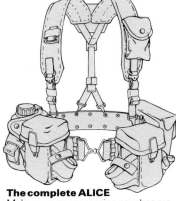

The complete ALICE
Make sure your magazine pouches are not too far forward on the belt, firstly because this restricts your movement, and secondly because it makes it difficult to get at your ammunition while lying prone.

Belt
If you have a thin waist you will have a problem carrying extra pouches, so pad the belt with foam rubber and a scrim scarf to get a snug fit. Equipment that doesn't fit properly is very tiring to carry over long distances.

Compass or field dressing case
Can be worn on the yoke, but it gets in the way when you are wearing a Bergen, so in that case put it on your belt. Secure your compass with a lanyard so that you don't lose it. Remember that everyone should carry their first field dressing in the same place.

Entrenching tool/cover
The US Army entrenching tool folds neatly away and can be used for scooping as well as picking, but it is nowhere near as tough as a proper infantry spade and is useless for serious digging.

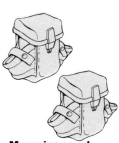

Magazine pouch
You normally carry two magazine pouches, but the webbing will take more. These US pouches can be closed with one hand and can be attached to British webbing for survival/first aid pouches. There is no right and left pouch, unlike the British system.

How to use the clips

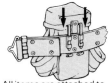

1 All items are attached to the webbing by the same method. Push the belt under the clips, then press the tops down to close.

2 Make sure the clip is properly closed, as shown on the left; the one on the right is undone.

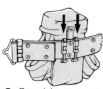

3 Once it is set up, tape and wire everything in position to stop the pouches moving or falling off during strenuous activity.

In jungle warfare, the lightweight Bergen with frame is far superior to the issue '58 pattern Large Pack, as it is lighter and less likely to rot.

thus defeating its function as a survival tool, or will be less than accessible among your belt order.

With sheath or clasp knives, do not choose something that has to be dismantled to be used. With all knives, remember to carry a sharpening stone or steel – a blunt knife is useless and dangerous. There may also be a place for a hatchet or machete if you are working in close jungle or bush.

If there is a threat of enemy artillery or mortar bombardment, your lightweight pick or shovel or entrenching tool is as important as weapon or NBC kit. The entrenching tool with its adjustable pick and spade blade is a

The 'H' frame Bergen carries the load high on the back and is therefore quite comfortable, but it is impossible to fire from the prone position while wearing it.

versatile tool – the current NATO item folds to a compact triangle which can be stowed on rucksack or belt order. Older entrenching tools may have a sharp edge ground on to one side of the spade blade to serve as an axe in a close combat action.

Compasses

Food and navigation come very close seconds after ammunition, and for simplicity we will look at navigation first. A good compass on your belt should be complemented by one either on your wrist, or in your combat smock pocket. Orienteering compasses are cheap and reliable, and fit easily into a pocket. Silva are good but make sure they are graduated in mils and not degrees.

The US Army Lensatic Compass or British Prismatic Compass are excellent for accurate navigation and night work. They can be stowed in their pouches on the right or your left-hand pouch – once again, this allows you to use them with your hand on your rifle – and ALICE equipment allows you to stow the compass on the yoke, though this position is more commonly used for the first field dressing. Your compass should be attached by a lanyard – drop it at night without a lanyard and you are in deep trouble. Night work also requires light: use your compass under a poncho and with a red filtered torch. Tough plastic pen torch designs with a lanyard and clip are now available and are ideal – they can be carried

in the smock pen pocket. The radioactive Beta light torch is probably best.

A map case may be attached to the belt order, or stowed inside the smock. It should have a green or camouflaged cover, and a clear plastic cover for the map – wet maps are useless maps, and a clear cover allows you to mark the overlay and not the map.

Food and water

Water should be in a plastic bottle with a metal mug, and your water-purifying tablets should be easily accessible. If they are not co-located with the water bottle there may be men in your patrol who forget to add them to untreated water.

The metal mug allows you to brew up – add some masking tape to the edge to prevent your lips from burning when you drink from it. Tough aluminium foil can also be packed in the water bottle carrier and used to cover the mug when you are brewing up; this reduces the heat loss from the open top.

You have a knife, so a spoon is all you need to eat. US Army MRE (Meals Ready to Eat) and C-rations come with a plastic spoon, but a larger spoon is handier when you are cooking.

Though plastic explosive in small blobs can be used instead of cooking fuel tablets, this is misuse and a waste of its proper potential. Fuel tablets, including the well-tried German Esbit, should be stowed in the belt order. They may be issued with rations, but this is by no means certain

A Survival Aids 'Crusader' Bergen buried underneath sleeping bag, kip mat, and hooped bivvy bag set. Note the extravagant number of bungees needed to hold all this together.

– nor is the issue of toilet paper! Keep spares of both.

The brew kit and basic rations on your belt order should be enough for two days of brews – eight to ten – and food enough to do two meals. US MREs in their retort pouches have minimal weight, can be folded and have their own liquid in them. Dehydrated meals need water and can be slightly bulky.

Salt and sugar may be needed, according to climate, and in almost any climate hot tea and sugar can be wonderfully restorative. Dried herbs, curry powder and other additives to issue rations make them more varied and take little space or weight. A gas cigarette lighter is a useful supplement to the matches that come with a 24-hour ration – solid fuel tablets can take a lot of lighting in wind or rain.

Protection

By now you are beginning to think that you have to have a waist the size of an all-in wrestler to take the load on a belt order – and there's more to come.

A poncho, waterproof clothing and other protective clothing is essential in temperate and tropical climates. A poncho with bungees and pegs and a foil space blanket take up a tube about 45 cms by 12 cm if they are rolled tightly. They allow you to erect a shelter without having to rely on the arrival of your large pack or rucksack.

Waterproof clothing ideally in a breathing fabric like Goretex, can also be carried. A smock and gaiters will provide protection without bulk, the gaiters protecting you against wet penetration through bracken or long grass. Nylon parachute cord will also assist in shelter construction and can be used as shoe laces.

Field dressings

A basic first-aid kit with your first field dressings – note you need more than one, a bullet has an exit hole as well as an entry point – is an essential part of your kit. It will allow you to do the running repairs on blisters, minor cuts, headaches and small burns.

With practice, you will decide on the most useful additions to the first-aid kit. In the tropics insect-repellant may be handy; if you are working in rough and rocky terrain, cuts and grazes may be common, and antiseptic swabs are important before you dress these cuts. A good pair of surgical scissors and a scalpel with blades are a vital part of the kit. A simple plastic 'fever scan' type thermometer which can be placed on the forehead is useful.

A belt order may seem a complex load to have slung around your middle, but with practice you will find yourself discarding some things and adding others.

In Vietnam, US soldiers carried up to 480 rounds of 5.56-mm ammunition each – one of the advantages the lighter calibre has over 7.62-mm NATO. This man wears the late-model flak jacket; webbing pouches can be clipped directly to it.

Combat Jacket and Webbing

Experience has shown that many soldiers lack the ability, knowledge and experience to prepare for and remain organised during long exercises and operations. It is vital that you keep yourself and your equipment in peak condition.

The aim here is to provide you with a practical guide to living and operating in the field. We will concentrate on equipment issued by the British armed forces, but will suggest items that can be bought to enhance the issue equipment.

In the Falklands, walking wounded are escorted to a Scout helicopter for casevac. Don't wait for a combat situation to find you are carrying the wrong kit.

The combat jacket and contents

You should pack your combat jacket as carefully as you pack your webbing. A packed combat jacket can weigh over 5 kg. Work out a place for everything (although some items will have to be carried in positions laid down by unit standard operational procedures).

There are several types of combat jacket available. The new issue type shown below is probably the worst: it is not very hard-wearing and the bulbous pockets are easily holed or torn off, and it is only three-quarters lined. The 'old type'

general issue combat jacket still commonly available is far more robust; all the seams are double stitched, it is fully lined and does not have bulbous pockets.

The para smock is generally good but a bit thin for really cold weather; unit SOPs may forbid its use. The SAS windproof smock is excellent if worn in conjunction with, say, a fibre pile jacket.

If possible, always dry clean new jackets; they have a treatment in the lining to reduce your thermal image.

The private soldier's kit

These are the things you must carry as a private soldier.

1 Around your neck are two ID discs, inscribed on which are your name, number, rank, blood group and religion. In wartime you would also carry morphine, an Omnopon syrinette.

2 A top pocket will contain various pens, pencils and chinagraphs and a notebook, waterproofed in a plastic bag. You use the notebook for writing down orders, stag lists etc.

3 One shell dressing, usually carried in the top right hand pocket, is woefully inadequate; carry as many as you sensibly can, and when treating a casualty use his dressing first. Dressings need to be sealed in plastic as well.

4 A lock blade or clasp knife attached to you by a lanyard will be far more use than any 'Rambo' style cutlass.

These are the basics, but essentials that you ought to carry include spare dressings, a small first-aid kit, and Dextrosol tablets; a survival kit; gloves; a few 7.62-mm tracer rounds for target indication; a pocket torch with the bulb painted red, and spare batteries; a lighter; spare flannelette (for weapon cleaning); plastic bags for covering wounds in a chemical environment; a headover; and at least 20 metres of dyed para cord. Pad the hard items with the soft stuff and you will avoid bruises when you take cover.

An extra 20-round magazine in the inside pocket is always a good idea, and your quilted combat liner or a thin waterproof jacket will fit into the 'bum pocket' inside the back of the jacket.

If your jacket is for field use only, you can sew strips of thick black elastic on the arms and body for local camouflage. A pair of old socks with the feet cut out and sewn on the inside of the wristbands will make it warmer and more comfortable.

Map, gloves and orders book

Maps should be protected in map cases or by Fablon: cover the map with Fablon and soak the paper off in water, leaving the detail stuck to the Fablon. Before you do this, highlight the grid references with a highlighter pen and colour in the mature woods, which on military maps are so light in colour you can hardly see them. Note the 'orders book' for giving orders to the section; this is a prepared book covering all the phases of battle, attack, defence, patrolling, withdrawal etc and is used in conjunction with the aide memoire.

Notebook, string, mine tape, face veil, torch

As section commander you have a notebook in which are recorded details of each section member. The 50-metre lengths of string are for use as communication cords in a patrol harbour or defensive position, or when setting up a linear ambush. The white mine tape is useful for various route-marking tasks. Face veils are good as sweat rags and as camouflage when thrown over the head. A reliable pocket torch is an essential, but a beta light (a radioactive source that gives out green light) is the better option for patrolling.

The section commander's kit

If you're the corporal in charge of the section, you need the above items in addition to your personal kit to enable you to command your section in the field and communicate within the section and with the platoon commander. Your second-in-command (usually a lance corporal) will carry exactly the same so that he can control his fire team and take over command of the section if you are wounded. He would carry issue binoculars and spare morphine around his neck.

Compass, protractor, para cord, route card

A Silva-type compass is a must: easier to use than the issue prismatic (but less accurate), and excellent for night patrolling. Your compass must be graduated in mils and degrees (the RAF works in degrees, and you may need to talk to them for casevac or an air strike). You will need two types of protractor. The knotted para cord is for counting the number of hundreds of metres you have covered during a patrol; after every 100 metres you pull another knot through your top pocket buttonhole. The plastic plate is a basic route card on which you write the distance and bearing of each leg of a patrol.

Dressings and medical/survival kits

Everyone has three field dressings and a larger burn/shell dressing. As section commander you will carry a supply of cam cream, some tracer rounds, and fire control orders. In addition to survival and medical kits you will also have a small model kit — a collection of coloured string and labels that enable you to make a detailed model of an operational area when briefing the section.

57

The primary function of personal load carrying equipment is the carriage of ammunition, water and rations or medical equipment.

The traditional system, the 58 pattern webbing, is a yoke or harness attached to a belt supporting an array of pouches containing the equipment. This spreads the weight between the waist and shoulders.

Disadvantages

Although now rather archaic, the 58 pattern is a well-designed piece of kit, very robust and reasonably comfortable when correctly fitted. But it is heavy and bulky compared to modern equivalents and shrinks badly when wet.

The ammo pouches do not exactly fit either SLR or SA80 magazines, and are very difficult to close with one hand. The water bottle pouch is an extremely tight fit – a particularly

What it's all about: a painful and exhausting bash across country. In the Falklands, yomping with kit well in excess of your own bodyweight was the norm, with a digging-in session and a fight at the end of it.

annoying fault, and adding the S6 respirator haversack and NBC equipment makes the webbing extremely cumbersome. But perhaps the major failing is that it is very difficult to decontaminate and will soak up chemical agents.

The new webbing, PLCE (Personal Load Carrying Equipment) is designed to accommodate 30-round SA80 magazines, is very light and easier to decontaminate, but it will burn and does not provide the limited degree of protection from fragmentation that the 58 pattern provides.

Handy hints

1 When you have assembled your webbing, check it for fit, jog around in it, make any adjustments and then tape everything down. Use about four bungees to hold it all together; this will stop the pouches bouncing around or falling off when you are running.
2 The 58 pattern was not designed for the extra demands of chemical warfare, so you need to devise some system of carrying your NBC suit and overboots when you are not wearing them. An empty poncho roll secured to your kidney pouches is a good solution, although the arm or leg ripped out of an old combat suit will do. There are also a few commercially manufactured NBC rolls available.
3 When it gets wet your NBC suit will no longer fit; it is worth fitting an adjustable pin buckle. The Burghams buckle (as used on rucksacks) is also suitable.
4 If you're large, you're at an advantage for once: you will be able to carry more pouches. A first aid/survival pouch and an extra water bottle are popular additions, and extra room for ammunition and grenades is always useful.
5 Black elastic sewn onto the pouches is essential for holding camouflage.

'Building your rig'

Assembling the British Army 1958 pattern webbing

To assemble your webbing you will need a screwdriver, a pair of pliers and some thick insulating tape. Your webbing is your lifeline in the field: if you make sure it fits correctly at this stage you will be able to fight in relative comfort. Ill-fitting webbing is as disastrous as an unzeroed weapon; it will tire you unnecessarily, and may fall apart.

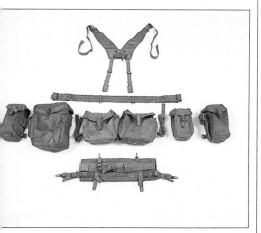

The component parts

From top to bottom, the yoke and belt; and from left to right the ammunition pouch, S6 respirator haversack, kidney pouches, water bottle pouch and another ammunition pouch. Finally, the poncho cape carrier.

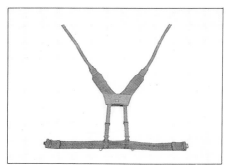

Putting it on
1 First adjust the belt to the right size for your waist.
2 Decide at this point if you are going to pad the belt with foam and face veil or kip mat material.
3 Attach the yoke to the belt; note that the metal rings in the belt point downwards. For a firm fit, work open the recesses which is adequate to hold it together when new, but when it's worn in the pouches will fall off unless fixed properly. The photograph shows the clips outside the recesses which is adequate to hold it together when new, but when it's worn in the pouches will fall off unless fixed properly.
4 Adjust the straps so that the Y of the yoke is at the nape of your neck and the belt just above your hips.

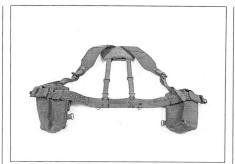

Ammo pouches
5 The right-hand ammo pouch has a smaller pouch on the side, and the left hand pouch has bayonet loops. The pouches slant rearwards and have attachments on the top for the yoke and on the bottom for the poncho carrier. Make sure you put the ammo pouches as far back as you can so that you can easily get to your magazines in the prone position. Again, you will need a screwdriver and pliers to fit them.
6 The yoke attaches to the flat metal ring on top of the ammo pouch. Push it through from the back, then up and down through the rings on the yoke.
7 Now adjust the front of the yoke so that the belt is horizontal all the way round your waist.

Kidney pouches
8 Each kidney pouch has two webbing tabs that secure loops over the belt and the yoke respectively. The top loops always come loose and flap about, so tape the whole thing down. You may have to undo it all for weapon training and range work (picture 3 is known as Weapon Training Order). The solution to the problem is to buy a second set; it is well worth while.

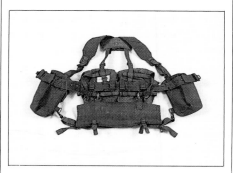

Pouch cape carrier
9 This has four clips on it, two on the top and one on each side. There is a pouch on the back of it designed to hold a pick helve. Make sure you put it on the right way round.
10 Use the adjusters to pull the ammo pouches right back. An alternative position is on top of the kidney pouches instead of below it.

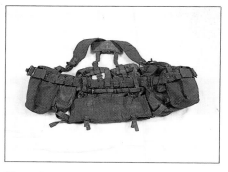

Water bottle pouch
11 Clip this on in the same way as the ammo pouches.
12 The respirator haversack can either be slipped onto the belt through its loop or carried using the strap over the shoulder. This will depend on unit SOPs but if the haversack is on your webbing you should never be more than five paces away from it at any time.
13 Practise to find out which is the best position for you to get at your respirator quickly.

Complete webbing
14 The basic 58 webbing is complete. Note the attachment on the yoke for spade or pick. There is another clip on the poncho which holds the other end of the spade.

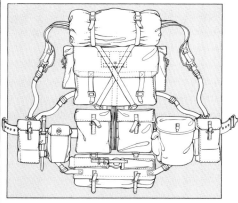

CEFO and CEMO
The webbing, or Complete Equipment Fighting Order (CEFO), is ideally what you actually fight in. With the large pack added it becomes CEMO, Complete Equipment Marching Order, and should contain all that you need to survive in the field. The large pack and webbing were designed as an integrated system, but the large pack is horribly uncomfortable and far too small for the sort of load an infantryman has to carry today. Also, if you come under fire with your large pack attached correctly as shown it takes a good 10 minutes to get it off!

Equipped for Battle

As a rifleman in an infantry section, you will fight in CEFO (Complete Equipment Fighting Order). We have already considered how the equipment is carried; here we show you what is carried and why. The contents shown are geared towards conventional war on NATO's Central Front in West Germany.

Essential items only

The weight of what you carry with ammunition may easily be in excess of 15 kg, so eliminate all non-essential items. The result will be a load consisting of basic individual requirements, basic unit/patrol requirements, and special task equipment.

Wartime changes

The kit on the right is the basic general layout that will be insisted upon during your training as a recruit at an infantry depot. However, in war this layout would certainly change to some extent to accommodate more ammunition. The kit details are not an official list but simply a guide, and you must not contravene your own unit's SOPs (Standard Operating Procedures).

With efficient management, you should be able to live on the contents of your webbing for at least 48 hours. SAS troopers are taught to live using the contents of their belt for weeks, not days.

Personal kit needs a good deal of time, expense and effort to make sure it works. Attention to this unglamorous detail shows the difference between an amateur and a professional.

The Royal Marines clear Grytviken, South Georgia. The one with the LMG (light machine-gun) is wearing an SAS-type windproof smock, gaiters and non-issue fell boots. The Northern Ireland gloves he is wearing are leather and easily become sodden and useless. The other one, with the GPMG, has Arctic-issue gloves; these are excellent for warmth, but restrict dexterity.

Complete Equipment Fighting Order: 58 Pattern Webbing

The 58 pattern webbing is due to be replaced by the new personal-load carrying equipment designed specifically for the *SA80*. Battalions issued with the *SA80* have the same webbing contents except for six 30-round magazines of 5.56-mm ball instead of five 20-round magazines of 7.62-mm ball, and a 150-round bandolier of 5.56-mm for the *LSW* instead of a *GPMG* belt.

Left ammo pouch

1 The bayonet and scabbard fit into the loops on the side of the pouch; the button on the scabbard goes in the cut in the loops. The bayonet itself is not designed for cutting or slashing and the handle is also a bit short for effective use as a fighting knife, so stabbing is really all it is good for. Practise firing your rifle with the bayonet fitted as it will affect the MPI (mean point of impact) of your shots.

2 Three SLR magazines and perhaps a spare 7.62-mm belt or an L2 grenade complete this pouch. You must not put anything other than ammunition in here.

NBC roll

Any future war in Europe would see extensive use of chemical weapons, which are an important element in the Warsaw Pact armoury. So unfortunately you have to carry the NBC suit and overboots with you on your webbing. The suit will protect you for 24 hours in a grossly contaminated environment.

Don't throw away the packets as you can use these to cover wounds, and don't unpack spare suits until you need them. The arm of an old combat jacket will accommodate the suit, though an extra poncho roll is a better solution.

Poncho roll

1 The poncho is a rectangular waterproof sheet with a hood in the middle and eyelets and press studs around the edges. It can be used as a waterproof garment that will cover both you and your pack, or more commonly as a 'basha'.

2 As a rifleman you will carry a spade or pick, for digging a shell scrape. The pick head is carried in a pocket on the poncho roll with the shaft secured on the yoke. Spades are simply fixed to the yoke and secured by a tab on the poncho roll. Digging tools must be camouflaged.

3 Toggle ropes and/or emergency stretcher can also be carried in the poncho roll, and the 66-mm LAW (Light Anti-tank Weapon) is best strapped to the back of your webbing.

Water bottle pouch and kidney pouches

The water bottle pouch contains your water bottle, cup and water sterilising tablets; keep your bottle full at all times.

The kidney pouches contents start on the left, below the water bottle.

1 Spare pair of socks sealed in plastic.

2 A small personal medical kit, spare batteries for the issue torch and rolls of green string for 'comms cord'.

3 A panscrub.

4 Sand bags.

5 Contents of the kidney pouches are best kept in two-litre plastic margarine boxes. A faceveil or sandbag wrapped round them will stop glimpses of white showing. The two items on the faceveil are issue insect repellent and ear defenders.

Right ammo pouch
1 This has a little pocket on it, originally designed for a grenade-launcher attachment long since out of service. It is a useful place for your knife, fork and spoon (KFS) and perhaps the blank firing attachment (BFA) for the SLR.
2 Two SLR magazines are carried.
3 The SLR cleaning kit (the green plastic box) has to be packed with flannelette so that it won't rattle.
4 Put L2 grenades in this ammo pouch if there is room.
5 Smoke grenades can be taped or clipped onto your webbing, but this is not really recommended.

Respirator haversack
1 This contains your S6 respirator, available in various sizes; a spare canister; NBC gloves, inner and outer; spectacles; an anti-dimmer outfit (the little green tube), which doesn't seem to work; and a number of no. 2 detector paper books.
2 For operations you will be issued three combopens which contain atropine, an antidote for nerve agent poisoning for intramuscular injection, and a diazapan (tranquilliser) tablet in the top.
3 The haversack also contains your personal decontamination kit, comprising a bottle and pads of Fuller's Earth.

Kidney pouches
1 These contain part of your 24-hour ration pack. This should be split up into what you can eat on the move, which goes in your pockets, and what you can't, which goes in your webbing.
2 Spare heavy-duty tape is a must for camouflaging rifle and equipment and for taping down things that rattle.
3 Your boot cleaning kit contains polish, brush, spare bootlaces.
4 The green plastic bottle is foot powder; use liberally whenever possible and change your socks frequently.
5 Camouflage cream should be re-applied whenever you sweat it off.

Kidney pouches
1 The wash kit should include half a towel, half a bar of anti-bacterial soap, half a toothbrush, half a plastic tube of toothpaste and a shaving mirror.
2 The hexamine stove is a reasonably effective cooker although the fuel can be difficult to light, so make sure you have a lighter.
3 Remove hexamine from the bottom of your mess tin with a pan scrub.
4 Brew kit.
5 Tie a can opener to a length of paracord and tie that into the loop inside the kidney pouch.
6 Always carry spare toilet paper in a plastic bag.

Preparing Your Battle Load

We have looked at the kit you will carry as an infantry soldier on exercise in peacetime. Now we see what you might carry in war, and how your kit can be modified to improve your chances on the modern battlefield. On exercise, you tend to carry items that make life easier and which would not necessarily increase your combat effectiveness.

There are considerable restraints placed on training during peacetime, so you must personally adopt a train-for-war attitude, starting with your kit. This is intended as a general guide, and what you are able to do will depend greatly on unit SOPs and tasks.

Right: Every time you pack your kit, think it through: do I really need it? Is this a logical place for it? Once you have established a routine, stick to it: always put kit in the same place. In wartime badly-arranged or useless kit could mean the difference between life and death.

A realistic combat load

The Falklands rewrote the book as far as some tactics are concerned. In training, a Company attack fighting through a platoon-sized enemy position from the EFL (Effective Fire Line) to Reorg would usually take about 20 minutes maximum, with a lot of running involved. The same attack in the Falklands took two or three hours at least, and involved a lot of crawling around and several reorganisation phases as the forward platoons worked through the position. Massive amounts of ammunition were expended, and maintaining the momentum of attacks became a real problem.

One paratrooper started an attack with 14 20-round SLR magazines and a sandbag slung around his neck containing a further 200 rounds of ball, together with 200 rounds for the GPMG; not forgetting a mixed bag of L2 and white phosphorus grenades and two 66-mm LAWs. He spent most of the attack from the EFL onwards skirmishing forward on his belly, used all his ammunition, and ended up rummaging through dead Argentines' pouches for spare FAL magazines.

Use this kit layout as a basis for ideas. Exercise is the place for trialling new pieces of kit and methods of carriage. Check out what is available, and decide whether each item of kit will help you in battle.

A realistic combat load

Ammunition carriages

A real step forward has been the adoption of the SA80 in 5.56-mm. This is an 'intermediate' cartridge and is a good deal lighter than the 7.62-mm NATO round, which means that you can carry far more ammunition into battle. You must get used to carrying a realistic ammunition load now. Load will vary according to task; you will need a lot of ammo for FIBUA and positional defence, with a minimum of at least 8-10 mags with a spare ball to 'replen' your mags plus a belt for a GMPG. The SAS magazine pouch shown holds 4×20-round SLR mags. You can get 7.62-mm ball ammo issued in bandoliers in five-round clips just like the 10-round stripper clips for the SA80, so you can replenish the magazine by using a stripper clip guide. This slots on top of the 20-round magazine and allows you to fill a mag quickly with four five-round stripper clips. The clip guide can be purchased from good gunshops or occasionally obtained from the older armouries. It is certainly faster than loading by hand, but takes practice and can lead to stoppages if the base of the rounds are not right up against the back of the magazine.

Rhodesian Army chest webbing

This is excellent for extra ammo carriage for 4×20-round magazines and a couple of grenades, and can easily be worn in conjunction with your ordinary webbing. It is supported by belt and shoulder straps

Customising your SLR

Very few units will allow you to go to town on an issue weapon, but some will, and there are some simple things you can do to overcome its disadvantages and maximise its good points.

The 7.62-mm round does a good deal more damage to the enemy than the 5.56-mm M193 ball (used for the M16 and Armalite) or the vicious new 5.56-mm SS109 ball (SA80 and M16A2). But this also means that it is overpowered for normal killing distances on the battlefield, uncontrollable in fully automatic fire and difficult to train recruits with, as well as being heavy and relatively slow to acquire a target. The opposition, equipped for the most part with AKMs and AK-74s, have a light, responsive and selective-fire weapon good for short-range and close-quarter battle, so you should exploit your long range advantage by bumping them off at a distance, which requires a very high standard of personal marksmanship. An infantry rifle group is meant to be able to engage at 500 metres.

Scopes

A good shot will improve with the use of telescopic sights rather than iron sights, and for a section commander or scout they are better than binoculars, as they are ready to hand and you are also ready to fire.

Scopes are commercially available with mounts specifically for the SLR, but the better makes are very expensive and only a few jobs would justify such a purchase. Telescopic sights were popular in the early days of the British Army involvement in the current troubles in Northern Ireland before being banned and replaced with the SUIT sight (Sight Unit Infantry Trilux), which is a version of the SUSAT (Sight Unit Small Arms Trilux) seen on the SA80.

Beware! Scopes are good for medium and long-range work, but they drastically reduce your field of view and are therefore no good for close-quarter battle. They are also vulnerable to damage and failure.

Bipods

These will improve accuracy when you are shooting at static targets and, although usually seen on machine-guns, they are useful for assault rifles as well. Remember, they will affect your point of impact, so zero the rifle without the bipod and then note the effect when the bipod is fitted.

Cheap clip-on bipods such as the M16 variety seen left are OK, but the better alternative is the fold-up variety that is attached to the handguard rather than the barrel. Some assault rifles have these fitted as standard.

Firepower

A useful modification is to add a pin into the bolt hold-open device, as on the FAL original design. This will hold the bolt open on your last shot – no more dead-man's click – and faster reloads. AKs have a 30-round magazine, which when fighting through a position could be a significant advantage: magazine change takes vital seconds. You can beg, steal or borrow 30-round LMG (Light Machine Gun) magazines which fit the SLR. These are the things to slap onto your SLR in a final assault position! Make sure you get a gunsmith to beef up the magazine springs, or you'll get stoppages (the LMG loads with the assistance of gravity).

Finally, some units prefer the SLR without sling swivels and carrying handles, and saw them off. A good spray paint job is useful for camouflage, but use your own rifle!

SA80 firepower

SA80 5.56-mm ammunition means more rounds to fire but, with automatic fire capability, faster ammo expenditure. Soldiers are trained in fire discipline to conserve ammo, but even so six magazines are not really adequate. M16 magazines are cheap and plentiful and fit the SA80; they come in 20, 30 and 40-round sizes and they also fit the LSW, so if you use these you no longer have to strip GPMG belt for ammo in an emergency.

Until the new PLCE equipment arrives, ALICE magazine pouches, shown here, are a good buy; they are made for 3×30-round SA80 magazines and they are light, have a clip closure and two pockets for grenades. You may still have to carry a GPMG belt, as the GPMG will be retained in service for fire support.

The pencil flare kit shown is usually carried by section commanders for signalling, illumination, identification etc. The right-angle torch is issue kit, but should have a red filter fitted; white light destroys night vision.

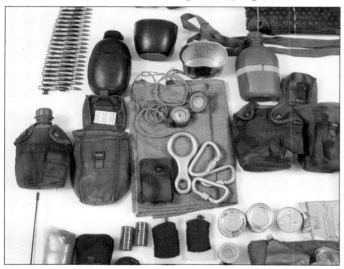

Specialist kit

Abseiling equipment is useful kit. The figure 8 piece can be used for abseiling and belaying in climbing. Karabiners are used in climbing and are also handy for clipping Bergens together to make Bergen rafts on river crossings.

Extra water is a must, especially in an NBC environment when you will sweat a lot and any local sources will be contaminated. American ALICE water carriers are cheap and simply clip onto your belt. A steel mug is far better than the issue mug, as you can cook in it and dispense with your mess tin if needs be. The black tape is for taping around the rim to stop you burning your lips.

The prismatic issue compass is more accurate than the Silva type; NCOs should carry a prismatic on the belt and a Silva spare.

Sleeping with your boots off in a tactical situation is courting disaster, so a sandbag over each boot will keep your sleeping bag clean. The small pouch is a first field dressing pouch from the ALICE system; these are handy pieces of kit and can be clipped to belt or harness.

SAS belt order

SAS troopers usually carry most of their equipment in their Bergens, and the belt order is not intended to carry the load usually carried by infantrymen in CEFO. There is a lot to be said for simply carrying ammunition, water and NBC kit and binning the rest into your Bergen: in war this is a likely scenario.

The weight of the belt is usually enough to leave you with your trousers round your knees, so use cross-straps to transfer some of the weight to your shoulders. If you wear your belt order without kidney pouches you will be able to use a longer-frame Bergen such as the Berghaus, which will enable you to carry heavier loads further and for longer in something less than agony! The small mess tin just fits the escape ration pouch.

Using paint on your webbing rots the material; animal dyes such as agricultural stock-marking fluid are excellent for the job.

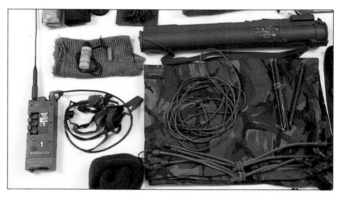

PRC 349 Clansman radio

Usually carried by both fire team commanders in the section, this is an excellent inter-platoon and inter-section radio. Its relatively limited range means you can use it as a chat net during a fire fight, and it uses a throat mike so you don't have to speak loudly to be heard, and it only requires one hand to operate it. Also, it is a lot easier to carry than the PRC 351.

The lightweight DPM basha is a vast improvement on the issue poncho, and does not have a hood in the middle, which is an advantage when you have to pack your webbing into it to keep it dry.

Gore-Tex bivvy bags are excellent kit as long as you can get out of them fast enough! If you are slumbering in a bivvy bag you are a good deal less aware of activity and noise around you. But the poncho, unfortunately, is nowhere near as dry and comfortable.

Variations on a theme

The new PLCE equipment will diminish the need to customise, as it is close to the ideal. The poncho roll on top of the pouches is a popular modification as it leaves the legs with completely unrestricted movement. Note the SAS ammo pouch and SUIT sight pouches on the top set, and the way the ammo pouches are tied well back.

Complete Equipment Marching Order

Whether it's 15 or 45 kg, a soldier carries his home on his back. All his operational needs for extended periods, without support, must be carried. What he carries and how he carries it is therefore of vital importance to his operational effectiveness. His loads will vary depending on the type of operation, the environment, the duration, and his role as a soldier.

Basically, the contents of a modern soldier's 'Bergen' (the name of the British Army's backpack) can be categorised as follows:
1 Rations
2 Sleeping bags
3 Shelter
4 Spare clothing
5 Personal Admin
6 Ammo
7 Water
8 Specialist equipment

Rations

Although he carries rations in his webbing, the majority of a soldier's rations are carried in his Bergen. It is common practice to pack only the tinned meals if you have to carry more than three days' rations and discard all but a few packets of biscuits. However, in some units it is a chargeable offence to throw rations away!

Arctic rations are much lighter and less bulky, but require a great deal of water when cooking. This poses less of a problem in the Arctic, although you still have to melt large quantities of snow.

Sleeping bags

Sleeping bags (GS type) weigh about 2 to 2.5 kg and take up the largest amount of space in the Bergen. They should always be packed inside a waterproof bag.

The 58 Pattern Webbing Large Pack, still on issue and widely used in training, has no frame and must be carefully packed to be comfortable.

Shelter

Ponchos or bivvy bags are commonly carried in your Bergen as opposed to on your webbing, since it's not sensible to separate shelter fron sleeping bag as you will usually not use one without the other.

Spare clothing

Spare clothing is the most variable of loads, but is best kept to a minimum. Spare socks and underwear are obviously needed, as is something dry to sleep in. It is common practice to carry one very warm spare item such as a fibre-pile jacket.

Personal Admin

Personal Admin equipment consists of articles such as washing plus shaving kit, boot brush and polish. While you're in training these items are carried in your webbing as well, but once in battalion this is not always

*The speed march in full **CEMO**: yomping around the countryside takes a fair proportion of the training time of a modern infantryman.*

Contents of the Large Pack

The large pack or Bergen, plus your webbing, make up Complete Equipment Marching Order, and contain the kit that enables you to live in the field for a protracted period. Weight and content vary according to task; this is intended as a guide to the basic elements.

1 Kip mat
Now on issue, these insulate you from the cold ground. They are light but bulky; you can save some room by cutting them down to your body size.
2 Survival bag or survival blanket
3 Spare straps
For strapping extra kit to your pack.
4 Sleeping bag
This must be in a thick plastic bag; it is filled with down, so is useless when wet and takes a long time to dry out. Dry clean only.
5 Spare shirt
The Norwegian army variety is better.
6 Spare combat suit
It is not impossible to destroy a combat suit on exercise; also, if you get hypothermia there will always be a dry suit to change into. And on longer operations, the rule is that you sleep in a dry set of clothes and put the wet one back on in the morning.
7 NBC overboot spares
In a contaminated area, NBC boots last for hours, not days.
8 Spare ammo
9 Combat smock liner
You could sew some sleeves in to improve it.

Fibre pile jackets are available on the civilian market, and are better as they will keep you warm when wet.
10 Notebook
11 Jersey
12 Cold weather trousers
You can put these on without taking your boots off.
13 Spare cooking fuel
14 Spare boots
15 Spare rations
As well as issue rations, always carry extra: freeze-dried stuff is light, but you will need water for it.
16 Large mess tin
17 Gym shoes (or trainers)
Use these for sleeping in if you get a chance to take your boots off.
18 Spare NBC suit
The one you are wearing will last 28 days, or 24 hours in a contaminated environment. And if you rip it you must replace it.
19 Aircraft recognition panel
20 Headover
21 Socks (at least four pairs)
22 Spare gloves
23 Sandbags

If you have to sleep in your boots, a sandbag over each one will keep your sleeping bag clean and will dry out your boots to some extent.
24 Spare shell dressings
25 Issue torch and spare batteries
26 Bin liners
Don't drop rubbish – this shows poor personal and unit discipline.
27 Helmet
If you are not wearing it (e.g. on night patrol).
28 Towel
29 Abseiling kit
30 Complete set of waterproofs
The jacket may be kept in your webbing.
31 Gaiters
Not issue, and not essential, but very useful in certain areas.
32 Spare thermal underwear
33 Spare water
An essential: fill it to the brim so that it doesn't make a noise.
34 Full washing and shaving kit

Specialist kit may also include field telephones and cable, PRC 351 radio batteries, wiring gloves, night vision aids, intruder alarm systems.

Common British Army Packs

The 58 Pattern Large Pack and GS Bergen

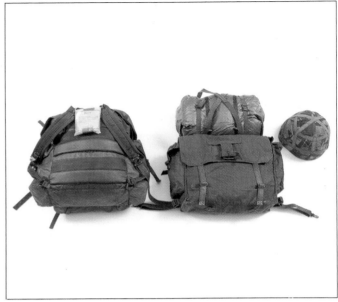

The 58 pattern large pack (right) has limited capacity and no frame. The sleeping bag is carried on top of the pack, and there are two side pockets. Padded shoulder straps can be added, making it easier to get the pack on and off quickly. The GS type Bergen (left) is the better issue option. It can be carried with or without a frame (it uses the same frame as the PRC 351 radio) and has three outer pockets, but is still quite limited in capacity.

The large pack has cross straps for attaching your helmet, and underneath there is an attachment for your digging tool. It is not waterproof, and is difficult to decontaminate, so purchasing a DPM rucksack cover is a good move. The GS Bergen has adjustable shoulder straps but no waist attachment. It is waterproof, and can be decontaminated. Without a frame it has to be much more carefully packed.

done. Despite its obvious importance, it should still be kept to a minimum: half a bar of soap; half a toothbrush (no handle); half a towel etc.

Ammo

In the field, most soldiers prefer to dedicate the weight and space on their belt to extra ammo, water, rations and medical kit. A large amount of ammunition is also carried in Bergens and indeed, when horror stories of 55-kg Bergens came back from the Falk-

The overall height of the military rucksack is critical. If you have a short back you can easily find that in the prone position you cannot fire your weapon as your rucksack forces your head into the deck. This soldier is having problems.

lands, ammo accounted for most of the weight.

Water

Water is just as important as food and you wouldn't last long without it, even in Europe. You should carry at least two pints in a bottle in the Bergen, plus the two on your belt.

Specialist equipment

This consists of items such as radios or observation or surveillance devices. All are heavy and bulky, and

PERSONAL MEDICAL KIT

Your personal medical kit should include treatments for minor ailments, dressings to deal with serious wounds, and some all-purpose surgical tools.

For minor cuts, pack antiseptic cream, a roll of heavy-duty, fabric-backed plaster (not assorted plasters), and some micropore tape (excellent for blisters).

For gunshot wounds you'll have your issue field dressing. This won't stop bleeding from deep, open cuts and gashes, however. These need a first-aid dressing that presses into the wound. Ordinary tampons are ideal for this, and you should carry as many as you've room for. Add a 2-inch crêpe bandage to hold them in place. Steri-strips are useful too for holding less serious wounds closed.

Don't forget pills for colds, headaches and diarrhoea. Beware of antihistamines: they can cause drowsiness. If you're allergic to any drug, carry some ID that warns the medics of your allergy.

Finally, make sure you have scissors, a scalpel and spare blades, and a set of tweezers. These are always useful, even if you come through a battle without so much as a scratch.

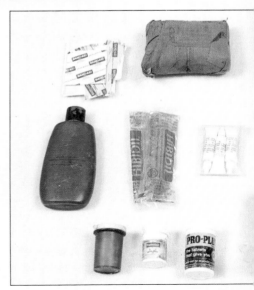

The SAS/Para Bergen and Berghaus Cyclops Roc Bergen

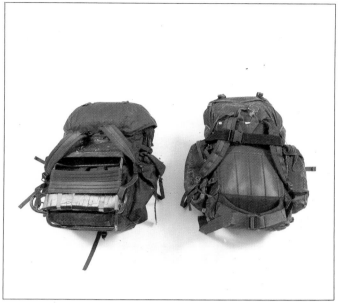

The SAS/Para Bergen (left) will fit over 58 pattern webbing; it is not on general issue but can be obtained. It has three large external pockets, an internal pocket, an internal zip pocket in the top and attachment points for more kit, and has sufficient volume for most tasks. Unlike some Bergens, it is possible to fire from the prone position while wearing it. But it is very heavy and, with no waist belt or chest harness, is tiring to run in. The Berghaus Cyclops Roc system (right), adopted as the model for the new PLCE, is not easily compatible with 58 pattern webbing. It has a light internal frame that bends to the contours of the back.

The Roc has good capacity and is the most comfortable way of carrying a heavy load for long periods: weight is distributed between the shoulders and the waist. A chest harness or strap can be easily added, and side pockets are detachable. The Roc is not completely waterproof so will benefit from a rucksack cover. There is no attachment for a spade or pick, so you will have to rig one up. The red square identifies the company within the battalion to which the individual belongs.

spare batteries should be distributed among the section.

The standard British Army Bergen (called the GS) is not really big enough to cope with infantry work, and many soldiers buy their own: either the larger Para Bergen designed for airborne forces, or one of the very good civilian packs available. The large pack that connects to the 58 pattern webbing is practically useless and is only used in training.

The Para Bergen is easily the most popular Bergen in infantry battalions.

It is a good idea to have two medical kits: a survival medical kit that goes in your survival kit and is sealed, and a larger version with considerably more items in your Bergen. After packing the basic items, you can tailor it to your needs: some useful items might be as follows.

Dioralyte
This replaces vital salts etc lost in dehydration; it is made for babies with the runs, but is also good for replacing sweat lost in an NBC suit.

Proplus
Careful how you use this: anhydrous caffeine will keep you awake and aware on exercise, but plays havoc with your sleep rhythm. There will be exercises, however, where there will be no other way to stay awake.

Delaquin
For sore throats.

Crepe bandage
Always useful to complement the shell dressings.

Flamazine
Anti-bacterial cream for boils and cuts.

Issue insect-repellent and sunscreen
Literally life-savers in jungle environment.

You also need something for constipation and the opposite. Everything in the kit must be clearly marked with labels that will not rub off!

SLR cleaning kit

This lives in your webbing but it is a good idea to carry extra oil and flannelette in your Bergen. SLR kit usually contains oil bottle, combination tool, pull-through, nylon brush, phosphor bronze brush and chamber brush. Additional items would be a Scotchbrite cleaning pad, a spare SLR gas plug and lots of flannelette, plus a small repair kit comprising foresight screws, extractors and spring, firing pin and spring – i.e. the bits that drop off SLRs with monotonous regularity.

CHAPTER FOUR

IF...

It can happen, a soldier can be taken alive by the enemy and not always, sad to say, in the thick of a fire-fight. Through the ages, whole armies have surrendered at various times, presumably to avoid further bloodshed. It rarely occurs today, but when it does the captors are then faced with horrendous problems in policing the large numbers of soldiers milling about. Every man has to be relieved of all weapons and ammunition, searched, interrogated, logged, and ultimately housed and fed.

In some cases, by their surrender fighting men will realise that only rarely is it worth dying for a lost cause. The kamikase airmen of the beaten Japanese forces in World War Two were an example of that, but different cultures have different concepts of honour, and for some death is preferable to dishonour and for them being captured alive is losing face in the worst possible way.

But even so, a few Japanese soldiers were captured before they could commit *harakiri*, to face – what? One of the classic psychological ploys in wartime is to convince the population that it hates the enemy, but fear and hate go hand in hand and for the soldier he will feel apprehension about the kind of treatment he might receive at the hands of his captors. How to control this understandable feeling is something for which training is given.

Evade capture if at all possible but if the worst comes to the worst today's soldier must be forewarned and prepared for a severe test of his fortitude and courage, for whatever rank he holds he will usually know something which will be of interest to the enemy Intelligence section, and all such bodies are very adept in obtaining that information by one means or another.

We begin this chapter of SURVIVAL by suggesting that escape and evasion will very often be the prime objective for many a soldier cut off from his unit. What to do when this happens is the basis of the article. How-

ever, some will be taken and the second article presents sound advice on how to act under interrogation, for all POWs will undergo it.

Forget the Geneva Convention, it is a noble concept but the fact is that any likely enemy will not abide by its tenets. Unpleasant reading though it is, we give ten of the techniques that have been used to force a POW to cooperate. They are not examples of bygone wars, these means have been used within the past decade.

Sooner or later the interrogation will stop and the POW compound with its monotony and frustrations will replace the evils of non-stop questioning. The sudden change from fast, adrenalin-pumping action to captivity is a traumatic experience and if one is to be able to cope with it there must be steadfastness and adaptability. This is the theme of our third article.

But there may come the moment when escape is possible. 'Over the wire and on the run': it is the story-line of many a book and film and the hero always makes it clean away. The reality – as usual – is different, the guards' guns are not loaded with blanks. Escape is a risky business and bravado is no way to go about it. We present three features which describe some of the hazards facing an escapee – dogs, not the cosy 'man's friend' but the dogs of war, trained to track and bring down people running away.

Dogs are but one problem, for there are many obstacles to face before any peace of mind can be expected. Once out of the compound or away from captors, total determination is the key. A quick escape from front-line troops gives a man a better chance than when he has been taken miles back in the enemy country and is in the hands of others.

When on the run, however, beware the use of civilian clothing if you are carrying a weapon. This can give touchy captors a good reason to label you a terrorist liable to a brief trial and execution.

An Argentinian officer captured and on his way to interrogation.

Evasion and Capture

To be taken prisoner is the worst thing that can happen to a soldier. Death is quick; a wound will see you evacuated to a field hospital for treatment; but capture exposes you to a nightmare of torture, indoctrination and exposure. An army is a part of a nation, an arm of government, and every government goes to great lengths to protect its soldiers from every danger, including that of mistreatment as a prisoner of war.

What to do

The United States Army issues Field Manuals – FM 21-76 and FM 21-78 – that deal only with evasion, escape and survival. This section is taken from those manuals. It deals with evading enemy forces and how to behave if you're captured. Later sections will tell you how to hold the line under interrogation, and how to cope with life as a prisoner.

The manuals put a new word into the English language – the evader. A man, probably on his own, being hunted by enemy troops in unknown country. The chances against him are enormous, but if he keeps his head

and remembers his training, he just might escape – against all the odds. Evaders are split into two types: short-term and long-term.

Short-term evasion

You're a short-term evader if you or your unit is temporarily cut off from the main body of your forces. This can happen quite frequently while you're on patrol, for instance, and is actually the way of life of long-range patrol units (known as LURPS in the US military).

When you know you're going to be separated from the main force, navigation and fieldcraft are your best friends. Knowing where you are and which direction you're heading in is going to help save your life, and your own skill at moving cross-country or through a town will finish the job.

9 points for successful evasion

1 Large groups are easily detected. If there are a lot of you, split into four-man teams, which are harder for the enemy to detect.

2 As long as you are wearing your uniform you can attack enemy military targets, but not civilians.

3 Do not disguise yourself as a local unless you do so convincingly. Amateur disguises and ignorance of local language and customs will quickly betray you.

4 If you landed by parachute, you should assume that the enemy spotted your descent and get out of the immediate area as fast as you can.

5 Observe the basic rules of camouflage,

concealment and movement at all times.

6 Take your time when travelling: hurrying makes you less alert and tires you out.

7 Avoid populated areas and busy routes wherever possible. If approached by strangers pretend to be deaf, dumb or just half-witted. It often works.

8 If you are being helped by the local population, do not make any marks on your map: if you are captured with it the enemy could work out who was assisting you.

9 Observe enemy troop movements, military positions, weapons and equipment if you have the chance – but do not write anything down, or you risk being treated as a spy.

Long-term evasion

Very few people have to evade the enemy for long periods of time or cross long stretches of enemy-held territory. The only people likely to have to undertake this most difficult and arduous task are aircrew who have been shot down, and escaped prisoners of war, though patrols are sometimes sent so far out that the same principles apply to them.

Try to relax. Fear and tension will only force you into making mistakes. Time is on your side. It doesn't matter how soon you get back to your own people, as long as you do get back.

This may mean lying up for weeks or even months, and applying all your survival skills.

Under United States law, a soldier must make every effort to return to his unit. If captured, it is his duty to try to escape – though very few ever do so successfully. Getting 'home' will be a lot easier before you're captured. You must use all the tricks of camouflage and concealment to stay hidden from the enemy.

On your own

Rely on your own resources. Don't trust civilians unless you absolutely have to. Their whole way of life will be strange to you. A gesture that in your home town might mean "welcome" could mean the very reverse in enemy territory.

It's not a good idea – ever – to try to disguise yourself as a native. Even if your colour and clothes don't give you away, and you happen to speak the language, the smallest gesture will be enough to show an experienced obser-

Shot-down aircrew often find themselves a long way behind enemy lines, faced with the prospect of long-term evasion and probable capture. If the enemy find you, your most dangerous moment will usually be at the moment of capture when the enemy soldiers are excited and pointing guns at you. Stay calm, and move slowly.

A US soldier surrenders to North Vietnamese troops in South Vietnam. It is said that you are less likely to be shot on the spot when trying to surrender if you get rid of your helmet first.

ver that you're not what you're pretending to be.

If you have been lucky enough to make contact with a friendly local group, be guided by them – but remember that no conventions of war apply to them. Any civilian found helping you will probably die for it.

Take every opportunity to distance yourself from your helpers. If you have to travel with a member of a local resistance group, for instance, don't sit together. Arrange a system of simple signals so that you don't have to speak.

Be ready to go it alone at any moment, and don't carry anything that could point a finger of suspicion at anyone who might have helped you. No names and addresses written down; no marked maps. Remember

that you're a representative of your country – perhaps the first one the natives have actually met. Even under the hardships that an evader must endure, it's up to you to make a good impression. Remember, you're fighting a war so that these people can live in freedom.

Communicating

If you do get the chance to talk to natives and feel secure enough to ask them for help, communicating is going to be a big problem. The chances are you won't speak each other's language, so you'll be reduced to making signs and gestures. To make this easier, the US Government issues each soldier with what is known as a "Blood Chit". A Blood Chit is an American Flag, printed onto cloth, with a message in English and all the other languages you are likely to come across in the area in which fighting is taking place. The last, and most important, feature of the Blood Chit is a

unique number that identifies the person it was issued to.

The message asks for help and assistance. It promises that this will be rewarded. Don't give up the Blood Chit itself. Any one who helps you will get their reward just by quoting the number. Give them the number but don't give up the chit itself.

Take care of the chit

If you lose your Blood Chit, report it straight away. It's a very valuable document. If it falls into the hands of the enemy's Intelligence Section, they could very easily use it to discover which members of the local population are likely to be friendly to you, and this will probably get them shot. It will certainly make sure that no-one trust the chit – or you.

It may be possible for your own people to rescue you, most likely from the

Searching and handling a prisoner

This is how you can expect to be treated by an enemy who 'plays by the rules'.

1 Standing position: arms stretched, body relaxed. They work from top to bottom and will check your clothing carefully.

2 Stress position: with your weight on your fingertips and toes, you cannot react quickly. Expect your groin and armpits to be checked as well.

3 If you are caught in a group they may position you like this to prevent fast reaction against the search.

4 Again, if you are in a group, you will be placed close together and your captors will not move between you.

air. To stand a chance of this being successful you must know the standard ground-to-air distress signals.

Don't call down a rescue attempt unless you are absolutely sure that the area is safe. Remember that a helicopter is most vulnerable to attack when it's taking off and landing. Make sure that any signals can be removed or covered up very quickly in case an enemy air patrol should appear.

Save the wounded

If there are casualties, make sure that they get off first. If you do have seriously wounded men in your party, you must always consider whether their best chances of staying alive are to surrender (United States law allows that). Obviously, local conditions will be important – a man with a light wound surrendering to troops who are known to kill all prisoners, de-

spite the Geneva Convention, is not helping himself!

Intelligence of all sorts – and evidence of the bloodthirstiness of enemy troops is only one sort – is really vital. Use every means you can to learn about enemy troop movements and placement and the attitude of local non-combatants.

Stay aware

Try and keep abreast of the progress of the war as a whole, too. You may be hiding for nothing! Remember that some Japanese infantrymen were still living concealed in the jungle of the South Pacific islands 25 years after the end of World War II, because they didn't know it was all over.

If the worst does happen and you face capture, your first decision will

Royal Marines of the Falklands garrison surrender to the Argentine Buzo Táctico Marine Recce unit. When captured you are obliged to give your name, rank, number and date of birth only.

According to Radio Hanoi, a US Air Force pilot was captured by a North Vietnamese militia woman. In a one-to-one situation you may be able to escape, but he (or she) who has the rifle may have the last laugh.

be whether to try and fight your way out. If you're alone and unarmed, this is not likely to be an available option, but if you're with your unit and your armament is up to strength, you may stand a very good chance of winning a fire-fight even against a larger enemy force, because surprise will definitely act in your favour – the last thing the enemy force will expect is an armed and trained group of soldiers behind its own lines.

If you are captured, you are required to tell the enemy only four things – your name, rank, serial number and date of birth. Say nothing else. Don't refer to your unit by name, don't talk about your superior officers, don't identify the leaders of your group. The smallest piece of additional information may be useful to the enemy.

5 A two-man arrest position: one fixes you with an armlock while the other applies pressure points.

6 One way of using a baton to support an armlock: with the baton under your arm and behind the neck you are immobilised.

7 Arresting method with a baton: by pushing this between your legs and grabbing you by the neck, the guard can move you easily by pushing your neck and raising his right arm.

Under Interrogation

To the army on the move, taking prisoners is more than a waste of time, it's a waste of precious manpower to guard them and rations to feed them. It's often only some respect for the laws of warfare and the fear that they would be treated the same way themselves that keeps them from shooting everybody.

To the intelligence specialist, though, the prisoner is not a waste of time. He's precious. He may be pure gold. The information about troop strengths and positions that he has in his head – perhaps not even realising that he has it – could be the difference between a battle lost and a battle won.

The US Army knows this, and spends a lot of time training its men how to combat enemy interrogation techniques. Field Manual FM 21-76 is the source for this section on how to get through a hostile interrogation while giving away as little information as possible.

The laws of war

The news of your capture is supposed, under the Geneva Convention, to be passed to a body called the Protection Power, often the Red Cross/Red Crescent, so that they can pass it on to your own government. That's the only reason for giving away even

US prisoners are herded through the North Vietnamese capital, Hanoi. These public displays were used to prey on the emotions of the prisoners' families in America and turn public opinion against the war.

such simple information as your name, rank, number and date of birth.

If you're captured by a terrorist group, they probably won't do this –

THE INTERROGATOR'S SKILL

The interrogator prepares himself before interrogating his prisoner. He adopts a three-phase approach:

1 Research
He gathers all the information he can about all his prisoners.

2 Selection
He chooses which prisoners to interrogate and determines the information he wants.

3 Extraction
He puts into operation his varied mix of extraction techniques.

1 Intelligence
The interrogator studies any information he may have acquired from initial searches, overheard conversations, and background material gleaned by intelligence workers operating in the captive's own country.

2 Weak or strong?
He also builds up a picture of the PoW's makeup: is he weak or strong? Can he take punishment? What gets to him? Is he cool or emotional? How has he adjusted to PoW life?

3 Softening up
You'll be softened up, either by rough treatment, starvation, thirst, sensory deprivation, sleeplessness or solitary confinement. The interrogator will set up the place where he'll ask his questions so that it's intimidating and unfriendly.

4 Disgrace
He will try to destroy your confidence by disgracing you in the eyes of your fellow prisoners or your family or comrades at home, or will simply try to make you feel ashamed of yourself.

5 Lesser of two evils
The captor will give you a choice between two evils, one of which is less damaging than the other. He knows that you will choose the least damaging, and that is the one he can use for his own purposes.

Forcing co-operation

These are some techniques that PoWs have been subjected to in recent times.

1 Torture
Technique: extreme dislocation of body parts e.g. arms, legs, back etc by twisting or pulling; beating, slapping, gouging, kicking; inserting foreign objects such as bamboo slivers under the fingernails; electric shocks
Effect: crippling; partial or total temporary or permanent loss of use of limbs and senses; loss of normal mental functioning; extreme pain; lowering or breaking of ability to resist captors' demands
TORTURE IS THE MAJOR MEANS OF FORCING COMPLIANCE

2 Threats
Technique: threats of solitary confinement, non-repatriation, death or beatings to oneself or other PoWs; threats regarding future treatment; threats against family
Effect: unreasonable anxiety; loss of hope and confidence; despair

3 'Now and then' treatment
Technique: occasional favours such as release of food packages and better living conditions; promise of big rewards for helping captors
Effect: tempts the PoW to go along with captors; presents the captors in a favourable light; makes resistance to questioning seem a bad idea

4 Isolation or solitary confinement
Technique: total or partial isolation by rank, race, degree of compliance etc; or total solitary confinement
Effect: keeps PoW away from anyone who can give any kind of support – moral, physical, psychological

5 Hints that captors are in full control of everything in camp
Technique: use of information from other sources to make PoW believe the captors know more than they really do
Effect: makes PoWs suspicious of each other and makes resistance seem futile

6 Show of power over life and death
Technique: use of executions or torture; introduction and withdrawal of better conditions and medical care; complete control over physical aspects of camp
Effect: breeds extreme caution and the belief that the captor is boss

7 Deliberately-caused physical deterioration
Technique: extremely long interrogation sessions; long periods in leg irons and stocks; bad food
Effect: drastic lowering of resistance to interrogation

8 Enforcement of minor rules and commands
Technique: overly strict demands for compliance with instructions and expected courtesies; forcing PoW or write or verbally repeat nonsensical words and phrases
Effect: causes automatic obedience to commands

9 Lowering of self-respect of PoW
Technique: lack of privacy; ridicule and insults; prevention of washing; keeping living conditions filthy, insanitary, full of vermin etc
Effect: humbles PoW and makes giving in an attractive prospect

10 Control over physical senses
Technique: placing in isolation with no stimuli or giving extreme stimuli such as no light or sound, or too much light or sound; dripping water on forehead
Effect: makes PoW think that captors have total physical control; causes extreme discomfort and distress

even some governments don't, which is why so many US prisoners of the Viet Cong and Pathet Lao are still recorded as MIA (Missing In Action) following the war in South East Asia.

You don't have to tell them what branch of the service you're from, though they may be able to guess that themselves from your uniform and equipment. Some personnel traditionally get a hard time, notably members of Special Forces units and fliers.

Try not to get noticed and singled out for interrogation. Don't exhibit bravado or humility. Just fade into the background.

Be polite

There's no point in not being respectful and polite – in fact, to behave in any other way is extremely stupid. It will only earn you harsher treatment and probably get you beaten up and deprived of food.

7 Hidden eyes and ears
You may have looked and found nothing, but the enemy has probably bugged the camp, so watch what you say, everywhere.

8 The silent treatment
You may be put into solitary confinement or held in a room with an interrogator who says nothing. Don't be afraid of silence; come to terms with it.

9 Repetition and monotony
Your interrogator may ask you the same questions in the same tone over and over again. Let him. If you get riled he'll win; if you maintain control the psychological victory will be yours.

6 The File
Your interrogator may start by asking you a harmless question about yourself. If you give a false answer, he checks his intelligence file on you and gives you the right one. You begin to think, "This guy knows everything. What's the use of holding out?" Don't give in. He is telling you the little he does know. If he knew everything he wouldn't have to question you further.

10 What's the use?
"Why hold out?" "Why suffer?" "You are at our mercy." "We'll get the information out of you anyhow." "Make it easier on yourself." These are all statements that you must learn to resist.

The Geneva Convention

The Geneva Convention is an international agreement first formulated in 1864 to establish a code of practice for the treatment of wartime sick, wounded and prisoners of war. These are the major elements of the Geneva Convention as it effects prisoners of war.

1 Interrogation
A PoW is required to provide only his name, rank, service number and date of birth. The use of physical or mental coercion to obtain information from PoWs is prohibited.

2 Movement
PoWs must be moved under humane conditions.

3 Environment
The internment environment must not be unhealthy or dangerous.

4 Food
Food must be of sufficient quality and quantity to maintain good health.

5 Clothing
Suitable clothing must be provided.

6 Health, Hygiene and Wellbeing
The detaining power must ensure that adequate hygienic facilities are provided. The PoW is entitled to treatment by medical personnel from their own country, where available. The seriously wounded or sick are entitled to special treatment and may be transferred to a neutral nation.

7 Protected Personnel
Captured medical personnel and chaplains are treated as protected personnel and are to be free to circulate among the PoWs tending to their spiritual welfare and health.

8 Religion, Recreation, Education and Exercise
Each PoW has the right to practise his religion, and to engage in physical exercise, education and recreation.

9 Work
All enlisted personnel below NCO rank are subject to work details, but these shall not be dangerous or unhealthy. NCOs may be called upon to work in a supervisory capacity; officers may work voluntarily. The Geneva convention prohibits the use of PoWs for mine clearance and lays down working conditions, pay, fitness for work, and the treatment of PoWs working for private individuals.

10 Outside Contacts
PoWs have the right to write to their families on capture. The convention outlines postal privileges and rights pertaining to the receipt of packages.

11 Complaints
PoWs have the right to complain to the military authorities of the detaining powers, and to representatives of the neutral protecting powers recognised by both sides.

12 Representatives
The senior PoW will be the prisoners representative. In a camp where there are no officers or NCOs the representative will be chosen by secret ballot.

13 Legal Proceedings
PoWs prosecuted and convicted for offences committed before capture retain the protection afforded by the convention. They may not be tried for any action which becomes illegal after the act is committed. The captors may not use force to gain a confession.

14 Punishment
Cruel and unusual punishments, torture, collective punishments or unfair punishments by a biased court are prohibited.

15 Escape
Attempted escapes, or non-violent offences committed only to aid escape and not involving theft for personal gain, the wearing of civilian clothes or the use of false papers, are subject only to laid-down disciplinary action.

This communist propaganda photograph was used to illustrate 'heroic' North Vietnamese troops who have just captured a shot-down American airman. It is impossible to avoid your captors taking photographs of you.

medical attention for someone badly wounded and not treated properly, or almost anything else that seems attractive. After all, they can promise you anything – you're not going to get it, anyway.

The double game
As well as trying to convince you that other prisoners have been co-operating, he will try to get information from you about them, which in turn will allow him to put subtle pressures on anyone you talk about. Don't give out any information about

At the same time, don't give the interrogator the idea that you might be willing to co-operate. All you'll succeed in doing is to prolong the interrogation.

There's a world of difference between acting ignorant and acting dumb. The interrogator may say something like 'We know there's a build up of troops at such-and-such a location. Does it contain armour?' If your answer were, 'I don't know, Sir, I've never been in that location,' it sounds a lot more convincing than 'Piss off'. But beware of seeming to be trying to be helpful.

Watch out for apparently innocent enemy personnel such as doctors, nurses, orderlies and cleaners. Never talk in front of them; they could well be intelligence agents operating undercover – perhaps not even revealing themselves to other enemy agents on the spot.

Solitary confinement or keeping you in tiny cages preys more on your mind than on your body. Psychological torture leaves no obvious scars, which would beg awkward questions at a press conference.

The enemy interrogator will be very keen to turn you into a collaborator, too. The two main methods are threats – of physical torture or death, to you or to another member of your squad, or promises – of better treatment,

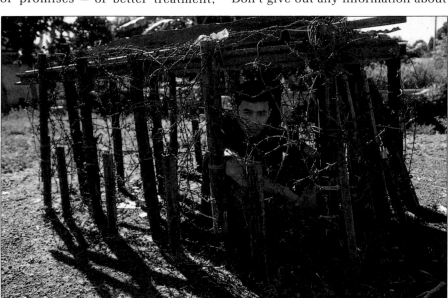

If the enemy forces you to co-operate by using torture, do not give up hope of further resistance. Consider each time you are forced to give in as one round in a long fight. You may lose some rounds but the fight is still open.

any of your comrades. Don't admit to being in the same unit with them.

Be on guard

Watch out for false questionnaires "for the Red Cross", for instance. The aid organisations need to know nothing more than your name, rank, number and date of birth. Any information you provide in a form like this is only for the enemy intelligence officers' use.

Never make any statement of any kind. Not in writing, nor spoken where it might be recorded.

The big shot

Don't try to impress the interrogator by boasting about things that you and your unit have done – whether they're true or not. He's not going to let you go because you make yourself out to be some sort of superman!

At the same time, don't try to decive him by volunteering false information, no matter how subtly you think you do it. He knows the wide intelligence picture and will recognise your lies, and will ask you the same questions over and over again, perhaps with days in between. He'll record everything you say, and look for differences in your answers.

Don't look into the interrogator's eyes. You may give away information without meaning to. Pick out a spot between his eyes or in the centre of his forehead and concentrate on that.

Once he has you talking, it won't take a skilled interrogator long to get the truth out of you. Don't put yourself into a position where you find that you're having a conversation with him. Let him do all the talking, and limit your answers to "No," and "I don't know anything about that".

Never drop your guard. You can be taken off for further interrogation at any time, at any hour of the day or night.

Victories

Try to win a victory every time you're interrogated, no matter how small. Having worked out how, pass it on to your fellows so that they are morally stronger.

The longer the interrogation goes on, the safer you are. More prisoners will be arriving and needing your interrogator's time, and your information will become more and more out of date.

What will prolong the nightmare is your partial co-operation. One snippet of useful information will convince your interrogator that he may be onto a good thing, and he'll carry on until he gets the lot, no matter what it takes.

Using this picture, the North Vietnamese were able to say 'Look how nice we are to the US prisoners'. Be on your guard against tricks like this.

THE PRISONER

A prisoner-of-war camp can be anything from a huge barbed wire compound holding tens of thousands of men to a crude shelter in a jungle clearing and one or two men in a bamboo cage. Once your interrogation is over you're of very little use to the enemy, unless he can exploit you for political purposes.

You're just a drain on his resources. The men he has to use to guard you, the food and medicines he has to send to keep you alive: all of these could be better used on the battlefield. So it's going to be tough. The US Government has spent a great deal of time and money to find out what gives its soldiers the best possible chance of getting through a period spent as a PoW. US Army Field Manuals 21-76 and 21-78 are the source for this section on life as a prisoner of war.

Strength through unity

No matter how few of you there are, you must have an organisation. One man must be in command. Chances are that your captors will try to force someone of their choice on you.

If they try to set up an organisation amongst the prisoners, then the best thing to do is to appear to go along. But you'll know who really is the Senior Ranking Officer. He, not the enemy's puppet, will appoint his Adjutant, his Quartermaster, his Welfare, Education and Entertainments Officers and set up rest of the PoW infrastructure.

Eat the food

You will get less, worse and stranger food than you ever had – a poor version of the stuff the enemy eats. If you are a finicky eater, get over it. Many men have died in a short period of captivity because they could not adapt to the food – they have starved themselves to death.

Add to your diet with roots, weeds, bark, a hidden garden, animals or reptiles. Ants and grasshoppers are good sources of protein. Cat, dog and monkey meats are staples of many diets.

Steal from your captors. If your Senior Ranking Officer approves, trade with the enemy, and share with those PoWs who need it at least as much as you do. If it's edible, eat it.

The enemy knows that lack of enough food or the right kinds of food decreases mental and physical powers, making you less able to resist and

The enemy will try to break the morale of all the prisoners: you must try to organise against this. You have an important role in maintaining the morale of your fellow captives.

easier to manipulate. Therefore he will withhold food to make you do what he wants.

Drink the water

You must drink, even though your water smells bad, is dirty and is alive with bugs. Strain or purify it with chemicals or by boiling if you can. Make a still to obtain water, or suck the juices from fruits. Tomatoes are an excellent source of fluid, as are some wild plants such as cacti. Catch rain or snow. If you think, you'll drink; if you panic, you'll dehydrate.

Exercise for survival

Try to take some sort of exercise every day. Keep up your muscle tone, but don't overdo it – you won't be getting the proteins and carbohydrates in your diet that will allow you to do strenuous exercise.

Keep your mind active, too. Try to be learning something new all the time. If you're in a large camp, with lots of other people, the chances are that you'll be able to learn pretty much anything you can think of. You'll have skills that others will want to learn, too.

Play can be just as important as

Inside the forbidding interior of the notorious 'Hanoi Hilton' – the old French prison where many captured US personnel were held by the North Vietnamese.

American prisoners look out at North Vietnamese guards in Hanoi. Give each guard an insulting nickname to use amongst yourselves: it'll make you feel much better.

work. Not just physical games and sports, though these are very important, but entertainments of all kinds. Painting and drawing and writing need very little in the way of materials, and they don't just keep you busy – they allow you to express yourself, your inner thoughts, in an important way.

Remember, it may be hard work trying to stay fit and healthy, but it's nothing compared with the job you've got if you lose your health and fitness and then have to get it back again. Your captors will like it a lot better if you just sit around doing nothing all day and every day, weakening your own morale and destroying your will to stay awake and alive. Don't do it! Your life is in your own hands.

Join in

The men appointed to the jobs of Sports, Education and Entertainments Officers will want to set up as many activities and events as they can. Get involved in these activities. It doesn't matter if you're not too

NGƯỜI GỬI (Addressor)

HỌ TÊN (Name in full): John H.

SỐ LÍNH (Service number): Fv

NƠI VÀ NGÀY SINH (Date & place of birt 14 November 1940

ĐỊA CHỈ (Address): TRẠI GIAM PHI (NƯỚC VIỆT - NAM
(Camp of detenti in the DEMOCRA

GỬI (Addressee)

HỌ TÊN (Name in full): Mr. and Mrs.

ĐỊA CHỈ (Address): 1238 N.

California

Dear Mom Dad and Family. How's everyone? I am in excellent health and still retain my optimistic outlook on everything, so don't worry a bit about me. The food and treatment here are very good. I got your packages, they were great. I think about you all much of the time and look forward to being home soon. Love, Spike

NGÀY VIẾT (Dated) 9 October 1969

GHI CHÚ (N.B.):

1. Phải viết rõ và chỉ được viết trên những dòng kẻ sẵn (Write legibly and only on the lines).
2. Trong thư chỉ được nói về tình hình sức khỏe và tình hình gia đình (Write only about health and family).
3. Gia đình gửi đến cũng phải theo đúng mẫu, khuôn khổ và quy định này (Letters from families should also conform to this proforma).

A favourite enemy trick is to allow you to write home, but whatever the truth of the situation your family will get a letter saying how well you are being treated. Another ploy is to get you to write something for the press or TV – they will then distort whatever you say to suit their propaganda machine.

good at whatever it is — what matters most is that you get busy and active and stay that way.

The folks back home

Keeping in touch with your family and friends is very important for both sides. You need to know you're not forgotten and they need to know that you're as safe and well as possible.

Letters and photographs are the only way you'll be able to keep in contact, and the enemy will know this and use it to weaken you. Be ready to share your letters, photographs and parcels, if you get them, with the people around you. The SRO will put someone in charge of mail, and keep an accurate list of letters sent and received.

Outgoing letters are often a source of intelligence for the enemy. Try to restrict yourself to a brief note like, "I'm alive and well," and if you're in any doubt about the value to the enemy of something you want to say in a letter home, ask the SRO's advice — that's another one of the many things he's there for.

Make sure that you circulate any scraps of news that you get in your letters. The best way is for a group of people to produce a camp newspaper. It needn't be more than hand-written sheets that get passed on from person to person around the camp. If that's not possible, then you'll have to do it by word of mouth.

Get one over

Let no chance go by to 'get one over' on the enemy, and make sure that everyone knows about every little victory. Give all the guards and camp personal nick-names — the crueller the better! Don't use them to their faces, of course, but in private use every chance you have to make fun of them. Leave them in no doubt of what you think of them.

Camp communication

There are many ways to communicate with other prisoners. The PoW isolation barrier and enemy-imposed ban on communication must be broken. If you can see, hear or touch other PoWs, or if articles are brought into and taken out of your place of confinement, you can communicate.

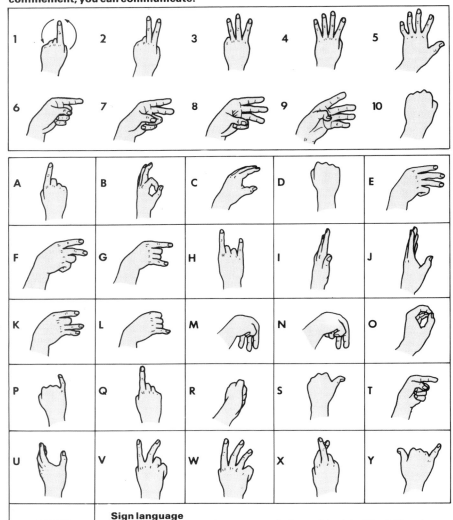

Sign language

The standard deaf-mute language may be learned, but it is difficult. There is a simple variation that is quicker to learn, using hand signals. Either hand can be used. Numbers are rotated to indicate that they are numbers and not letters. The code uses the standard US Navy hand signal numbers; zero is shown by rotating the letter O. Let your hand drop slightly after each series of letters or words.

To indicate 'I understand' or 'I do not understand', the receiver may nod slightly in a prearranged manner. Different body movements such as blinking the eyes, flexing the hands or arms, shrugging the shoulders etc — all natural and meaningless to the enemy — can be worked out in advance to indicate different responses.

Tap codes

The Morse code can be learned quickly. But it has a serious drawback: it consists of dots and dashes that sometimes cannot be distinguished. There is a better system that consists of a square marked off in 25 subsquares; 5 across and 5 up and down, with the letters of the alphabet in the subsquares (the letter K is not used because it sounds like C). The squares running from left to right are rows; the squares from top to bottom are columns.

Taps are used to identify letters. The first series of taps gives the row; after a short pause, the second series of taps gives the column. The letter is in the block where the row and column meet. To find the letter O, for example, three taps would designate the third row (L-M-N-O-P); a slight pause followed by four taps would designate the fourth column (D-I-O-T-Y); the row and column meet at the letter O.

A longer pause indicates the end of a word. Two taps indicate that the word has been received. A series of rapid taps indicates that the word was not received, i.e. not understood. When a receiver has enough letters to know what the word is, he gives two taps and the sender goes on to the next word. Each time the code is broken by your captors, you can rearrange the letters.

The methods of getting a message across with this code are almost unlimited. The code can be tapped, whistled, winked, coughed, sneezed or hummed; you can nudge the guy next to you; you can use finger movements, eye movements, twitches, broom strokes, pushups; or you can bang objects together.

2. Then tap these columns.

	1	2	3	4	5
1	A	B	C K	D	E
2	F	G	H	I	J
3	L	M	N	O	P
4	Q	R	S	T	U
5	V	W	X	Y	Z

1. Tap these rows first.

This is how to tap the message
HEADS UP

```
1 2       1 2 3         1   1 2 3 4 5
■ ■       ■ ■ ■ (H)     ■   ■ ■ ■ ■ ■ (E)

1   1     1 1 2 3 4       1 2 3 4   1 2 3
■   ■ (A) ■ ■ ■ ■ ■ (D)   ■ ■ ■ ■   ■ ■ ■ (S)

1 2 3 4   1 2 3 4 5
■ ■ ■ ■   ■ ■ ■ ■ ■ (U)

1 2 3     1 2 3 4 5
■ ■ ■     ■ ■ ■ ■ ■ (P)
```

Mail deliveries
As well as personal deliveries, messages can be left in any hiding place — latrines, trees, rocks, crevices, holes etc; the best places are those that the enemy would expect you to visit normally. The hiding places should be changed frequently, and couriers should deposit and collect their despatches at different times.

Talking through the wall
Roll up a blanket in the shape of a ring doughnut and put it against the wall. Put your face in the centre of the doughnut and talk slowly. The receiver puts his ear against the wall on the other side, or presses the open end of a cup against the wall with his ear against the other end.

Different noises
Various sounds such as grunting, coughing, sneezing, blowing your nose, whistling or humming can be used as prearranged signals to pass messages such as 'all is well', 'enemy around', 'stop', 'go' etc.

Word of mouth
This can sometimes be dangerous. To disguise the content from the enemy, language variations can be used; subculture language (street language of minority groups), for example, or pidgin English, ordinary slang etc.

Writing messages
You will not usually have writing materials available. But you can improvise: use charred wood, fruit juices, ashes mixed with any fluid etc. Use any pointed object as a writing implement. Leaves, wood, cloth, toilet paper and any other material can be used as a writing surface.

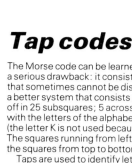

Escape, Rescue and Release

The best chances to escape will come straight after your capture. You'll still be close to your own forces, and so you'll know which direction to head in, and you may even be familiar with the country. You'll be fitter and healthier than after time spent in captivity, and if you can keep your wits about you, you may be able to take advantage of the confusion that is usually to be found just behind the fighting front, with reinforcements and resupply trying to go forward and medevac and empty resupply units trying to move back.

The first hours

You'll be in the hands of combat troops, not people trained in holding prisoners, and their inexperience may give you opportunities. But at the same time they'll be psyched up for battle, so will probably shoot rather than ask questions. They might just shoot you for the fun of it.

For all these reasons, every army has a plan for dealing with prisoners of war, for getting them out of the combat zone as quickly as possible, so that they can be interrogated while the information they have about troop strengths and movements is still worth something.

The chances are that if you're captured on your own, or as part of a

Take advantage of the confusion associated with your capture. You will be passed between different enemy units and transit camps, and security here is often the weakest.

The possibilities of escape

Escapes are much more likely to succeed if the prisoners are properly organised with an escape committee and a chain of command. It needs many hands to forge documents, create disguises and provide tools for the job. When you make your bid for freedom other prisoners can create a diversion to distract the guards.

The gate
Perhaps the best escape route is through the front gate, hidden in enemy vehicles.

Bluff
You may be ab way past the g disguised as a remember, yo be complete.

On the outside
Outdoor working parties provide the best opportunities for escape: at least you're beyond the camp wire. And you should have a couple of hours clear before the next head-count.

small group, you will be held somewhere like the regimental command post, and then transferred to the rear echelon headquarters run by intelligence security units, military police or internal security troops. This will not be far from the fighting front.

In transit

When enough prisoners have accumulated, you'll be moved back, being kept to open country and avoiding towns and villages. The enemy is likely to be short of motor transport – or, at least, will give a very low priority to the transportation of prisoners, so you may well find yourself evacuated on foot.

He'll be short of personnel, too, so the PoW column may have too few guards, who may even be not fit for active duty – walking wounded perhaps, themselves on their way to rear echelon hospitals. That means that there will be more chances to escape.

If the guards are placed at the head and tail of the column, as is often the case, pass the word through the ranks of prisoners to spread out and make the line of marching men as long as possible.

Keep the pace as slow as you can. At a bend in the road, you may suddenly find that the head and the tail are out of each other's sight, which means that men in the centre of the column can slip away to either side of the road and get quickly into some kind of cover.

The larger the number of men who make a break, the greater are the chances of their absence being noticed straight away. One or two men missing probably won't be noticed until the next head count is made, and that may not be until the end of the day.

Take advantage of any diversion, too. Artillery bombardment and attack from the air or extreme weather conditions, for instance, are likely to cause a lot of confusion, and may permit men to slip away while the guards' attention is distracted.

Road transport

If you're being transported by truck out of the combat zone, you will probably be moved by night. If the guards are not alert and you are not locked inside the vehicle, you may get a chance to jump for it when the truck

Tunnel out
Tunnels are a big undertaking and require an organised team. Getting rid of the spoil is as big a problem as digging the tunnel itself.

Tools
Collect anything that will serve as a tool. If you find a proper tool on a work party out of camp, hide it away for a few days or weeks before smuggling it back in.

Tunnel around
If you can't tunnel out, perhaps you can tunnel from one part of the camp to another – perhaps to a food store or another group of prisoners.

Sleeping dummy
Move your bed into a corner of your cell as far as possible from the guards' view, some weeks before your escape attempt so that they can get used to it. Then put a dummy under your blankets before you go missing.

The wire
There have been many successful attempts at going through the wire, but beware mines and electronic sensors.

Cover
Plan your escape to coincide with rain and bad visibility. Your guards' senses will be less effective in bad weather.

slows down – climbing a hill, for instance, or negotiating a section of damaged road. Try to sabotage the vehicles – put sugar or sand in the petrol, for example – so that they are forced to stop. Once again, an air raid may give you the necessary cover and distraction for an escape attempt.

On the railways

Permanent PoW camps are usually placed as far away as possible from the battlefield and from borders with neutral or enemy territory, so the last move will probably be made by train. Large groups of prisoners in transit are usually locked into freight cars, the guards relying on the physical security of the locked wagons to stop escape attempts.

Ex-PoWs receive a briefing from a reception officer after their release from North Vietnamese prison camps. Many vets were mentally and physically scarred; others didn't make it back at all.

The conditions inside these cars, especially during a long journey in the middle of summer or winter, can become lethal, and the fact that you'll probably be packed in very tightly doesn't help. Even so, because you'll have long periods without observation, this may provide your best chance. Try to break through the floor, the walls (especially at a window or a ventilator), or the roof.

If you're travelling in passenger coaches, then you have two other advantages, even though you may have guards to worry about: it's much easier and quicker to break out through a window than the solid sides of a freight wagon, and you'll probably be able to communicate in some way with prisoners in other compartments or even in other carriages.

Try to create a disturbance to divert the guards' attention; then a whole group may be able to break out and scatter across the countryside. Some, at least, are likely to get far enough away from the immediate vicinity to stand a real chance of getting clean away. One thing to remember – watch out for oncoming trains on adjacent tracks before you jump.

Never start a fire in the van if locked in (as shown in many PoW films) – the guards may respond too slowly.

Don't relax for a moment, but always stay alert to any possibility, because you never know if you'll ever get another chance. If you're not in a position to escape yourself, help others to do so even if it means that you'll be punished for it later.

Temporary camps fairly near the battlefront offer better opportunities for escape than established Prisoner of War camps far behind the lines.

In the camp

Escaping from an established prisoner-of-war camp is a much more difficult task than making a break from a train or from a column of marching men.

The camp itself will have been built specifically to keep you in: barbed wire, electronic surveillence, floodlights, watch towers, dogs and thermal imaging for tunnel searches are just some of the weapons at the enemy's disposal. And even if you do succeed in getting out of the camp itself, you're still faced with a difficult and dangerous journey through enemy territory, where just your physical appearance may be enough to give you away.

The escape committee

Part of the prisoners' secret organization in the camp will be devoted to the business of escaping. There will be very few ways of making an escape from a camp, and each time an attempt is made it will cut down those possibilities even further.

The Escape Committee will coordinate escape attempts, to try to ensure that each one has the best possible chance of success, and also set up the infrastructure that each will need – tools, diversions, false documents, intelligence and so on. You should collect and hoard everything, even useless articles: these will mask the

Rescue from the jaws of captivity

As technology takes over from human observation and scrutiny, escape has become more and more difficult. But what technology has taken away with one hand it has given back with the other. Spy satellites and high-altitude observation flights give intelligence officers a clear view of every part of the earth's surface. That means you have a way of signalling to your own people, no matter where on earth you may be.

There's no need to rush it. You can trace out the letters of a message in the soil of a compound – or even stand around in groups that shape the letter in human bodies – in such a way that the enemy won't even be aware that you're doing it.

Make certain that each arm of each letter is at least 2 metres long, or it might not be seen from above. But remember, it's as likely to be seen by enemy satellites as your own.

Once your position has been identified – either by this method, or by a successful escaper being de-briefed, a coded letter getting through, or an enemy national selling the information – it may be possible for a rescue mission to be put together. Even if you're four or five hundred miles from the nearest friendly border or sea coast, your own authorities may be able to get a rescue force through.

The odds on a successful rescue will be a lot greater if there's a channel of communication from the would-be rescuers to you, and that probably means coded radio messages. There have been many cases of prisoners building radio receivers in camps, and here technology lends a hand once again, modern radio receivers being small enough to be easily hidden in all sorts of places.

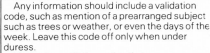

Any information should include a validation code, such as mention of a prearranged subject such as trees or weather, or even the days of the week. Leave this code off only when under duress.

Every piece of information that you can exchange with the people planning the rescue attempt will increase its chances of success. One of the most vital will be to set up the signalling system you'll use to call the rescue force in at the last moment.

The chances are that it will be helicopter-borne, and the pilots and mission commanders will need to be shown exactly where to land to be most effective; wind direction; where to expect resistance; and perhaps even where the prisoners they've come to rescue are to be found.

Be patient, and above all, be secure. A rescue attempt that fails because the enemy have got to know about the plan will not only cost the lives of the rescue force, but also give the enemy a huge propaganda victory.

useful ones if you are searched by camp guards.

Most escape attempts will need this sort of organisation – but that doesn't mean that you shouldn't go for it on your own if a chance presents itself unexpectedly, perhaps from a labour party working outside the camp.

Documents and disguises

Before you get too far in your escape planning, you have to think how you'll cross the enemy territory that lies between you and neutral or friendly forces. There are two methods – either you try to blend in with the local population, or you try to stay hidden.

If you try to fit in, you'll need clothing, documents, money and at least some knowledge of the language, all of which will either have to be produced inside the camp or stolen once you get outside.

In order to forge documents, you have to know what they look like to start with, and you must have the right sort of raw material available – paper,

inks and dyes, pens, and so on, not to mention the skill to do it. And as magnetic encoding like that used on credit cards gets more common, the chances decrease of producing forged documents that will pass any sort of examination.

The other option is to travel in secret, using your survival training to keep out of enemy hands. In many

If you are shot down over enemy territory it may be possible for US aircraft and helicopters to mount a rescue mission. Here a US pilot brought down over North Vietnam managed to maintain contact with US aircraft. He is picked up by helicopter while other US aircraft provide security.

ways this is more practical, and at least you know where you are when you depend only on your own skills.

Improvised signals to aircraft

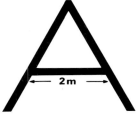

Unless aircraft are flying slowly at low altitude you will probably not be seen. To attract the attention of friendly aircraft you need to make a large sign which will stand out: letters should have arms of not less than two metres.

Alternatively, you can send the emergency 'SOS' signal in Morse code. Look around for any useful material: stones, fertilizer sacks, anything that can be arranged into a shape to catch the pilots' attention. Or, when on parade in POW camp, form your parade up so that it spells out the letters 'SOS' as shown above.

Escape and Evasion in Hostile Territory

There are two types of evasion: long-term and short-term. The long-term evader is likely to be a PoW who has escaped from a camp inside enemy territory or has ejected from a fighter-bomber aircraft or become detached from a deep penetration patrol. Short-term evaders, however, can be on the run almost anywhere. They can be recently-captured PoWs who have just escaped. They may be men who have become detached from a night patrol when it was 'bumped' in the darkness. They can be the survivors of a position that has been attacked and neutralised by superior forces.

The distinction between the two groups is that the short-term evaders may be armed and carrying equipment that will assist them, but they will be playing everything by ear — they will have no escape plan. The long-term evaders have the problem that they are often hundreds of miles from friendly forces and are enclosed in a PoW camp.

Paratroopers taken prisoner are searched by SAS personnel at the end of an Escape and Evasion exercise prior to the next phase, tactical questioning. Note that their boots have been removed.

Points to remember

1 In any future conventional war in Europe, evasion will be essential: modern tactics make surrendering a very difficult option. Warsaw Pact forces are not renowned for their fair treatment of PoWs.

2 If you are captured, the sooner you escape the better. The further down the line you go, the more thoroughly you will be searched. More kit will be taken off you, and the ground will become more unfamiliar.

3 You may not get any second chances; capture could mean death. Do not take risks.

4 Preparation is essential. Lessons learned must be applied: E & E kit must be carried on all operations — on you, not in your Bergen — and you must be skilled in its use.

5 Proficiency in unarmed combat is a considerable advantage, not only for physically resisting capture but also for promoting the right mental attitude of self-reliance.

They do, however, have time to plan and prepare clothing or equipment to assist them. Crucially, they can produce civilian clothes if the appearance of the locals will allow them to blend as civilians. If, however, their captors are physically very different then disguise is no assistance.

Short-term evasion is best conducted by small groups of about four men – larger numbers are hard to conceal, while smaller groups do not offer the protection and support nor the numbers to mount guard in a hide. So if there are more than four, you should divide up with group leaders – in this way, if some of you are captured, others may evade and exfiltrate to friendly forces.

Wild food

Evasion in a temperate environment is easiest in early autumn, when fruits, nuts and fungi are available and the weather is not too cold. The most difficult time to evade is during deep winter or even very early spring: it is cold, and there is very little natural food about.

Unless you are fighting in one of the great wild temperate areas of the world such as Canada or deep in the USSR, temperate areas usually have a civilian population, which means you can try to get hold of their food. But try to avoid any contact with the local population – get to know the layout of a farm, for instance, so that you can steal food from the kitchen and vegetable garden or raid the hen coops or cow sheds. Beware: farms have dogs and a disturbed cow can make a lot of noise.

On one evasion exercise British special forces managed to extract some freshly laid eggs from a coop. When they started to boil them, they discovered that one of the eggs was made of china, placed by the farmer to encourage the chickens to lay.

Bury the bones

If you intend to catch and butcher a sheep, remember that they can run very fast. If you do catch one you will need to drain the blood into a stream and bury the offal and bones – farmers feel very strongly about their sheep. They will report stolen sheep and the location of fires and signs of butchery.

In conventional and unconventional war there are refugees who will

Avoid this situation: the better option is to swim the river at night rather than risk a bridge. In rural areas those who operate a toll bridge will know all the locals, and you will be noticed.

A prisoner's fate

In a tactical situation, prisoners may outnumber the captors, who can ill afford the manpower for prisoner escort. Wounded prisoners put an additional strain on resources. In short, the enemy may have plenty of good reasons for killing you as a prisoner.

In the picture on the right, a Vietnamese marine gives water to a captured VC who was badly wounded in the legs and abdomen. The prisoner said he had been forced from his home by the VC and used as an ammunition bearer. Below, 30 minutes later, the same prisoner is shot dead by another marine.

have left their homes and there will be some food stocks. Enemy soldiers may ditch some of their rations, so it is worth checking their bivouac sites: you may find pieces of equipment that will assist your evasion efforts.

Corpses of friendly troops will also have water and rations, and a former friendly position is worth checking.

It is best to move by night – this allows you to check navigation from the stars or simply with your compass. Keep a simple orienteering-type compass in your combat jacket pocket: you live with what's in your Bergen, fight with what's on your belt and survive with what's in your pockets. This should include a compass as well as an escape map, a simple first aid kit and water purifying tablets. A good pocket knife will complete a kit that can be adapted according to the individual's priorities.

Resting by day

With this kit, the evader moves at night – when it is cold – and rests up by day when it is warm. When resting up, avoid obvious locations, including the temptingly dry outbuildings on a farm.

Try to find a place where you can see approaching search parties and have an escape route. A small patch of scrub may be better than a wood; searchers are more likely to overlook the scrub. Remember that they may have dogs or cordon-and-search-teams in helicopters – you must camouflage from the air as well as from the ground.

In a temperate area such as Europe there are always polythene agricultural sacks in the fields. These are not

A foraging raid

Do not attempt a foraging raid unless you have exhausted all other means and are desperate. Apart from the obvious danger of being spotted, thefts from a farm will be discovered rapidly, perhaps while you are still nearby.

Hunger
Your attitude, morale and will to survive will be affected after about four days without food. You will begin to suffer loss of weight, weakness, dizziness and blackouts, a slowed heart rate, a feeling of cold, and increased thirst.

Stealing chickens
The odd chicken may not be missed. But if you do not have specialist knowledge you shouldn't try to simulate a fox or dog raid; a gamekeeper will easily spot an amateur job and may put the enemy on your track.

Stealing eggs
If you are going to take eggs, take only a few. A farmer knows that hens sometimes do not lay properly, but he will not accept the loss of the entire contents of the hen coop.

Personality
This is perhaps the most important factor in an evasion situation. You must be decisive, adaptable, calm, optimistic but realistic, patient, able to improvise and to cope with isolation, and able to assess and predict the action of others.

Care with sheep
Hill sheep die on moorland all year round and a missing one is unlikely to be noticed; but be careful on the more closely monitored lowland farms. When gutting the sheep, always check the liver; it should not look grey or have any yellow patches when you cut into it.

Short-term evaders prepare a shelter. It is vital that you have enough in your webbing to survive for several days; the habit of taking most of your kit out of your webbing for a night patrol could backfire badly if you are separated from it.

only completely waterproof but are also a common sight and therefore good camouflage in themselves. Take care, however, to check what they have contained: some agricultural chemicals are toxic or at least harmful to humans. Farmers also use twine and cordage, and this is useful for building shelters and hides.

Remember, however, that farmers do not take kindly to having their hard-earned stock used by men on the run and they also have a very good

Caves for cover

A boulder cave provides an excellent hide for an evader. Be careful to cover your tracks near the cave, and establish a strict trackplan so that disturbance to surrounding vegetation is kept to a

minimum. Do not try to improve the cover to the entrance too much, as farmers and game keepers will notice any changes in ground cover.

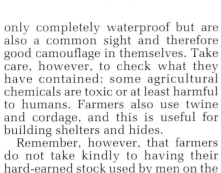

Recce the target
Carry out a careful reconnaissance, and plan the operation to cover every eventuality.

Assess the risk
Before going ahead, decide whether the likely takings are going to be worth the risks.

Cover group
This may be unconventional warfare, but do not discard conventional common sense. If you are operating as a four-man team, at least one person should cover the others from a position where he can see the whole target area and provide adequate warning of enemy or civilians.

Plan your pickings
You can take a lot of stuff that will last for several days, and move on rapidly, or stay in one place and steal small amounts that may not be noticed.

Take your chances
You must be constantly on the look-out for things that could be useful. Work out how to use them later.

idea of the layout of their land. Anything that looks out of the ordinary will attract their attention and they may pass this on to the hunters who are trying to find you or your group.

Civilian disguise

Disguise in civilian clothing can take various forms. At its simplest you can use a coat or mackintosh over your uniform to conceal its colour or pattern. Or you may be able to find civilian clothes that fit and look acceptable. If, however, you adopt this course remember that if you are captured in civilian clothes and have a weapon, many enemy soldiers and governments will see you as a terrorist and beyond the normal rules of war.

If you do opt for disguise you need a washing and shaving kit, since dirty or bearded civilians are more likely to attract attention even near a war zone. Avoid children; unlike adults, they are uninhibited about staring at strangers.

Even the most junior soldier is a useful member of his national armed forces. Also, your return to friendly forces increases your country's knowledge of enemy tactics and operations.

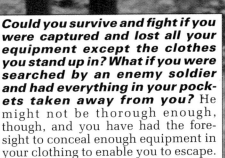

Could you survive and fight if you were captured and lost all your equipment except the clothes you stand up in? What if you were searched by an enemy soldier and had everything in your pockets taken away from you? He might not be thorough enough, though, and you have had the foresight to conceal enough equipment in your clothing to enable you to escape.

If you are captured, the man searching you is going to be so interested in retrieving stuff such as notebooks, maps and knives that he will not even think about looking in the other places where small items of equipment can be concealed.

Hiding places

He will find the tobacco tin containing your survival kit, and it is probably best not to hide any equipment in your jacket or smock as this will probably be taken off you straight away. Your shirt, jersey or trousers are, however, ideal hiding places for escape and evasion equipment.

Useful things to conceal are:

1 A wire saw
2 A compass
3 A sharpened hacksaw blade
4 A fishing kit
5 A sewing kit
6 Condoms
7 Scalpel blades
8 Map
9 Firelighting oil

You can usually feed the wire saw into the waistband of your combat trousers; remove the rings from the saw, and replace them with bootlace or nylon cord. Likewise, you can feed fishing line into the seams of your clothing or under the collar of your shirt. Some soldiers remove all the buttons on their trousers or pockets and re-sew them using fishing line.

Fishing-hooks are, however, a different problem. If you sew them into clothing unprotected, they may pierce the cloth and injure you: wrap them in PVC first. The same applies to needles and scalpel blades.

Boots are often cited as good hiding places for escape and evasion equipment, but beware. Walking is probably the only way you will be able to

Selecting your equipment

The items you need to take are largely dependent on the environment you are going into, so you will need to make one up for each potential deployment area. In preparing your kit, choose things that can be used for more than one task.

You need:

1 First aid items
2 Signalling items
3 Water and means to obtain drinkable water
4 Fire starting equipment
5 Food and kit to help you obtain food
6 Shelter kit
7 Weapons

travel, and if your boots are uncomfortable or unable to protect your feet you will be in trouble.

Step on it

If you have very thick shock-absorbent insoles in your boots, you can hide things beneath them, but check regularly to make sure the insole is not being worn away. Obviously only very thin items can be concealed this way, and nothing over about 8 cm long, as it may puncture the insole and your foot when the sole of the boot flexes.

Survival rifle

A Ruger 10/22 silenced semi-automatic rifle, complete with folding stock and 4×40 scope, will definitely keep the larder stocked.

SAS Belt Order

Sabre squadron troopers always carry E and E equipment as part of their belt order. This is not the definitive layout: individuals are allowed to carry what they like once they are on squadron.

1 Belt, pouches and water bottles
2 SLR magazines
3 Rifle cleaning kit
4 Purse net
5 Fishing kit
6 Snares
7 Mess tin lid and rations
8 Torch and filters
9 Button-compass
10 Wire saw
11 Fire starting kit
12 Lock picks (note: these are illegal in UK)
13 Clasp knife
14 Prismatic compass
15 Miniflares
16 Millbank bag (for filtering water)
17 Field dressing
18 Survival ration
19 Heliograph
20 Silk escape map

Condoms also need to be concealed with care: if they are unprotected the plastic wrapper will eventually wear and damage the contents, so when you come to use one in a survival situation it has a hole in it! Wrap them in PVC tape (ideally, a minimum of five should be carried).

If you can safely conceal a flint and steel firelighter in your clothing, so much the better, but make sure you know how to use it before sewing it in, otherwise the space is wasted.

Compasses and maps

Small compasses are fairly easy to conceal and the small RAF button compass can even be swallowed and retrieved at a later date! However, these compasses only really give an indication of magnetic North, and are not accurate enough for bearings.

Rough maps of your operational area are not as difficult to construct as you may think. Pilots and Special Forces are often issued with elaborate maps, printed on cloth or silk and disguised as handkerchiefs or sewn into the lining of clothing.

Major details

Your escape map should be a very simple affair, with only large towns, major roads, railways and rivers marked on it. Any other detail would be useless and confusing. Combined with your simple compass, it just makes sure you walk in the right direction. It is best drawn on rice paper or airmail paper, folded and wrapped in cling film or seran wrap and sewn behind a unit or rank patch or hidden under the insole of your boot.

Above: Even if you are captured you should be allowed to keep your helmet and respirator, and the former can be pressed into service for cooking unless it is a new issue one.

Right: Three belt orders containing survival kit. Pistols can be useful but ideally you should not get into a position where you have to use one. The bottom set really needs a yoke to spread the weight.

Left: Useful things can be sewn into combats. The RAF issue button compass is excellent, and can be swallowed prior to capture and retrieved later. Also, some kit can be taped down behind your scrotum, and you can hide kit in your nether regions. Beware of injuring yourself if you use this method of concealment, and remember that, although inexperienced troops may not be very keen to search this area, your bottom will definitely be on the checklist.

Right: A Marine recruit builds a survival shelter on Dartmoor. Effective training, a minimum of equipment and local resources will provide the determined evader with all he needs. Inset: The commando wire saw in action.

Condoms can be used as:

1 Water carriers
Each one will take about 1½ pints. Remember to put the whole thing in a sock for support.

2 Surgical gloves
Bullet wounds are usually already highly contaminated, but if you are clearing out a wound put condoms on your fingers to reduce the chances of further infection.

Signalling devices
Useful for ground-to-air signalling: simply blow them up and place them on the ground in the desired pattern.

4 Waterproof containers
You can use them to protect kit or maps and for hiding things internally, and for keeping water out of weapons and radio equipment.

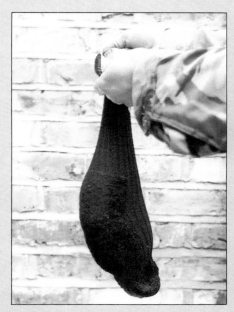

Above: When you're searched by the enemy, the chances are that you will lose the most useful of survival tools – your knife. If you can successfully hide a sharpened edge of some kind, e.g. a razor blade, you can still make survival tools: it just takes longer. This fox was skinned with a flint flake. The sinew, extracted with a knife from along the back, is an excellent source of strong cordage for making tools: having to dig them out with your teeth is less pleasant.

Remember

1 Every piece of kit you smuggle through the first search will help you escape.

2 If they keep searching, eventually they will find everything.

3 Make sure the piece of kit can be retrieved once you have escaped, e.g. that it is not so well sewn in that you can't get at it.

4 Make sure you know how to use the kit you've hidden.

Urban Evasion

Urban evasion, like its rural equivalent, varies according to the climate and wealth of the country you are operating in. For example, a country with strong family or local loyalties or with a restrictive political regime will be harder to move about in than one in which there is a large 'floating' population, a high level of personal wealth and public transport and facilities. The important consideration will be the sense of national threat and suspicion that has been generated by war.

Win some, lose some

A large Western city can be a very anonymous place. Even to members of ethnic minorities it offers a level of concealment. Citizens will keep to themselves, and as long as your manner and appearance do not attract attention you can move fairly freely. Always include a shaving kit in your E&E gear – unshaven men will always attract attention. Trains, entertainment centres etc. can offer protection from the weather by day and sometimes by night: evasion is not helped by standing around.

Food can be a problem, depending on how you intend to work. If you go into deep cover and remain concealed in a 'safe house', you will depend on your hosts. There may be problems where food is rationed or controlled.

A Shi'ite Amal militiaman questions a Palestinian woman as she is evacuated from Bourj El Barajneh refugee camp. In a society at war your chances of remaining under cover are not good unless your knowledge of local language and custom is faultless. For this reason SAS patrols operating in Germany always include one member trained to a very high standard in colloquial German.

Derelict housing can provide a good spot to go to ground, but beware: dossing is not socially acceptable as a way of life in most Communist bloc countries. Civilians may be eager to inform on you and derelict housing may be regularly searched by security forces.

A household will either have to share food with you, or they will need to have false ration books and documents. They should not tell shopkeepers or suppliers that they are concealing someone: even the most trustworthy of friends may be indiscreet.

For the evader, the problem can be one of boredom. Books, videos, radio and television, board games and simple keep-fit routines will pass the time, but you must keep noise down, avoid appearing at the windows, and not produce domestic noises or cooking smells that are incompatible with the lifestyle of your host.

Hiding place

Within the house you will, as in an OP, need a look-out position and, most importantly, a place to hide. Many modern houses are built to well-known specifications; a search team will perhaps have plans, they will at least have a good knowledge of the type of house. Older houses, on the other hand, may have common roof space that allows you to move from house to house in a run of terraced buildings. Flats that have been converted from larger buildings offer good hiding places, but may be less soundproof.

The ideal hiding place should be small so that its presence does not detract from the space or comfort of the house. However, it should not be so small that a prolonged occupation becomes uncomfortable. Water and a bucket for waste matter are the basic priorities, and good ventilation is

The most difficult period is the transition from short-term evasion on the battlefield to deep cover. In finding people who are likely to be sympathetic you may have to recce several households for a considerable period.

essential. A bench or seat is welcome.

The walls of the hide should be thick enough not to sound hollow. Various types of sound insulation can be added to the inside to give the impression of a solid structure. Lay in a store of simple foods that will not deteriorate over time and which have basic wrappings.

When you have prepared the hide, you should practise a 'crash move' – getting into the hide from 'a standing start' from somewhere else in the house or flat.

When you are under cover, the householder will have to remove any trace of your presence in the building. This can include extra food and

Beirut provides one of the most demanding evasion environments. Deep religious and political divisions between groups within the Palestinian community alone means that everyone must belong to one particular faction, and an individual will stand out conspicuously.

Slumming it

One way of surviving is by becoming a vagrant. This is not as easy as it may sound. In many cities there is a well-developed underworld of vagrants and drop-outs and your arrival among them will not go unnoticed. The vagrants may include informers or drug addicts who are an easy target for pressure by the police or enemy security forces.

If you can degenerate to a low enough level you will become an unlikely suspect. You may have problems with your health and in protecting yourself against bad weather if you adopt this technique.

Foraging for food is easy in a wealthy environment as long as you are prepared to examine the contents of cafe and restaurant dustbins. This type of behaviour will also add to your cover as a vagrant.

The vagrant approach to urban evasion depends on the society in which you are on the run. A European vagrant could be the object of great interest in some African or Far Eastern cities, and this would not assist your attempts at concealment. But in North America and all of Western Europe you could easily pass as a victim of war or civil disturbance. In this environment you can effectively pretend to be insane.

Dustbins are an excellent source of food and useful kit. Use the lid to sort through the stuff, or lay it out on some paper so that you do not make a mess. If you take things away you must fill the bin with newspaper and try to leave the top layer undisturbed; people notice how full their bins are.

Movement by night

Virtually all evasive moves should be made at night. Do not be over-confident: remember the enemy has night vision devices. You will always have to compromise between choosing the easiest route and not going where the enemy expect. Remember:

1 Learn the route.
2 Unless you have foolproof documentation and the right clothes, never move on roads.
3 Never cross bridges; use improvised rafts or swim.

Capture
If you are caught in civilian clothes you will not be able to claim protection as a PoW: you will probably be treated as a spy and eventually killed.

plates, books and magazines, clothing of the wrong size or sex and even the extra toothbrush or towel in the bathroom.

This type of concealment assumes that your evasion is assisted by relatively well-paid people with a circle of reliable contacts. Such people do not normally have a traditional fear of authority but nor do they have the skills of deception and concealment.

The grey man

The mid-way approach to evasion is to adopt the 'grey man' technique. Here you aim to have as anonymous an appearance as possible. Clothing should be neutral, and your behaviour will have to be that of a 'solid citizen' — such people do not sit around in public parks or search through dustbins: they are on their way to or from work.

But this can be very tiring, and you will need a good command of the local language. The advantage is that,

Passing cordons
If you have to cross a road near a cordon, wait until a car with lights on has just passed the cordon and cross immediately. The light will have destroyed the enemy's night vision and flare night vision devices.

Evasion

There are any number of situations where you as a soldier will need the skill to evade, for example:

1. *A breakout from a PoW camp or holding area.*
2. *An escape from a surrounded position in small numbers or as an individual.*
3. *As a result of the disruption of boundaries between units after a tactical nuclear exchange.*
4. *As a result of becoming lost on patrol and straying into the enemy positions.*
5. *When your defensive position is overrun and not cleared.*

Weapons
You will have a good chance of bluffing your way out of a stop-and-search check if you have the right documents and kit and know the language. In this case, do not blow your chances by carrying a weapon. If you have no chance of bluffing then consider carrying a weapon: silenced firearms are ideal, but otherwise choose something that is concealable or not in itself harmful e.g. a screwdriver or chisel. Silenced firearms are ideal, but realistically a meat skewer is more the sort of thing you can hide in your kit.

—FORSEY—

unlike the vagrant, you are less vulnerable to assault by other vagrants or bored members of the enemy police force. Your travel through the country is less likely to be questioned, but — and this is critical — you will need the right paperwork, work permits, identity cards, even documents for travel in restricted areas such as the border, and you must also have money.

It may be that you can make the transition from deep cover to a grey man role. During your time in cover you will be able to learn some language and local knowledge before venturing out.

Seasonal advantages

Though evasion and escape can be easier in the country in spring, summer and early autumn, the city can have attractions in the winter. The major disadvantage is that contact with enemy citizens or even occupying powers is inevitable, and this can compromise you.

Security forces

Border guard units are picked for their loyalty or high degree of political indoctrination. Soviet GRU and NKVD will be highly active in occupied towns and cities rounding up undesirables: however, other units within the Warsaw Pact armies are not so closely aligned with the USSR that they will go out of their way to kill you.

Movement by day

Generally, moves by day are not a good idea, but are sometimes unavoidable. If you have to move by day:

1 Be confident; look as if you know where you are going, do not loiter, and do not appear furtive.
2 Obtain some unobtrusive clothing and try to assume a definite identify, e.g. steal a donkey jacket and carry a spade.
3 Keep clean, and shave if possible.
4 If you can get hold of a bike you are doing well, but assess the risk before you steal it. Use public transport if you are completely confident that you know how the system works.
5 Keep away from stations and bus terminals.
6 Rivers are an excellent escape route, but the larger ones will be watched.
7 Watch out for children and dogs.

Avoid children

Children are not bound by grown-up conventions of social behaviour, and when they see something peculiar they will point it out loudly.

Cordons

These are relatively easy to pass at night. If you observe the enemy position for up to two hours, they are bound to compromise the sentry position by noise, movement or simply sentry changeover. Then choose your route carefully.
If you have to cross a road near a cordon, wait until a car with lights on has just passed the cordon and cross immediately. The light will have destroyed the enemy's night vision and flare night vision devices.

Checkpoints

If you have to pass through an area covered by a checkpoint, imitate the silhouette of the enemy sentries as far as possible, especially headgear, which is a common recognition feature. Learn at least one phrase in the local language, along the lines of 'Don't shoot, you idiot, it's me' — and make sure it is fluent.

Jungle Evasion

Evasion in an environment such as tropical jungle, savannah grassland or deep temperate forest can be a case of survival rather than evasion. Enemy hunters may find searching for you or your group as difficult as locating the proverbial needle in the haystack. But your movements may be predicted by shrewd hunters, and they can place ambushes or stop lines on features.

You will probably have a compass and basic survival kit and even if you escape from a PoW camp or convoy you need a sense of direction, particularly if moving by night. Hunters will try to put stops between you and friendly forces, or an open border or sea coast. They will also look at the easy routes, for instance tracks or river lines. Roads and railways are often covered by transport police or civil security forces.

Security vs speed

You will be faced by a trade-off between security and speed. Movement by day is faster, and in deep jungle movement by night is almost impossible. But grassland should be covered at night since helicopters or fixed-wing aircraft can cover large areas very easily by day.

Jungle varies between primary and secondary, and though the high canopy of trees in primary may obscure the horizon and make navigation difficult, it is excellent cover from the air and the going on the ground is

Map coverage in most jungle areas where modern armies have not recently operated is usually very poor. This, in combination with horrific weather and high mountains, results in aircraft constantly going down, even without enemy ground fire.

In the jungle, survival rather than evasion can rapidly become the priority for the inexperienced. However, if you're well trained the jungle provides the ideal situation for long-term evasion.

Getting the locals on your side

US Special Forces made extensive use of the indigenous population of the highlands of Vietnam, Cambodia and Laos. These aboriginals, collectively known as the Montagnards, were very effective as mercenaries trained and led by the Green Berets.

As an evader, getting the local population on your side is of paramount importance. If you are going to approach a village a thorough recce is essential. Before going in, decide whether you stand a reasonable chance of winning if you have to fight. If you come to the conclusion they would easily kill you, do not risk provoking them; stash your rifle where it can be retrieved later.

When you approach the village, do so openly so that they have plenty of warning and will not be forced into a snap decision, such as killing you. Take off your helmet, and bin anything that makes you look like a spaceman. They are less likely to kill you if you look vaguely like them.

easy. However, it does not adequately conceal you from enemy troops.

Secondary jungle gives excellent cover, but is very hard going on foot and can house dangerous plants and animals. But among these threats to life and health there will be edible plants and scope to make animal traps. Trapping food does pose two problems – you have to wait for the trap to be sprung, and it may be found by local people who will report its presence to the enemy.

Finding water

Water can be collected from plants or as rainfall, but avoid streams unless you have sterilising tablets in a survival kit. There are a vast number of killing or incapacitating organisms in rivers.

Savannah and bush have water holes and do give you a better chance to kill game, but remember that you

Combat ranges in the jungle are very short, so you have no great tactical advantage over the natives armed with single-barrelled shotguns, slingshot and bows and arrows. As an evader with the locals on your side, you could still do considerable damage to an enemy.

will have to cook it. Cooking takes time, requires a fire and the trade-off of the nutrition of the meat against time and vulnerability is a decision that you or your team will have to make on the ground. Dried or smoked meat is one way of making the most of game that you may have killed.

Talking to the locals

You may be obliged to enter a village, perhaps because you need urgent help or simply through bad navigation. Most villages have dogs, and dogs bark. This will warn the locals that there is a stranger about. Avoid crossing rivers downstream of the village: they may be sewers as well as the 'launderette'. Remember that infection can enter your body through your skin as well as your mouth.

You will be an object of great interest to the locals, but not necessarily an object of hostility. Your colour, clothing and equipment will be observed. Items such as survival knives, water bottles or footwear will be examined; be prepared to demonstrate them in the spirit of mutual interest – the locals are professional hunters who kill to live, and should be extended respect and courtesy.

Village leaders

It is a fair bet that the older men are the village leaders. Treat them with respect and you will ensure that the village will respect you – if you are brash, threatening or offhand with them you will probably find enemy troops on your tail within hours of your exit from the village.

Local hospitality

It is worth remembering that not all villages in remote rural locations or deep jungle see their government as friendly. You may have more in common with them than they with the soldiers, and a lost, perhaps wounded and frightened man will merit traditional hospitality extended to any stranger. But do not overstay your welcome – the villagers' resources may be limited, your presence will become known through tribal gossip, and sweeps by enemy soldiers may pick you up.

The longer you stay, the more vulnerable you make the villagers to enemy reprisals. One night – or a brief stop – can always be explained away to the enemy: they can say you were armed and threatened them. If you stay longer it will be obvious that they co-operated with you.

Respect for women

An important rule when visiting a village is to extend a dignified respect to the women – whatever their age. It is very unlikely that they have the same values as your culture. If you are in a group, keep an eye on anyone who is likely to breach the social etiquettes.

Disguise your route

If you discuss your proposed route with the villagers, do not tell them which one you decide on, and do not leave in the direction you intend to travel. Go west if you plan to go north, and change route after you are away from sight. The villagers may wish to guide you on your way; accept with gratitude, and when they have gone cover your tracks. Even if they have been friendly, they may be naïve people who will subsequently betray you.

A village elder. If you do not speak the language, an understanding of body language is essential. Do not make the mistake of giving offence by talking to the wrong man: it should be obvious after careful recce who the key individuals are. If you observe the village for several days you should also build up some idea of tribal custom: at least the method of greeting. You should also have an idea of patterns of movement and therefore the best time to approach.

Ground air emergency code

If friendly forces are going to be looking for you, all means of communication are important, so do not assume the radio will work. This signalling system will work wherever you have air superiority: hilltop village sites are usually clear enough to set this up.

Note: leave a space of about three metres between each element where possible.

1 Require doctor, serious injuries
2 Require medical supplies
3 Unable to proceed
4 Require food and water
5 Require firearms and ammunition
6 Require map and compass
7 Require signal lamp with battery and radio
8 Indicate direction to proceed
9 Am proceeding in this direction
10 Will attempt takeoff
11 Aircraft seriously damaged
12 Probably safe to land here
13 Require fuel and oil
14 All well
15 No
16 Yes
17 Not understood
18 Require engineer

Main picture and above: In many jungle areas, the villagers farm small gardens outside the village as well as hunt. This usually means that the village is relatively deserted during the day, with all the young children and one or two adults all concentrated in one hut, but don't bet on it. If you decide the village is too much of a risk, you could always raid a garden and move on.

Maintaining the will to survive

Knowing that you may have to travel hundreds of miles over a period of months may be a little upsetting; having to survive alone in a strange environment for this period may make dying look like the easy option.

The determination to survive must be maintained at times by sheer will power: most of the obstacles you will have to overcome will be mental rather than physical. The factors that make all the difference are:

1 A sense of responsibility: loyalty to your unit and a sense of duty.
2 Family and home ties: having something worthwhile to survive for.
3 Self-control: thinking the problem through rather than panicking.
4 Planning: preparing a plan that makes use of all available resources.
5 Endurance: pain, discomfort and other unpleasant conditions must be accepted as normal.
6 Leadership: the strong help the weak.
7 Knowledge of escape and evasion and survival techniques.

Surviving the Dogs of War

Every breath you take, every move you make, a dog can detect it. Perhaps as much as a mile away under the right conditions. And an attack dog, trained to silence, can be on you literally before you know it: travelling at 15 metres a second and weighing anything up to 45 kg, it is as lethal as any bullet. What can a man working behind enemy lines do to protect himself against these killers? In this section we're going to examine some of the dog evasion techniques taught to British Special Forces units.

Dogs of war are trained to do specific jobs. Guard and attack dogs are trained to detect, engage and, in some cases, to savage intruders or evaders either under the command of a handler or running free.

Search dogs are adept at picking up and finding the source of airborne scents and are allowed to run free, going over an area of ground yard by yard. Tracker dogs, on the other hand, run on a long leash with a handler. Ground scents are the trackers' speciality.

Search and tracker dogs lead their handlers to their target, but do not usually assault the fugitive, leaving that to the attack dogs or to the handlers or their combat back-up.

Eyes, ears and noses

Like most mammals except man, dogs have very poor eyesight. They don't see colours at all, but only shades of grey, and then not very clearly. They can see you moving, of course, and this is very likely to

For this evader it's too late to escape. But there are lots of ways to avoid letting the dogs get so close, so learn the evasion drills before you get into this situation.

The dog and his handler work as a team. Destroy their confidence in each other, and you stand a chance.

Evading Tracker Dogs

So, what can you do to fool the dog? Let's split the mission up into four phases: lying up, pre-contact, distant contact and close contact.

Lying up

If you have to spend any length of time in a lying-up place, always obey these simple rules, even if you have no proof that a search dog is operating:
1   Keep as close to the ground as possible.
2   Put most of your clothing over you, so that the ground absorbs your scent rather than letting it out into the open air.

3   Breathe down into the ground, or at least into the vegetation.
4   Keep as still as possible.
5   Bury rubbish under where you are lying.
6   No smoking, no fires wherever possible.
7   If you're discovered by anyone, move away as fast as you can.

Pre-contact

Use all the normal physical camouflage tricks to blend into the environment, plus a few that are designed to throw the dog off the scent.
1   Travel over ground already used by other people or by animals. This makes the dog work much harder to keep on your track.
2   If you're travelling as part of a group, split up from time to time. Double back on yourself. Leave a false trail wherever possible.

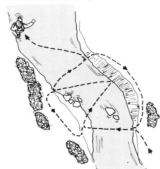

3   Use streams and running water to confuse the dog, but don't try to walk for too long in the stream itself – it will slow you down too much. Instead, cross the stream diagonally, doubling back perhaps two or three times so that the dog can't tell which of your exit tracks is the real one and which ones are dummies.

4   When you're preparing food, pay close attention to the direction of the wind. You must bury all wrappings and containers, but remember, too, to handle them as little as possible. The smell of the food is one thing – your smell on the wrappers tells the dog that it was your food. When you bury the remains, don't touch the ground with your hands. Use a metal tool of some sort. Whenever you can, sink the rubbish in deep water. The same goes for urine and faeces.

Distant contact

If you're sighted from a distance, speed becomes important.
1   Try and tire the dog and handler team; it will be easier to destroy their confidence in each other if they make mistakes through tiredness.
2   If you're part of a group then split up straight away, and arrange a rendezvous for later.
3   Make for hard ground. A road or a rocky surface makes and holds much less scent than a soft one.

4   If you are in wood country or scrub, double back and change your direction as often as you can.
5   The tracker dog will be on a long lead; if you can get him tangled up, you can increase the distance between you and him, and maybe break off the contact entirely.

Close contact

If the dog catches up with you, you're in deep trouble. Not so much from the dog: he's done his job in finding you. Now you're in trouble from the handler and whatever combat back-up he may have available.
1   Forget the dog for the moment. You'll know from the look of him whether he's an attack dog or a tracker. If he's a tracker, he probably won't come near you.
2   Move as fast as you can. Get out of sight of the handler.
3   Get rid of loose pieces of clothing, food (especially food – the dog may be distracted by it when he comes looking for you) and any other pieces of kit that aren't vital to your mission or your survival.
4   If the dog sticks with you, you must kill or immobilise it.

attract their attention. Because their eyes are low down to the ground they're quick to see movement above the skyline.

If a dog's eyesight is only half as good as man's, its range of hearing is twice as good. How far away they can hear you is affected by weather conditions, especially wind and rain. If the wind is blowing away from you and towards the dog, he's a lot more likely to hear you. Rain creates a background noise and makes individual sounds much more difficult to pick out. So take advantage of rain to get on the move.

It's not just that a dog can hear you a long way off; he can also hear sounds that man can't. High-pitched squeaks and whistles that you don't know exist are part of a dog's everyday life. So tape loose pieces of equipment to stop

Forty-five kilos of German shepherd dog races towards its quarry. It's impossible to stop such a powerhouse. Let it attack a protected left arm, grab the dog tight to your body, roll onto the ground and get behind and on top of it to immobilise it.

them rubbing and catching. Think about the way you use radios and other items of hardware. A clink of cooking utensils, a match being struck, even the sound of the flame when you're cooking your meal can give away your position to a well-trained dog.

Amazing sense of smell

In fact, if you were cooking a meal, the chances are that he would smell you first – from anything up to a couple of miles away under the right weather conditions! Because while a dog's hearing is a lot keener than ours, his sense of smell is many thousands of times better.

The strongest human body odour comes from the sweat glands, especially under the arms. Moving quickly, particularly when carrying a heavy load and wearing too many clothes, makes you sweat heavily. So does being tense, nervous or frightened. Eating various types of strongly flavoured food makes it worse, and so does not washing regularly.

Everyday clues

And it's not just the natural smells of our bodies that provide a target for the tracker dog's nose. Clothing, especially when it's wet; soap and deodorants; leather; tobacco; polish and preservatives; petrol; oil; and many, many more smells that are a natural part of our everyday lives can give a

An East German border guard feeds his attack animal. These dogs are trained killers: left to run loose while leashed to a chain, they can bring down and savage an escapee within seconds, night or day.

dog a clue to your presence.

A dog picks up scent in two different ways: from the air, and from contact with the ground, trees, plants and buildings. Airborne scents do not last very long: they are blown away by the wind quite quickly.

Traces of movement

A ground scent, on the other hand, may be obvious to the dog for anything up to 48 hours. Ground scents are caused not just by you leaving your own smell on things you touch, but by the movement itself. If you're walking on grass or pushing through vegetations you will crush leaves and stems with every movement.

Even on bare ground you will release air and tiny quantities of moisture that have been trapped in the soil, which smell quite different from the fresh air above ground. From the scent "footprints" that you leave behind a dog can even tell in which direction you're moving.

And because you push off each step with your toes, the front of the footprint is more obvious than the heel and it only takes a few steps for a dog to work out which way you're travelling.

Just as each person's footprints look slightly different to the eye, so to a dog is the mixture of scents in the smell footprint slightly different. The dog recognises this difference, and so may be able to track one person even where there are a number of people travelling together or where there are animals present.

Methods of evasion are detailed in the special sections, but remember the general point: although a dog can outhear, outsmell and outrun you, you can out-think him. To do that you must assess the skills of the dog opposing you, and use your wits and tactics to confuse all or most of its senses. Outwit the dog or the handler, and you may escape where others may not.

German shepherd dogs are the world's favoured guard and attack dogs; they're alert, fast, strong and aggressive. But other breeds are also used, including Dobermann pinschers, Rottweilers, mastiffs, boxers and giant schnauzers.

Combating Attack Dogs

Guard dogs and attack dogs either operate with a handler or are left to run free in a confined area. A dog that is running free in a compound may not even recognise his handler, but will attack absolutely anyone who comes into his territory. But whether the dog is on a leash or running free, its training is designed to do just one thing – catch anybody who shouldn't be there.

You do have one slight advantage when dealing with a guard dog – he's fixed in one place, more or less.

1 Always approach from down wind.

2 Take it slowly and easily to minimise exertion, and thereby cut down the amount of smelly sweat you secrete.

3 Keep as low as possible and use natural features of the ground. Windborne scent doesn't quite travel in straight lines, but any natural obstacle will help.

4 Approach along paths used by other people.

5 When you get within 200 metres of the objective, don't stop for anything – dogs have been known to pick up scents even against the wind at this sort of distance.

6 If you're dealing with a dog guarding a building, try to get above the ground floor if you can; dogs have difficulty in detecting people way above their heads.

7 If you find yourself close to a dog and handler unexpectedly, keep still. Guards have been known to pass within 10 metres of an intruder who's keeping perfectly still without detecting him.

Try to get above the dog's level; this will make his job more difficult.

Sacrificial defence

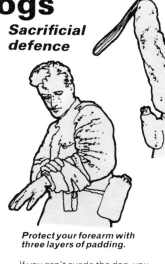

Protect your forearm with three layers of padding.

If you can't evade the dog, you have to immobilise him. And you can't do that effectively until the dog is within attack range. You have to let the dog bite you. Wrap protection around the forearm of the hand you don't use by choice. Arrange it in three layers. A soft one on the inside, as padding; a hard one next, to stop the dog's teeth penetrating; and lastly another soft layer to give the dog something to get his teeth into. Don't discourage the dog from attacking you, but make sure he takes the offered target; he will be more difficult to deal with the second time. When he's sunk his teeth into the padding, he's within reach, and you can deal with him. ★

Allow the dog to grab your protected arm. If you're still standing, you can club the animal.

If the dog leaps on you, roll over with him and keep his body tight to yours. Work your way around onto the top and back of the dog to immobilise it.

Snakes, Crocs and other Varmints

When you're living off the land, you have to be on the lookout for anything and everything that's edible. That means being prepared to catch and eat some pretty unfamiliar dishes — anything, from an insect to a reptile. Better a venomous snake for supper than slow starvation. Snakes and lizards, in fact, are delicious, and there are some restaurants in the world that charge high prices for snake meat. In this section of the survival course you can learn how to trap and cook lizards, snakes, turtles, frogs, newts and salamanders — not to mention crocodiles.

Take care

All snakes found on land or in fresh water are edible, whether they are poisonous or not. If you don't know if the snake you're hunting is poisonous, assume it is and act accordingly. Take extreme care when approaching the snake, and use a long stick or a hefty stone to kill it.

Kill the snake

You can, if you prefer, pin it to the ground by the head before killing it. Pick up the snake from behind. Put your index finger on the top of its head, and your thumb and middle finger on each side, just behind the

Frogs usually make good eating, but not these. Their skin contains one of the world's most deadly poisons. Central American Indians roast the beasts on sticks and scrape the resulting toxin onto their hunting arrows. One millionth of an ounce of the poison will kill a 6-kg monkey. Generally, avoid all brightly-coloured small animals.

jaws. You must keep your index finger on top of the head to stop the reptile turning inside its skin and biting you.

Next, chop the snake's head off, making the cut a couple of inches behind the head itself. But don't relax your guard. Even after you've cut it off, its reflexes may still be active

This anaconda snake is just about to squeeze the life out of an interfering human. Constrictor snakes such as these (some grow up to 12 metres long) live in jungles around the world and wait in low-lying tree branches before dropping onto hapless victims who wander underneath.

Tree-dwelling green mambas are from a group that kills more people than any other. Three drops of their venom will kill you, and as they only deliver a small proportion of their venom each time, they can go on to kill a few of your mates as well. And they can move at up to 5 mph.

enough to make the severed head bite you. Be careful!

Snakebite

Snakes kill their prey in one of two ways: constrictors squeeze it to death, the rest bite. Not all snakebites are poisonous, and very few poisonous

Cobras generally live in tropical scrub farmland and often make their homes under peasant huts, so be careful where you bed down for the night. Though they usually rear up and bite their victims, some species spit their venom up to 2 metres, aiming for the eyes. The poison can be absorbed into the bloodstream through the eyes, and you can be dead inside the hour.

Preparing a snake for eating

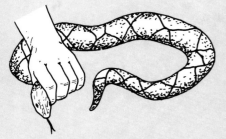

1 Hold the snake firmly behind the head.

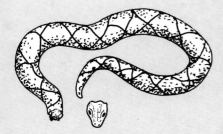

2 Cut the head off with a knife.

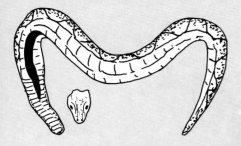

3 Slit open its belly and remove its innards. Use these to bait snares and traps.

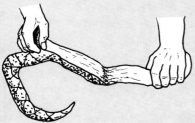

4 Skin the snake. You can use the skin for improvised belts, straps or similar items.

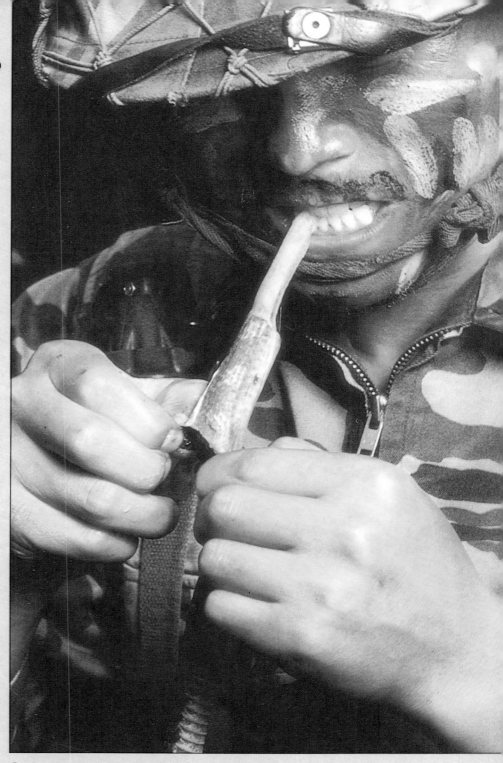

Snakes are good to eat and, according to this Japanese soldier, this is the best way to skin them. Before trying it yourself, make certain that you've cut the head off with at least 5 cm of body. Otherwise you'll get a mouthful of venom!

bites will kill you if you treat them promptly enough.

Walking around, the place you're most likely to get bitten is on the lower leg, well away from the heart. Unless the snake manages to hit a vein by chance, you have time to act before the poison can spread into the bloodstream. These are the signs of a venomous snakebite:

1 Between one and four puncture marks at the site of the wound
2 Local pain
3 Local swelling within the first two hours after the attack
4 Paralysis, twitching, numbness and general weakness within two hours

Remember, the poison has to spread in the bloodstream before it can do serious, lasting harm. If you panic or get excited, your pulse will speed up, and that will cause the poison to spread faster. Stay calm.

You don't need to be quite so careful with lizards: there are only two poisonous species in the world, the

First aid for snakebites

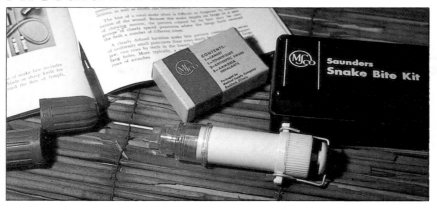

In a snake kit the lancet is used to open the wound so the blood carries the poison out of the body. Tourniquets restrict the circulation and limit the spread of the poison. In an emergency a bit of broken glass and some rope will do the job.

All snakebites should be treated as poisonous, and first aid must be given at once. The US Marine Corps manual recommends that you carry out the following while waiting for evacuation to the nearest hospital or aid station.

1 Kill the snake if possible. If you can identify it, this may help in deciding on the treatment. Call for medical evacuation immediately.
2 Keep the victim quiet and calm. Keep the bitten part still and below the level of the heart.
3 Place a constricting band between the bite and the heart. Tighten the band just enough to produce slight bulging of the surface veins. Make sure that circulation has not been stopped.
4 If swelling develops above the constricting band, remove the band and apply it above the swelling.

Nerve poison

For neuro-toxic (nerve poison) snake bites, such as cobra, coral snake or sea snake, medical evacuation and immediate administration of anti-venom is essential but you may have to act quickly in the meantime.

1 The venom will attack the nervous system and the victim may stop breathing. If he does, apply artificial respiration.

2 If heartbeat and breathing stop, apply CPR (cardiac pulmonary resuscitation).
3 Do not suck the wound; you may ingest the poison.

Blood poison

For haemo-toxic (blood poison) snake bites, such as rattlesnake, copperhead and viper, take the following action if the victim cannot be at a hospital within an hour of the bite.

1 Make a cut over each fang mark, parallel to the bitten limb. The cuts should be no more than half an inch long and a quarter of an inch wide.
2 Apply suction to the wound. If a snakebite kit is available, use its suction pump. If not, suck by mouth, spitting out the blood and other fluids frequently. Haemo-toxic venom is not harmful in the mouth unless there are cuts or sores and even then there is not much risk. Suction should be kept up for at least 15 minutes before loosening the tourniquet.

ALL SNAKEBITE VICTIMS SHOULD BE TAKEN TO HOSPITAL. The Mojave green rattlesnake has a slow-working haemotoxin; the snake can bite you and you'll feel fine, but 10 hours later you'll be dead.

The Puff Adder is one of the largest of the viper family and lives in the drier parts of the East African bush. Thick and heavy snakes, they like to enter camps in the bush, so watch out for them, especially in piles of logs. Their poison is not very strong but they give you a very large dose of it.

Gila Monster and the Beaded Lizard. They are both found in the Americas, roughly between Panama and the south-western United States. Club them, or catch them in a running noose on the end of a long stick.

Skin and clean snake before you cook it. First, cut off the head, then make a cut down through the belly as far as the tail. Don't throw the entrails away – you can use them for baiting traps. Now peel off the skin, just like peeling a banana. Don't throw it away, either. Snakeskin and lizardskin are useful materials even before they're cured.

Lizards

Treat large lizards just like snakes (they're not quite as easy to skin). Small lizards can be impaled on a stick through the head and roasted, without skinning and gutting them first. You'll know they're cooked when the skin starts to bubble and crack.

Reptile meat is very much like chicken, light in colour, moist and tender. Remember that in some parts of the world snake meat is regarded as a delicacy!

Down by the waterside

Don't ignore the larger reptiles, like crocodiles, alligators and cayman. They, too, are edible, and the meat from just one large specimen will keep you going for a long time. Shoot them, if you can – in the back of the head or neck – but if you don't have a firearm available you could try trapping.

Avoiding spiders and scorpions

1 Check your bedding before you get into it.
2 Check clothing, socks and shoes before you put them on.
3 Avoid sleeping or leaving clothes near damp places; dampness appears to attract these creatures.
4 If you feel an insect or spider crawling on you, remain still. Sudden movement may cause it to bite or sting.
6 Never step in the shade of a bush without visually checking the spot.

First Aid for scorpion stings

1 Keep the patient quiet and send for medical aid.
2 Place a tourniquet between the point of puncture and the heart.
3 Cool the area for 10 or 12 inches around the puncture point with ice, if available.
4 Remove the tourniquet after 10 minutes and keep the part chilled for at least two hours.

Not a nice way to go – death by crocodile. They lie in wait in the shallows of lakes and slow-moving rivers, waiting for an animal (or you) to come down for a drink or a swim. The crocodile shown above contained the body of an Australian camper.

These big reptiles are rather hard to skin. The best way is to heat them over a fire to loosen their armour and then skin them out in the normal way. The belly skin makes the most useful leather and, like all reptile skin, should be kept for use as bindings and straps. Skin from the rest of the animal is of little value.

Small but nourishing

Also not to be overlooked (and easy to find) are smaller aquatic animals. Frogs, newts and salamanders (a type of aquatic lizard) will all provide protein, and so will keep you alive where all else fails.

Frogs are best hunted at night, when you can locate them by their croaking. Skin and gut them before cooking. All the meat is edible. You will find newts and salamanders are to be found wherever there are frogs. Look in the water and under rocks and rotten logs. As with frogs, skin and gut them before you cook them.

But do beware: certain frogs and salamanders have poisonous sacs in their skin.

Desert and tropical jungle abound with various types of dangerous invertebrate animal life such as ground-dwelling spiders, scorpions and centipedes, together with insects of almost every type. Drawn to man as a source of moisture or food, lice, mites and flies can be extremely unpleasant and can carry diseases such as scrub typhus and dysentery.

The stings of many scorpions and the bites of centipedes or spiders can be extremely painful, though seldom fatal. Some species of scorpions and

Watch out for scorpions. They live under stones and in dark, warm, humid places in all warm countries. Your biggest danger is when walking around barefoot, putting boots back on, finding them in your armpits when asleep, or having a crap in the bush.

black widow or recluse spiders, however, can cause death. When you camp, check your clothes and shoes every morning.

Don't worry too much about tarantulas. These large, hairy spiders do have venom, but it rarely causes serious reactions in humans; you'll usually only get a slight swelling, numbness and itching.

113

Remember: In many countries, including the UK, it is illegal to kill, injure or take reptiles.

Crossing a River

If you are on the run or are operating in wild terrain, you are likely to encounter water obstacles that you may have to cross. They may be fast-moving rivers or large, marshy areas of clinging, stinking and tiring mud. Each has its dangers, but also its drills for survival. Here we deal with rivers, using techniques from US Army Manual FM21-76.

Finding your crossing-point

A river or stream may be narrow or wide, shallow or deep, slow-moving or fast-moving. It may be rain-fed, snow-fed or ice-fed. Your first step is to find a place where the river is basically safe for crossing, so look for a high place from which you can get a good view and look out for the best crossing point. If there is no high place, climb a tree.

Crossing a water obstacle can be highly dangerous, especially to the untrained. If you are not equipped with inflatable rafts or other crossing equipment, you may need to build your own if you have to get kit or wounded men over the river.

Your first step

Check the river carefully for the following features:

1 A level stretch where it breaks into a number of channels. Two or three narrow channels are usually easier to cross than a wide river.

2 Obstacles on the opposite side of the river that might hinder your travel. Try to select the spot from which travel will be the safest and easiest.

3 A ledge of rocks that crosses the river. This often indicates dangerous rapids or canyons.

4 A deep or rapid waterfall or a deep channel. Never attempt to ford a stream directly above or even close to such spots.

5 Rocky places. Avoid these; you can be seriously injured if you fall on rocks. An occasional rock that breaks the current, however, may assist you.

6 A shallow bank or sandbar. If possible, select a point upstream from such a feature so that the current will carry you to it if you lose your footing.

7 A course across the river that leads downstream, so that you can cross the current at about a 45° angle.

The depth of a fordable river or stream is no deterrent if you can keep your footing; in fact, deep water sometimes runs more slowly and is therefore safer than fast-moving shallow water. You can always dry your clothes later, or you can make a raft to carry your clothing and equipment across the river.

British paratroops are seen using a raft to carry their equipment across a river during jungle warfare exercises. Deep, slow-moving water is easier to cross than shallower but faster-moving water.

Rafting a river

Rafting rivers is one of the oldest forms of travel, and is often the safest and quickest method of crossing a water obstacle; however, building a raft under survival conditions is tiring and time-consuming unless you have proper equipment and help.

Brush and Australian poncho rafts

If you are with a companion and each of you has a poncho, you can construct a brush or Australian poncho raft. With this type of raft you can safely float your equipment across a slow-moving stream or river.

Brush raft

The brush raft will support about 115 kg if properly constructed. Use ponchos; fresh, green brush; two small saplings; and a rope or vines.

1 Tightly tie off the neck of each poncho with the neck drawstring.
2 Attach ropes or vines at the corner and side grommets of each poncho. Be sure they are long enough to cross to and tie with those at the opposite corner or side.
3 Spread one poncho on the ground with the tied-off hood upwards.
4 Pile fresh, green brush (no thick branches) on the poncho until the brush stack is about 45 cm high.
5 Pull the poncho neck drawstring up through the centre of the brush stack.
6 Make an X-frame of two small saplings and place it on top of the brush stack.
7 Tie the X-frame securely in place with the poncho neck drawstring.

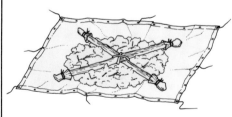

8 Pile another 45 cm of brush on top of the X-frame.
9 Compress the brush slightly.
10 Pull the poncho sides up around the brush and, using the ropes or vines attached to the corner and side grommets, tie diagonally from corner to corner and from side to side.

11 Spread the second poncho, tied-off hood upwards, next to the brush bundle.

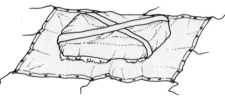

12 Roll the brush bundle onto the centre of the second poncho so that the tied side faces downwards.
13 Tie the second poncho around the brush bundle in the same way as you tied the first poncho around the brush (10).

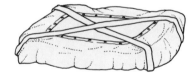

14 Tie one end of a rope to an empty canteen and the other end to the raft. This will help you to tow it.

Australian poncho raft

If you do not have time to gather brush for a brush raft, you can make an Australian poncho raft. Although more waterproof, this will only float about 25 kg of equipment. Use two ponchos, two 1-metre poles or branches, and ropes, vines, bootlaces or comparable material.

1 Tightly tie off the neck of each poncho with the neck drawstring.
2 Spread one poncho on the ground with the neck upwards.
3 Place and centre the two poles about 45 cm apart on the poncho.
4 Place the rucksacks, packs and other equipment between the poles, including items that you want to keep dry, such as boots and outer garments.

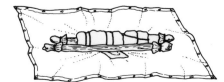

At this point you will need your companion's help to complete the raft.

1 Snap the poncho sides together.
2 Hold the snapped portion of the poncho in the air and roll it tightly down to the equipment. Make sure that you roll the full width of the poncho.
3 Twist each end of the roll to form pigtails in opposite directions.
4 Fold the pigtails over the bundle and tie them securely in place using ropes, vines or bootlaces.

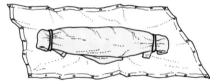

5 Spread the second poncho on the ground with the tied-off hood upwards. If you need more buoyancy, place some fresh, green brush on this poncho.
6 Place the equipment bundle, pigtail side down, on the centre of the second poncho.
7 Wrap the second poncho around the equipment bundle following the same procedure as you used for wrapping the equipment in the first poncho.
8 Tie ropes, vines or other binding material around the raft about 30 cm from each end of the pigtail.

9 Place and secure weapons on top of the raft.
10 Tie one end of a rope to a canteen and the other end to the raft. This will help you in towing the raft.

When launching or landing either type of raft, take care not to puncture or tear it by dragging it on the ground. Let the raft lie on the water for a few minutes to ensure that it floats before you start to cross the river or stream. If the river is too deep to ford, push the raft in front of you while swimming.

Crossing a fast river

If you are going to ford a swift, treacherous stream, remove your trousers and underpants so that the water will have less grip on your legs. Keep your shoes on to protect your feet and ankles from rocks and to give you firmer footing. Tie your trousers and important articles securely to the top of your pack; if you have to release it, everything will be easier to find.

Carry your pack well up on your shoulders so that you can release it quickly if you are swept off your feet. Being unable to get a pack off quickly

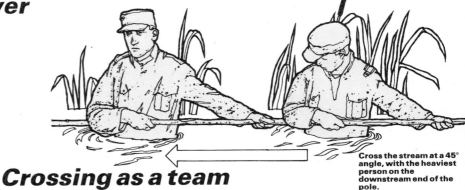

enough can drag even the strongest of swimmers under. Don't worry about the weight of your pack, as this will help rather than hinder you in fording the stream.

Find a strong pole about 12 cm in diameter and 2 to 2½ metres long to help you ford the stream. Grasp the pole and plant it firmly on your upstream

Crossing as a team

If there are other people with you, cross the stream together. Make sure that everyone has prepared their pack and clothing as above. The heaviest person should be on the downstream end of the pole and the lightest person on the upstream end. This way, the upstream person will break the current, and the people below can move

side to break the current. Plant your feet firmly with each step, and move the pole forwards, slightly downstream from its previous position, but still upstream from you. With your next step, place your foot below the pole. Keep the pole well slanted so that the force of the current keeps the pole firmly against you.

with comparative ease in the eddy formed by him. If the upstream person is temporarily swept off his feet, the others can hold him steady while he regains his footing.

As in all fording, cross the stream so that you will cross the downstream current at a 45° angle. Currents too strong for one person to stand

Cross the stream at a 45° angle, with the heaviest person on the downstream end of the pole.

This is a bird's-eye view of a four-man t

Rapids

Crossing a deep, swift river or rapids is not as dangerous as it looks. If you are swimming across, swim with the current – never fight it – and try to keep your body horizontal to the water. This will reduce the danger of being pulled under.

In fast, shallow rapids, travel on your back, feet first; use your hands as fins alongside your hips to add buoyancy and to fend off submerged rocks. Keep your feet up to avoid get-

ting them bruised or caught by rocks.

In deep rapids, travel on your front, head first; angle towards the shore whenever you can. Breathe between wave troughs. Be careful of backwater eddies and converging currents as they often contain dangerous swirls.

If you are crossing near the mouth of a silt-choked river avoid flat shores, which may have localised quicksands on either side of the water. If you encounter one, lie flat and move slowly out of the area.

Floating across

If the temperature of a body of water is warm enough for swimming but if you are unable to swim, make a flotation device to help you. Some things you can use are:

1 Trousers
Knot each leg at the bottom and button the fly. With both hands grasp the waistband at the sides and swing the trousers in the air to trap air in each leg. Quickly press the sides of the waistband together and hold it under water so that the air will not escape. You now have water wings to keep you afloat. These have to be re-inflated several times when crossing a wide stretch of water.

2 Empty containers
Lash together empty tins, petrol cans or boxes and use them as water wings. You should only use this type of flotation in a slow-moving river or stream.

3 Plastic bags
Air-fill two or more plastic bags and securely tie them together at the mouth.

4 Poncho
Roll green vegetation tightly inside your poncho so that you have a roll at least 45 cm in diameter. Tie the ends of the roll securely. You can wear it around your waist or across one shoulder and under the opposite arm.

5 Logs
Use a stranded drift log if one is available, or find a log near the water's edge. Test it before starting to cross, however, as some tree logs, palm for example, will sink even when the wood is dead.

6 Bulrushes
Gather stalks of bulrushes and tie them in a bundle 25 cm or more in diameter. The many air cells in each stalk cause it to float until it rots. Test the bundle to make sure it will support your weight before attempting to cross.

against can usually be crossed safely in this manner.

Do not rope your team together in fast-flowing water; the action of the current may hold any fallen member down.

Flash floods

Beware rapidly-increased water flows. Flash floods are a common feature in the tropics, and can arrive suddenly many miles from any apparent storm. Try to cross steadily but quickly. Heat loss will be substantial, and you could quickly become weak. Once out on the other bank, take your clothes off and wring out as much water as possible. Change into dry kit if you can; otherwise, put your wet clothes back on – they'll soon dry out as your body warms up.

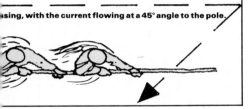

ssing, with the current flowing at a 45° angle to the pole.

Avoid bubbly water under falls; it has little buoyancy.

Avoid cold water

Be sure to check the water temperature before trying to cross a river or water obstacles. If the water is extremely cold and you are unable to find a shallow fording place, do not attempt to ford it. Devise other means for crossing; for instance, you might improvise a bridge by felling a tree over the river. Or you might build a raft large enough to carry both you and your equipment.

Other water obstacles

You may also face bogs, quagmire, muskeg or quicksand. DO NOT try to walk across: trying to lift your feet while standing upright will make you sink deeper. If you are unable to bypass them, you may be able to bridge them using logs, branches or foliage.

Another way to cross is to lie face downwards with your arms spread and swim or pull your way across. Be sure to keep your body horizontal.

In swamps, the areas that have vegetation are usually firm enough to support your weight and you should be able to crawl or pull your way through miles of swamp or bog. In open mud or water areas without vegetation, you can swim.

Log raft

This will carry both you and your equipment if you are unable to cross in any other way; if you have an axe and a knife you can build it without rope. A suitable raft for three men would be 12 ft long and 6 ft wide, You can use dry, dead, standing trees for logs, but spruce trees that are found in polar and sub-polar regions make the best log rafts.

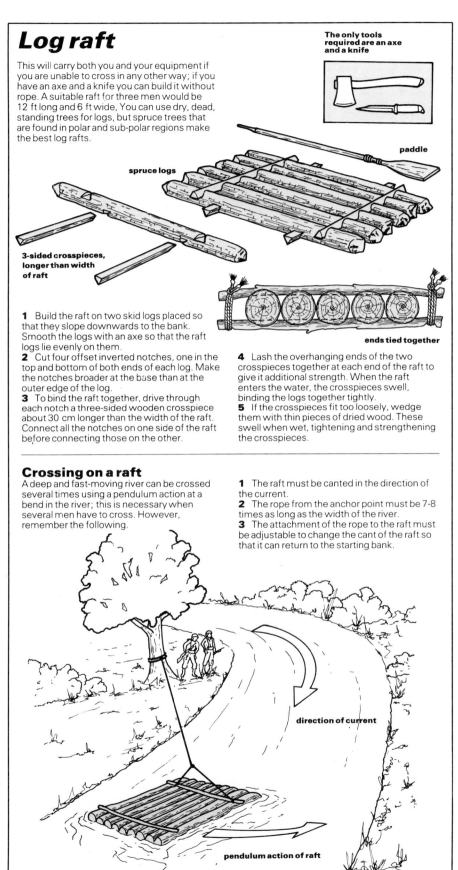

The only tools required are an axe and a knife

paddle

spruce logs

3-sided crosspieces, longer than width of raft

ends tied together

1 Build the raft on two skid logs placed so that they slope downwards to the bank. Smooth the logs with an axe so that the raft logs lie evenly on them.
2 Cut four offset inverted notches, one in the top and bottom of both ends of each log. Make the notches broader at the base than at the outer edge of the log.
3 To bind the raft together, drive through each notch a three-sided wooden crosspiece about 30 cm longer than the width of the raft. Connect all the notches on one side of the raft before connecting those on the other.

4 Lash the overhanging ends of the two crosspieces together at each end of the raft to give it additional strength. When the raft enters the water, the crosspieces swell, binding the logs together tightly.
5 If the crosspieces fit too loosely, wedge them with thin pieces of dried wood. These swell when wet, tightening and strengthening the crosspieces.

Crossing on a raft

A deep and fast-moving river can be crossed several times using a pendulum action at a bend in the river; this is necessary when several men have to cross. However, remember the following.

1 The raft must be canted in the direction of the current.
2 The rope from the anchor point must be 7-8 times as long as the width of the river.
3 The attachment of the rope to the raft must be adjustable to change the cant of the raft so that it can return to the starting bank.

direction of current

pendulum action of raft

CHAPTER FIVE

THE ART OF SURVIVING

One of the great problems when a person is adrift in a small boat at sea is that while the body can do without food for a week or more water is quite another matter. We must have a liquid intake to replace the body's natural losses and in the tropics those losses through the skin can be considerable. This is, of course, not the problem that the average soldier in temperate zones anticipates, although it has been known when troopships have met with some natural disaster or sunk by enemy action. The soldier's liquid requirements are only a problem in very dry areas where natural rainfall is minimal and natural water is out of reach.

Snow looks woolly, white and pretty on Christmas cards, but when it is deep and hiding man-trapping obstacles or crevasses its attractions wane fast. In this chapter you will find a lot of interesting advice on moving about in arctic conditions.

Water apart, there are many hazards waiting for the soldier in exposed places under the blazing tropical sun, or in deadly arctic cold, but there is shelter available for the eye trained to know what to look for and how to use the terrain. We begin Chapter Five by describing the first essential, shelter. If there is one part of the world where shelter is absolutely necessary for survival it is on one of the icecaps. Here, the correct clothing is a must and there are stringent rules for what a soldier must wear and we describe this here as well as the danger from frostbite, which can cripple and when combined with freezing conditions can even kill.

From the extremes of cold to the fatiguing effects of tropical heat SURVIVAL tells you about the three things which the jungle stands for, summed up as Heat, Humidity and Hygiene. Should the soldier ignore any one of these he will soon be in trouble, for unlike cold, where there are few dangerous living things, the jungle is home for biting, crawling, sucking insects most of which carry diseases harmful to man.

One of man's first steps towards early civilisation was his discovery of fire, how to make it and more importantly how to control it. There are times when soldiers still need to make fire, especially in the field and on active service. Apart from the obvious risks – fire and smoke can be seen by an enemy – fire is necessary for warmth, it can become very cold in the desert at night, it keeps predatory animals at a distance, the smoke wards flying insects away, it dries wet clothing. Science has provided soldiers with the means of heating food with chemicals, but the ability to construct a simple oven to cook food can come in very handy at times.

The second of the articles on fire concentrates on making one in difficult conditions. The garden bonfire presents few difficulties because dry ignition materials are always to hand, but when one has nothing but what nature provides (hopefully you do have a box of matches!) it is not as easy.

Lastly, the unseen enemy, the microscopic killers which lurk in the dank, humid jungles. Their size bears no relation to their ability to lay men prone and make them totally useless as alert fighting units. Be warned when you read the last article, for you will never see the malarial parasite the mosquito injects into your bloodstream, neither will you notice that tapeworm egg lurking in the tasty but undercooked meat. And very soon you will be sorry that the meat was not thoroughly cooked. An unpleasant subject, but one every soldier in the tropics must have in mind.

Learning how to survive in a Belize jungle.

Shelter for Survival

Finding shelter from sun in the desert, or from the freezing cold of the Arctic, is even more important in such places than looking for food or water. Exposure to extremes of heat or cold can kill you in hours, and not just in exotic latitudes. Even 'soft' climates like that of the south of England can be deadly on a bad winter's night. You'll discover in this section of the Survival Course how to protect yourself from extreme conditions, and how to make yourself comfortable and secure in more friendly environments too.

Choosing a shelter site

You must start to look for somewhere to hide or spend the night at least two hours before it gets dark. This will give you time to find the spot, clear away enough undergrowth or rocks to make a sleeping area, and time to get the material together to make your shelter as well.

There's one more thing you may have to look for in a survival site: protection from enemy forces. Where this is important you have to consider these factors:
1 Concealment from the enemy
2 Camouflaged escape routes
3 Ability to signal to friendly forces
And don't forget ordinary things like protection from the elements, insects, rock falls, and wild animals.

A survivor will always look out for certain types of ground, and avoid them by instinct. Flash floods can be upon you in seconds as a result of heavy rain falling miles away. So you must avoid apparently dry gullies in and around the foothills of a mountain range. Avalanches and landslides don't give you a lot of warning, either, so if you're forced to sleep in country that might produce either one, make sure your shelter site will give you protection from anything that might come down from above.

Be wary of river banks, in case the water level rises suddenly. The same applies to the sea shore; make certain you're above the high water mark.

The season of the year has to be considered, too. In winter, you need protection from winds coming out of the north, and a source of fuel for your fire; in the summer, what you need most is a water supply and protection from biting, stinging insects. The ideal shelter in one season might be a completely different spot at another time of year.

Types of shelter

The type of shelter you'll build depends very much on the kind of material you have available. If you have a poncho, a groundsheet or a parachute, or even a plain sheet of plastic, you're at a very big advantage.

In general, don't make shelters bigger than you need to. This is especially important in winter. A one-man

Nobody can function efficiently without shelter from the weather. A good shelter protects you from heat or cold, from rain or snow and from enemy observation; and it can provide a feeling of relative well-being and help maintain the will to survive.

Making a poncho shelter

If you are in an unfamiliar environment, begin looking for your shelter s▌ at least two hours before sunset. It is important to know how to constr▌ a variety of different shelters so that you can use whatever is to hand.

Improvised lean-to
Making the maximum use of available cover, this lean-to is built against a wall on a simple framework of branches.

Poncho lean-to
A poncho tied between two trees makes a quick and easy shelter. Tie a short (10 cm) stick to each rope, about 1 cm from the poncho: this will stop rain water running down the rope into the shelter.

parachute tent, for instance, can be kept just about bearable by the heat from a single candle. If you use it in a snow fall, though, you'll have to keep the weight of snow off it constantly, so that it doesn't all cave in on top of you. The smaller your shelter, the easier this job will be.

The simplest form of shelter is a lean-to made from a poncho, a length of rope, and two trees. First of all, make sure that the back of the lean-to will be into the wind. Tie support ropes to two corners of one of the long sides of the poncho. Tie off the neck opening. Secure the two support

ropes to two trees at about waist height (lower if concealment is important), and peg out the free side with three short sticks. If there are no trees around, you'll have to cut poles to use instead.

A poncho can be used to make a two-man shelter known to British soldiers as a 'bivvy'. In a wooded area, lay the poncho out on the ground to ensure that you have enough room, then clear the ground area of cones, roots, stones etc. Attach the poncho to four trees by its corners and make sure that it is stretched taut.

In a tactical situation it should be no more than 50 cm above the ground. Tie the hood off and tie it to a branch to raise the centre of the poncho so that the rain can run off.

In a desolate area where there are no trees, lay the poncho on the ground and, using it as a template, trace out its outline. De-turf the area 15 cm or so inside the cut line, and build a low turf wall around the shape of the poncho, leaving one end open. This will be the entrance to the poncho/tent and should be positioned facing the direction of any enemy threat.

Place one 60-cm tent pole at each end and peg down the corners and sides to make the poncho into a tent. The sides should overlap the layer of turfs and the poncho is again pulled taut and the hood tied off. Do not rest anything against the poncho or it will let in the rain.

If you have a parachute, you can make a very spacious teepee-type tent by lashing three poles – between three and four metres long – together into a

Poncho tent
This is lower than a lean-to and gives protection from the weather on both sides. On the other hand, it has less space and restricts your field of view.

Low silhouette shelter
Positioned no more than 50 cm above the ground, a poncho can make a good shelter. The diagram on the right shows a one-man shelter made with a parachute and three logs.

Building an 'A' frame basha

A 'basha' is an improvised shelter made from whatever material you can find. Wherever man has been, he leaves rubbish; the survivor exploits this, finding many uses for all sorts of discarded items.

1 Put a simple 'A' frame together to form the entrance to the basha and push a strong pole into the bank. This will be the framework for a substantial shelter.

2 Dig branches into the ground at about 30 cm intervals, and rest them against the top pole. Then weave other branches horizontally to make the sides.

3 Turfs take a long time to cut and position, but they are waterproof if slanted at 45° and they provide good insulation. Lay them from the bottom upwards, overlapping each row.

tripod, and then spreading the material over this frame. Extra poles will give more support, but you can just lean these against the first three; there's no need to lash them.

You can tie the top of the parachute to the branch of a tree, and then keep the lower edge spread out with pegs. This type of tent doesn't work well if you need to conceal yourself – its height and sharp lines make it very easy to see.

Even if you're on the move all the time, you can still use your parachute to make a rough and ready shelter. Fold the canopy into a triangle and run a line, something over head height, from a tree to the ground, five or six metres away. Drape the para-

chute over the line and peg out the sides.

If you have a little more time, cut a pole about five metres long and use that instead of rope to make the ridge. Cut two shorter poles and use these instead of pegs to keep the sides out. Tuck the canopy sides around the side poles until the fabric is taut, and then use the extra fabric as a groundsheet. Wedge another pole between the two lower ones to keep the mouth of the bivouac open.

This basha is constructed in the jungle, using the same methods: an 'A' frame supporting a leaf roof. These British troops have an American hammock in the background: a prized bit of kit because it has a built-in mosquito net.

If you have no man-made materials, you can still make a very effective shelter, although it will take a great deal longer. Don't be too ambitious to start with. Just make a simple lean-to at first; you can always make another side to it later on, if you don't have to keep on the move.

Find two trees that are close together and face in the right direction – the line between them should be at right angles to the prevailing wind. Cut a straight pole, about 2½ cm in diameter, and long enough for you to lash to the two trees, one or two metres off the ground. Cut six or eight three-metres poles and lean them against the first one. Weave saplings, vines and twigs through and around the sloping poles. Then cover these with leaves, grass, pine needles or anything else that's to hand, starting at the bottom and working up. Put more of this same material inside to make your bed.

Natural materials

One advantage of the lean-to made from local materials is that it blends in with its surroundings, and so is far more difficult to detect than one made from a poncho.

Shelter can mean more than just a roof over your head. In swampy or marshy country, for instance, it will be just as important to build a sleeping platform that is well off the ground, so that you can stay dry. Remember that a bed like this will have to bear all your weight. There's no point in trying to make one unless you have really substantial poles available.

Instead of building a platform, you can make a simple hammock out of a poncho, groundsheet or parachute canopy. Trees make better supports

4 Don't cut holes in plastic sheeting: they tear or let water in. Put a small pebble in the corner and twist the plastic around it until you have a small neck to tie against the side.

5 This side of the basha has been built using a poncho, a piece of plastic sheeting found in a field and a section of corrugated iron. All are secured in place with string and old bootlaces.

6 The basha is camouflaged with dead bracken cut well away from the campsite. The telltale shape of the 'A' frame is broken up with a bit of scrim netting.

than poles that you have to drive into the ground.

Natural shelters

Often, you'll find it easier and more rewarding to spend time looking for a natural shelter rather than in building one of your own. Look for caves, crevices, rocks on the side of hills away from the wind, fallen trees and large trees with low-hanging branches.

There are some places best avoided. Stay away from low ground if you can: these areas get cold and damp at night. Thick undergrowth is often infested with insects; check for snakes, scorpions, spiders and other pests. And wherever you settle, make sure there's nothing loose above that could fall on you in a storm.

You'll learn more about making shelters in exotic environments like

the Arctic and deserts in later sections of the Survival Course. But no matter where you find yourself, remember that the effect on your morale of having a place to 'come home to', even if it's only a lean-to made out of brush wood, could mean the difference between life and death. Your will to live is what will really keep you alive, and anything that strengthens it is another stroke in your favour.

SPOT THE BASHA

This photo was taken from the other side of the valley, about 75 metres away from the basha built in the sequence above. Normally, bashas wouldn't be built in such open terrain; erect them within dense cover and on the flank of the hill where the sun doesn't shine and produce shadows that will highlight the shape.

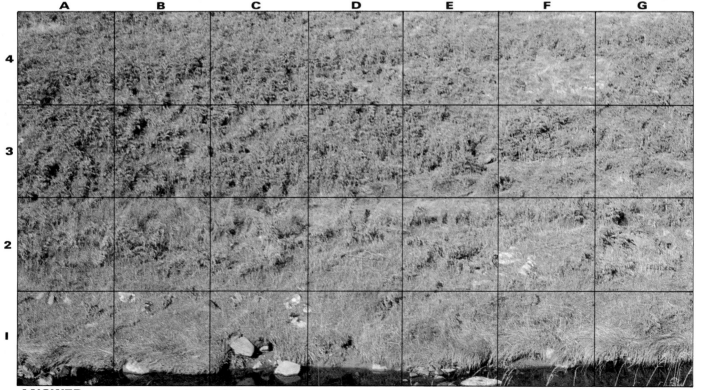

ANSWER: The basha is located in area 'Foxtrot Three', on the grid, in the top left of the quadrant.

Combating the Climate

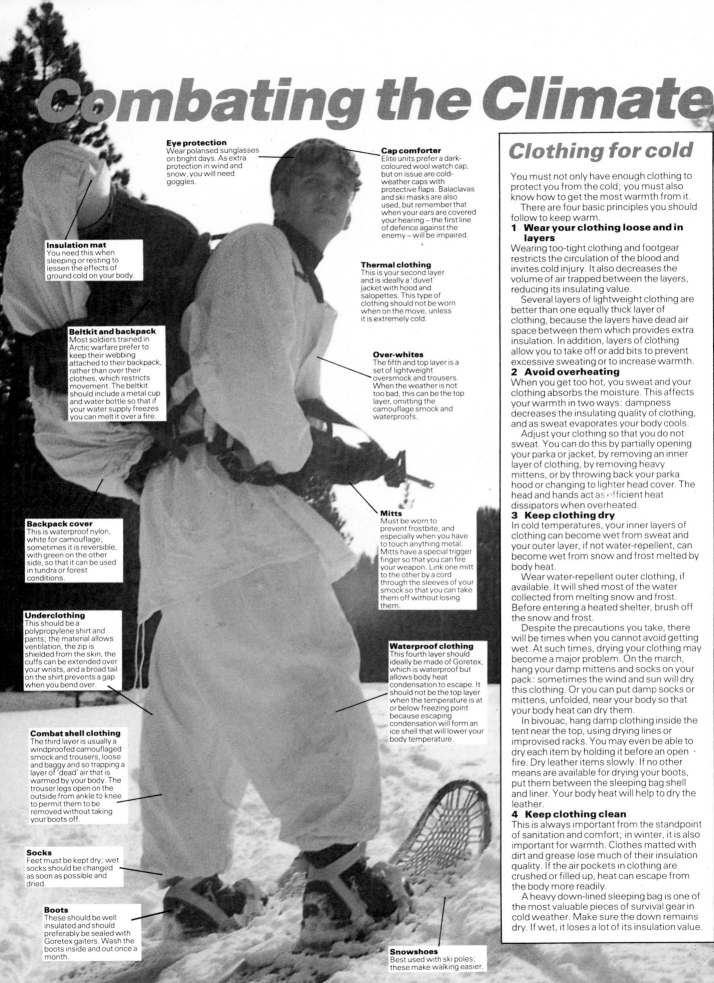

Eye protection
Wear polarised sunglasses on bright days. As extra protection in wind and snow, you will need goggles.

Cap comforter
Elite units prefer a dark-coloured wool watch cap, but on issue are cold-weather caps with protective flaps. Balaclavas and ski masks are also used, but remember that when your ears are covered your hearing – the first line of defence against the enemy – will be impaired.

Insulation mat
You need this when sleeping or resting to lessen the effects of ground cold on your body.

Thermal clothing
This is your second layer and is ideally a 'duvet' jacket with hood and salopettes. This type of clothing should not be worn when on the move, unless it is extremely cold.

Beltkit and backpack
Most soldiers trained in Arctic warfare prefer to keep their webbing attached to their backpack, rather than over their clothes, which restricts movement. The beltkit should include a metal cup and water bottle so that if your water supply freezes you can melt it over a fire.

Over-whites
The fifth and top layer is a set of lightweight oversmock and trousers. When the weather is not too bad, this can be the top layer, omitting the camouflage smock and waterproofs.

Backpack cover
This is waterproof nylon, white for camouflage; sometimes it is reversible, with green on the other side, so that it can be used in tundra or forest conditions.

Mitts
Must be worn to prevent frostbite, and especially when you have to touch anything metal. Mitts have a special trigger finger so that you can fire your weapon. Link one mitt to the other by a cord through the sleeves of your smock so that you can take them off without losing them.

Underclothing
This should be a polypropylene shirt and pants; the material allows ventilation, the zip is shielded from the skin, the cuffs can be extended over your wrists, and a broad tail on the shirt prevents a gap when you bend over.

Waterproof clothing
This fourth layer should ideally be made of Goretex, which is waterproof but allows body heat condensation to escape. It should not be the top layer when the temperature is at or below freezing point because escaping condensation will form an ice shell that will lower your body temperature.

Combat shell clothing
The third layer is usually a windproofed camouflaged smock and trousers, loose and baggy and so trapping a layer of 'dead' air that is warmed by your body. The trouser legs open on the outside from ankle to knee to permit them to be removed without taking your boots off.

Socks
Feet must be kept dry; wet socks should be changed as soon as possible and dried.

Boots
These should be well insulated and should preferably be sealed with Goretex gaiters. Wash the boots inside and out once a month.

Snowshoes
Best used with ski poles; these make walking easier.

Clothing for cold

You must not only have enough clothing to protect you from the cold; you must also know how to get the most warmth from it.

There are four basic principles you should follow to keep warm.

1 Wear your clothing loose and in layers

Wearing too-tight clothing and footgear restricts the circulation of the blood and invites cold injury. It also decreases the volume of air trapped between the layers, reducing its insulating value.

Several layers of lightweight clothing are better than one equally thick layer of clothing, because the layers have dead air space between them which provides extra insulation. In addition, layers of clothing allow you to take off or add bits to prevent excessive sweating or to increase warmth.

2 Avoid overheating

When you get too hot, you sweat and your clothing absorbs the moisture. This affects your warmth in two ways: dampness decreases the insulating quality of clothing, and as sweat evaporates your body cools.

Adjust your clothing so that you do not sweat. You can do this by partially opening your parka or jacket, by removing an inner layer of clothing, by removing heavy mittens, or by throwing back your parka hood or changing to lighter head cover. The head and hands act as efficient heat dissipators when overheated.

3 Keep clothing dry

In cold temperatures, your inner layers of clothing can become wet from sweat and your outer layer, if not water-repellent, can become wet from snow and frost melted by body heat.

Wear water-repellent outer clothing, if available. It will shed most of the water collected from melting snow and frost. Before entering a heated shelter, brush off the snow and frost.

Despite the precautions you take, there will be times when you cannot avoid getting wet. At such times, drying your clothing may become a major problem. On the march, hang your damp mittens and socks on your pack: sometimes the wind and sun will dry this clothing. Or you can put damp socks or mittens, unfolded, near your body so that your body heat can dry them.

In bivouac, hang damp clothing inside the tent near the top, using drying lines or improvised racks. You may even be able to dry each item by holding it before an open fire. Dry leather items slowly. If no other means are available for drying your boots, put them between the sleeping bag shell and liner. Your body heat will help to dry the leather.

4 Keep clothing clean

This is always important from the standpoint of sanitation and comfort; in winter, it is also important for warmth. Clothes matted with dirt and grease lose much of their insulation quality. If the air pockets in clothing are crushed or filled up, heat can escape from the body more readily.

A heavy down-lined sleeping bag is one of the most valuable pieces of survival gear in cold weather. Make sure the down remains dry. If wet, it loses a lot of its insulation value.

Survival in Arctic and sub-Arctic conditions is survival against constant attack. Day and night, without respite, the cold lays siege to your body. There is no let-up; staying alive requires attention to detail for 24 hours a day. Clothes, shelter and food are your major weapons against the cold – plus a strong will to survive. Without the will, the battle is already lost.

Air temperatures of −40°C and wind velocities of 30 knots are common in Arctic and sub-Arctic terrains. In these conditions, without clothes, you would be dead in about 15 minutes.

The most effective clothing provides a system of layers that trap warm air to form an effective insulation. If you are caught out in Arctic conditions due to vehicle failure, air-crash etc, improvise layered clothing and insulation.

Warm and windproof

Outer-shell garments should be windproof. Arctic conditions are usually dry, and waterproof outers (unless they are of 'breathing' material such as Goretex) should be avoided, as they cause condensation to build up inside, soaking your inner garments.

Many fabrics lose their insulating efficiency when they are wet. Goose and duck down, very popular in dry-cold outer garments, clump disastrously when wet, losing the 'lofted' air spaces that give them their insulating qualities.

Cotton garments and kapok quilt fittings also become heavy and cold. Wool, on the other hand, functions well when wet, as do a range of modern synthetic materials such as

polyester, which can be woven into single-layered clothing, used as quilting fillers, or processed into thick piles and fleeces which have the added advantage that they 'wick' moisture away from inside layers.

The effort expended in keeping warm should be regulated carefully to avoid overheating and sweating. Chopping a tree down to make a shelter could be a fatal expenditure of energy, burning up vital resources and soaking clothing with perspiration.

Frostbite

The prime dangers of cold-weather conditions are frostbite and hypothermia, as the cold strikes at both the outer and inner body. Your extremities – hands, feet, ears and noses – are particularly susceptible to frostbite, but any exposed skin is at risk, and the risk is multiplied by wind speed.

The wind-chill factor transforms

Keep active, but take your time. Everything takes longer. The cold slows you down, the kit is awkward and the snow exhausts you. As long as you're prepared for that, you can cope.

Preventing frostbite

It is easier to prevent frostbite or to stop it in its early stages than to thaw out and take care of badly-frozen flesh.

1 Wear enough clothing for protection against cold and wind.
2 Clothing and equipment must not restrict the circulation.
3 Do not touch cold metal or oils at extreme low temperatures.
4 Avoid unnecessary exposure to strong winds.
5 Exercise the face, fingers and toes to keep them warm and to detect any signs of numbness.
6 Watch your mate for signs of frostbite; he should do the same for you.
7 Thaw any frozen spots immediately.

modestly-cold temperatures into deadly, tissue-destroying assaults on the body. An 18-mph wind in a 9.5°C temperature results in a −23.3°C wind-chill temperature. At wind-chill temperatures below −6°C, exposed flesh freezes in 60 seconds or less. An ambient temperature (measured by thermometer) of −28.8°C is converted by a 35-mph wind into a deadly −59.4°C wind-chill temperature. At this level, flesh freezes in 30 seconds.

Removing a mitten long enough to undo clothing and urinate can result in frostbitten fingers. Deep frostbite, which can result in lost fingers, toes or even limbs, kills by incapacitating the victim. But gangrene can also easily set in, and that will indeed see you off unless you get medical help.

The first signs of frostbite may be a waxy whiteness on the skin. Keep a close eye on your mates for these

The 'wind chill effect' is a vital point to bear in mind when you're trying to survive in cold conditions. An already cold air temperature combined with a strong, freezing wind can lead to an equivalent chill temperature that may be deadly. This table will help you work out the likely effect of the wind on your body.

WIND CHILL EFFECT

WIND SPEED		TEMPERATURE (°C)																			
CALM	CALM	4	2	1	−4	−7	−9	−12	−15	−18	−20	−23	−26	−29	−31	−34	−37	−40	−43	−45	−48	−51
KNOTS	MPH	EQUIVALENT CHILL TEMPERATURE																			
3-6	5	2	1	−4	−7	−9	−12	−15	−18	−20	−23	−26	−29	−32	−34	−37	−40	−43	−45	−48	−51	−57
7-10	10	1	−7	−9	−12	−15	−18	−23	−26	−29	−32	−37	−40	−43	−45	−51	−54	−57	−59	−62	−68	−70
11-15	15	−4	−9	−12	−18	−20	−23	−29	−32	−34	−40	−43	−45	−51	−54	−57	−62	−65	−68	−73	−76	−79
16-19	20	−7	−12	−15	−18	−23	−26	−32	−34	−37	−43	−45	−51	−54	−59	−62	−65	−70	−73	−79	−82	−84
20-23	25	−9	−12	−18	−20	−26	−29	−34	−37	−43	−45	−51	−54	−59	−62	−68	−70	−76	−79	−84	−87	−93
24-28	30	−12	−15	−18	−23	−29	−32	−34	−40	−45	−48	−54	−57	−62	−65	−70	−73	−79	−82	−87	−90	−95
29-32	35	−12	−15	−20	−23	−29	−34	−37	−40	−45	−51	−54	−59	−62	−68	−73	−76	−82	−84	−90	−93	−98
33-36	40	−12	−18	−20	−26	−29	−34	−37	−43	−48	−51	−57	−59	−65	−70	−73	−79	−82	−87	−90	−95	−101
WINDS ABOVE 40MPH HAVE LITTLE ADDITIONAL EFFECTS		LITTLE DANGER				INCREASING DANGER (Flesh may freeze within 1 minute)					GREAT DANGER (Flesh may freeze within 30 seconds)										
		DANGER OF FREEZING EXPOSED FLESH FOR PROPERLY CLOTHED PERSONS																				

many layers of clothing, you may be unaware that you are losing body moisture. Your heavy clothing absorbs the moisture, which evaporates in the air. You must drink water to replace this loss of fluid. Your need for water is as great when it's cold as when it's hot.

One way to tell if you are becoming dehydrated is to check the colour of your urine in the snow. If it makes the snow dark yellow, you are becoming dehydrated and need to replace body fluids; if the snow turns light yellow or remains normal, you're OK.

There's also a condition called 'cold diuresis', which is an increased output of urine caused by exposure to cold. It decreases body fluids, which must be replaced.

patches. If you are on your own, periodically feel your face and ears for the typical numbness.

If you encounter frostbite, rub snow onto the area until the whiteness or numbness disappears. Alternatively, gently compress the affected area with a warm hand. Do not rub the frostbitten area directly; you are likely to break the skin, leading to an open wound and infection.

Hypothermia

Hypothermia occurs when the temperature of the inner body-core, which houses the vital organs, falls below 35°C. The normal inner body temperature is 36.8°C.

As hypothermia sets in, movements slow up, thought processes are dulled, and you begin to lose co-ordination. You're dying on your feet, though you probably won't know it. Your speech becomes slurred. When your body temperature falls to 25°C and below, death is almost inevitable.

One of the best ways of dealing with hypothermia is to put the victim naked inside a sleeping bag with another person, also naked. A second person can also administer the warm, sweet drinks (such as honey, dextrose, sugar or cocoa) and food necessary for recovery. DO NOT FORCE AN UNCONSCIOUS PERSON TO DRINK.

If you manage to get back to civilisation, the hypothermia victim can be immersed in a warm bath. But start with the trunk area first, otherwise there's a risk of cardiac arrest and shock.

A victim will also need some time to recover, because the attack will have profoundly affected the circulation system.

Trench foot and immersion foot re-

In extreme cold a combatant or evader can become depressed, irritable and indifferent to essential tasks. Stay fit, maintain a determined will to win, and follow the drills. You'll survive.

sult from many hours or days of exposure to wet or damp conditions at a temperature just above freezing. The feet become cold and swollen and have a waxy appearance. Walking becomes difficult, and the feet feel heavy and numb. The nerve and muscles suffer the most damage, but gangrene can also occur in extreme cases, and it may become necessary to have the foot or leg amputated.

The best preventive is to keep the feet dry. Carry extra socks with you in a waterproof packet. Wet socks can be dried against the body. Wash your feet daily and put on dry socks.

In cold weather, bundled up in

Snow blindness

It is vital to protect your eyes in bright sun and snow. Wear your sunglasses. If you don't have any, improvise. Cut slits in a piece of cardboard, thin wood, tree bark or other available material. Putting soot under your eyes will help reduce glare.

Sunburn

Exposed skin can become sunburned even when the air temperature is below freezing: the sun's rays reflect at all angles from snow, ice and water. Extra sensitive areas of skin are

Two degrees of frostbite

Superficial frostbite causes just the skin or the tissue immediately beneath it to turn white or waxy. After re-warming, the area will become numb and mottled and will swell, sting or burn for some time. In more severe cases blisters will occur, drying up to become hard and black. **Deep frostbite** goes down into the tissue, sometimes as far as the bone. It is accompanied by blisters or swellings. The area goes blue, violet or – the worst – grey and can be very painful. In acute deep frostbite the affected area may auto-amputate: in World War II, German soldiers at Stalingrad in Russia sometimes found loose toes rattling about in their boots.

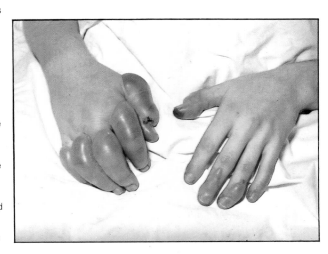

SAS men landed by helicopter on South Georgia during the Falklands war of 1982 came perilously close to freezing to death after a 'whiteout' made flying impossible out on the glacier. The real enemy was the Antarctic weather, not the Argentines.

the lips, nostrils and eyelids. You should apply sunburn cream or lip salve whenever you are out in the sun.

You can get sunburn more easily at high altitudes during the same time of exposure to the sun.

Snow blindness

This is caused by the reflection of ultra-violet rays caused by the sun shining brightly on a snow-covered area. The symptoms of snow blindness are a gritty feeling in the eyes, pain in and over the eyes that increases with eyeball movement, eyes watering and becoming red, and a headache, which intensifies with continued exposure to light.

Prolonged exposure to these rays can result in permanent eye damage. To treat snow blindness, bandage the eyes until the symptoms disappear.

You can prevent snow blindness by wearing sunglasses.

Constipation

If you put off relieving yourself because of the cold, eat dehydrated foods, drink too little liquid and have irregular eating habits, you may become constipated.

Although not disabling, constipation can cause discomfort. Increase your fluid intake to at least two quarts per day and eat fruits, if available, and other foods that will loosen your bowels. Eating burnt wood and charcoal may help!

Making a sleeping bag

If you do not have a sleeping bag, you can make one out of parachute cloth or similar material and natural dry material such as leaves, pine needles or moss. Place the dry material between two layers of parachute cloth.

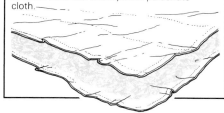

Although washing yourself daily may be impractical and uncomfortable in a cold climate, you must do it. Washing helps to prevent skin rashes that can develop into more serious problems.

In some situations, you may be able to take a snow bath. Take a handful of snow and wash your body where sweat and moisture accumulate, such as under the arms and between the legs, front and rear, and then wipe yourself dry.

If you cannot bathe, periodically wipe yourself dry in these areas. If possible, wash your feet daily and put on clean, dry socks. Change your underwear at least twice a week. If you are unable to wash your underwear, take it off, shake it, and let it air out for an hour or two.

If you are with natives or are using a shelter that has been used before, check your body and clothing each night for lice. If your clothing has become infested, use insecticide powder if you have some. Otherwise, hang your clothes in the cold, then beat and brush them. This will help get rid of the lice, but not their eggs, which will persist in the folds of your clothes.

Trench foot: Curse of the Falklands

Trench foot (or immersion foot) was a common affliction suffered by English and Argentine soldiers during the Falklands campaign. It results from prolonged exposure of the feet to temperatures near (but not necessarily below) freezing.

In the early stages the feet and toes are pale and feel cold, numb and stiff; walking becomes difficult. If preventive action is not taken, the feet will swell and become painful. In extreme cases the flesh dies and amputation of the foot or leg may be necessary.

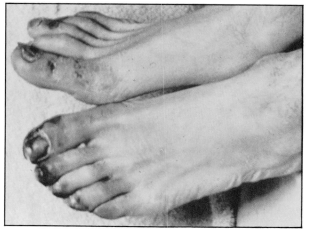

Travel in the Arctic

Deep snow means deep trouble if you're on the move. On foot or in an ordinary vehicle, you've got very little chance unless you've taken precautions beforehand. As well as the difficulty of moving through the snow itself, there are other less obvious things to worry about.

To start with, deep snow will change the appearance of the countryside, turning navigation by map into a nightmare. Secondly, the snow will hide all sorts of obstacles and dangers. Falling into a ditch filled with three metres of soft snow may sound like it could be fun, but the reality is deadly. You would find it very difficult to climb out before you were overcome by exhaustion and died of exposure. That is, unless you drowned in the snow first.

Consider and conserve

So what can you do to make your way through Arctic, sub-Arctic or Alpine conditions?

Firstly, you must stay calm and conserve as much energy and body water as possible. If you're carrying a heavy

load of equipment, weapons and ammunition you'll be unable to travel far if there's more than half a metre of untrodden snow on the ground – even if the country is flat.

You have to spread the weight of your body and your load. The two most usual ways of doing that both have their drawbacks – skis are hard

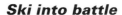
Swedish Fältjägarna Special Forces on the move deep inside the Arctic Circle. Despite the cold and hostile environment, individual movement and fighting is a vital part of the overall defence strategy.

to control unless you know how and, anyway, are almost impossible to make from the sort of material you'll be able to gather. Snowshoes, the other real way to get about, are very tiring unless you're used to them, but they can be improvised using natural materials.

If you're properly equipped, of course, you'll have both available: skis to use when you're travelling any distance, and snowshoes for use in camp, where there are lots of people about – or in heavy brush or undergrowth, where two metres of ski on each foot would make you a little clumsy!

Ski into battle

A fit, experienced skier can keep up a solid 10 kilometres an hour for days on end, even when carrying a full load of equipment. That's an awful lot more than you could manage on foot, and it requires a lot less effort, so there is much to be said for learning how to do it.

There are two main types of ski: Alpine skis are the shorter of the two types, and have fastenings for both the toe and heel of the boot; cross-country or Nordic skis are longer and narrower, with a hinged fastening at the toe only, so that the heel can be raised. This allows you to do a push/step movement that covers the ground remarkably quickly.

Military cross-country skis

The standard military issue ski is 208 cm long (big by Alpine standards). They have holes in the tips, to allow you to tow them in an improvised sledge, and are grooved at the heel to accept mohair 'climbers'.

To the non-skier it may come as a surprise to learn that you can actually walk uphill wearing skis. Originally, people stuck strips of sealskin onto the soles of their skis, with the pile of the short, stiff hairs pointing backwards. The British Army uses mohair instead, but the effect is the same.

The length of a pair of skis isn't terribly important, but the length of the poles is. They're much longer than the poles used in downhill skiing, coming to just below the shoulder. In the British forces they come in three lengths: 51 inches (130 cm); 54 inches (137 cm); and 58 inches (147 cm). Don't damage the points of your skis. They are intentionally sharp, to allow you to get a purchase on hard ice.

Awareness of avalanches

Avalanches come in four different types:
1 Soft slab: snow fallen on lee slopes which fails to bond with older snow.
2 Hard slab: a deceptively hard surface formed by high winds and cold air temperature.
3 Airborne: new snow falling on an already hard crust.
4 Wet snow: usual in spring thaw, often after a rapid temperature rise.

Some avalanches can reach 200 miles per hour, and carry with them thousands of tonnes of snow, ice and rock debris, burying a victim up to 10 metres below the surface. Here are some basic precautions to keep you away from danger areas:

1 Stay high.
2 Don't ski across rotten snow, new falls or very steep slopes.
3 Don't travel alone, but do keep a safe distance between group members.
4 Stay out of gullies — you never know what will come down from above.
5 Keep a close watch on the temperature, both of the air and of the snow: check them often, especially in the spring. Sudden changes bring about avalanches.
6 Dig pits from time to time to check on the condition of the snow lower down.
7 Watch for recent avalanche signs: they often come in groups.
8 Keep a very, very careful listening watch.

9 Don't assume, because one group's got across, that it is safe: they could have triggered off an avalanche.
10 Avoid convex parts of a slope; this is where fracturing of the slab commonly occurs.
11 Keep below the treeline; it's generally safer.
12 Keep away from slopes of angles of between 30 and 45 degrees, which are often the most dangerous.
13 The deeper the snow, the greater the danger.
14 Avoid new snow; it takes a minimum of 2-3 days to settle.

15 Travel in the early morning before full sun-up.
16 Do not adopt a 'lightning never strikes twice' attitude, or assume that if there's been an avalanche the danger's passed. Avalanches occur in the same place all the time.
17 On ridges, snow accumulates on the lee side in overhanging piles, called cornices. These often extend far out from the ridge and may break loose if stepped on, so do not stray unless you are sure of your ground.

The elite Mountain and Arctic Warfare Cadre of the Royal Marines trains throughout the harsh Norwegian winter. Despite their own and their hosts' professionalism, 16 Norwegian soldiers were killed in a single avalanche in 1986 during a joint exercise.

Crossing a danger area

Do everything you can to stay away from areas that look or feel like they might be about to avalanche. There may come a time, however, when you just have to go through one. Here are some rules that will increase your chances of making it safely — and some hints as to what to do if you get caught:
1 If you have to cross an avalanche area, travel across the slope one at a time.
2 Follow in the same tracks as the man in front of you.
3 Loosen your ski bindings and take your hands out of the loops on your poles.
4 Slip any rucksack straps off your uphill shoulder so that you can ditch it easily.
5 Fasten your smock hood over your nose and mouth to reduce the chances of drowning if you go down in powder snow.
6 Walk downhill; don't ski.
7 Go straight down, not in a traverse.
8 Keep high and stick to concave slopes.

Caught in an avalanche

If you feel or hear an avalanche coming, you must move fast but carefully — a fall now will almost certainly mean your death. Don't panic. If you stay calm you have a good chance of coming out of it unscathed.
1 Ditch your kit.
2 Find out where you are in relation to the avalanche. You may not be in its path. If it's going to miss you, don't move.
3 Look out for your team mates. Remember their positions. You may have to dig them out.
4 Ski away in a steep traverse. Don't go straight down the fall line. The avalanche may be travelling at anything up to 200 miles per hour.
5 If you get caught at the side of an avalanche, dig outwards — it's easier.
6 Make an air space around your nose and mouth, but keep your mouth shut. In a powder avalanche, try to get a cloth over your nose to act as a filter.
7 Determine which way is up and down, perhaps by dribbling.
8 Start digging your way out before the avalanche has time to settle and freeze into position.
9 If you're covered in powder snow, try a swimming motion. Backstroke is the most effective.

Improvising snowshoes

The traditional snowshoe looks a bit like a big tennis racket, but more modern versions are a rounded oblong shape, around 50 cm long and 25 to 30 cm wide, made up of a lightweight frame interlaced with straps of some sort.

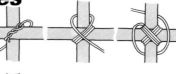
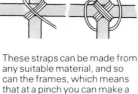

These straps can be made from any suitable material, and so can the frames, which means that at a pinch you can make a pair of snowshoes for yourself. Use stripped straight branches for the frame, and webbing, animal hide cut into strips, or even bark for the cross-straps.

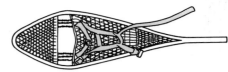

You don't need clever bindings: a single piece of rope, doubled and knotted twice around the foot and ankle, will do fine.

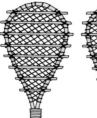
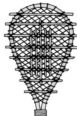

Do not bind the ankle to the snowshoe – allow it to lift in the same way as your heel lifts while walking normally.

Walking at night

In an operational or hostile situation, travel during darkness, unless the weather has closed in sufficiently during the day to hide you in low cloud or fog. Even then, take care; bad weather can lift very quickly, leaving you exposed and unprotected.

And beware travelling in 'whiteout' conditions: the lack of contrasting colours makes it impossible to judge the nature of the terrain. And do not travel during blizzards – they are deadly.

Moving at night can be tricky, as any light from stars and the moon is made even brighter when reflected off the snow.

Plan your moves

Make a plan to work from one feature to another, for shelter and concealment, rather than to trek straight out into open country.

Sounds travels easily in cold climates, so you should keep very quiet and stop to listen every so often.

Always cross a snow bridge at right angles to the obstacle it crosses. Find the strongest part of the bridge by poking ahead with a pole or ice axe. Distribute your weight by crawling or by wearing snowshoes or skis.

Cross streams when the water level is lowest. Normal freezing and thawing action may cause a stream level to vary as much as 2 to 2½ metres, per day. This may occur at any time, depending on the distance from a glacier, the temperature, and the terrain. You should also consider this variation in water level when selecting a campsite near a stream.

Choosing your course

Consider rivers, frozen or unfrozen, as avenues of travel. Frozen rivers are frequently clear of loose snow, making travel easier than on the land. Avoid snow covered streams: the snow, which acts as an insulator, may have prevented ice forming over the water.

Your course should be determined by your location and the terrain. In mountainous or wooded areas, it is advisable to follow rivers downstream towards populated areas (Siberia, where rivers flow northward to the high Arctic, is an exception).

When travelling cross-country, try to follow the contour of the land: however, note that valley floors are frequently colder than slopes and ridges, especially at night. Head for a coast, major river, or known point of habitation.

Going the right way

Navigation is tricky in the Arctic. You're near the magnetic pole, so compass readings may be erratic: take more than one, and average them out. Use the shadow tip method or use the sun and stars to show you in which direction north and other points of the compass lie. These techniques will be life-saving at times.

Nature itself gives you a few clues:

Crossing thin ice

If you have to cross thin ice, remember these rules:

1 One man at a time.
2 Take your hands out of the loops on your ski poles.
3 Put your equipment over one shoulder only, so you can shrug it off.
3 Loosen the bindings on your skis or snowshoes.
4 Think about distributing your weight by lying flat and crawling.
5 Bear in mind these thicknesses of ice and their corresponding loadbearing capabilities:
5 cm supports 1 man
10 cm supports 2 men side by side
20 cm supports a half-ton vehicle.

If you fall through the ice, get your kit off and up onto the ice; use your poles to help you out. Don't get too close to a team-mate who's fallen through; you'll only end up in there with him. Throw him a line so that you can help him out from a safe distance. Hypothermia will set in very quickly after immersion, so carry out emergency re-warming straight away.

The water is 0°C, and this Royal Marine's body temperature is supposed to be 37°C. So it's only a matter of minutes before the water wins. Unless he gets out he'll collapse when his temperature reaches about 33°C, and die when it gets to 25°C.

The essence of Arctic travel is to get somewhere in a fit state to do a job of work. Pace yourself; work to a steady rhythm, and concentrate. Be in command of the situation – don't let the situation command you.

1 A solitary evergreen tree will always have more growth on its south side.
2 Bark on poplar and birch trees will always be lighter in colour on the south-facing side.
3 Trees and bushes will be bent in the direction that the wind normally blows, so if you know the direction of the prevailing wind you can work out north and south.
4 The snow on the south side of the ridges tends to be more granular than on the north.
5 Snowdrifts usually are on the downwind side of protruding objects like rocks, trees or high banks. By determining the cardinal points of the compass and from them the direction of the drifts, the angle at which you cross them will serve as a check point in maintaining a course.

In the southern hemisphere, of course, the opposite polarity applies.

Pay attention to staying on the right track. You'll get some help in this during clear weather by looking back at your tracks in the snow.

But, of course, that's a sure sign to enemy forces that you're around. You have to be very cunning in the snow to cover up your tracks: stick to the treeline wherever possible, or use existing tracks and patches of broken snow. If you're travelling as a team, keep in each other's tracks.

Be careful how you plant your poles: always put them in the same holes as the guy ahead of you, then the enemy won't know how many there are of you. Alternatively, makes lots of holes to confuse them!

Distance

It's very difficult to judge distances in the Arctic as there are so few visual clues, and the clear air makes estimating distances difficult: they are more frequently underestimated than over-estimated.

The simplest way of estimation is to pace out a given distance yourself, but this must be practised to be anywhere near accurate.

Another method is for a rope or some signal wire of a given length (say 50 metres) to be strung between two men. The first man moves off, and when the slack is taken up the first man stops and the second man joins him, then repeats the exercise. Simple mathematics can be used to estimate the distance achieved after a number of repetitions.

Arrive and perform

Your task is to survive and remain fit to carry out your mission. Arriving as a casualty or, even worse, not arriving at all, puts your whole team and operation at risk. So remember the drills.

Jungle Survival: The Fundamentals

The jungle is an uncomfortable and dangerous environment. Some dangers are readily apparent, like the insects that carry disease and infection. Others are less obvious: rotten branches falling from the jungle canopy, barbed vegetation, and contaminated water. But if jungle presents you with most problems, it also offers you the greatest chances of survival. With the right skills and expertise, you can stay alive in the jungle, at peak combat efficiency, almost indefinitely.

Heat, humidity and hygiene

Your first priority is hygiene. Jungle conditions make a prize breeding ground for bacteria, so personal hygiene is number one. A minor scratch, blister or chafe can all become a major problem if infection sets in. So clean even the slightest wound immediately and keep it covered.

Wherever your skin is exposed you are vulnerable to malarial mosquitoes, leeches, poisonous thorns, knife-edged grasses, even the sap from some of the plants you'll have to slash your way through. Ideally, therefore, your clothes should cover as much of your skin as possible. Wear long trousers, tucked into your socks, and use webbing or strips of cloth to seal your boot-tops to your trouser bottoms. Wear long-sleeved shirts. Wrap your head in insect netting or a spare shirt, especially at dawn and dusk.

One result of protecting yourself like this is that your clothes will be soaked with your sweat and the air's humidity. Clothes made from natural fibres soak up sweat more efficiently and chafe less than artificial fibres, but you will still be prey to rashes and 'jungle rot'. The best way to prevent them is to smear yourself with vaseline, especially your armpits and genitals. In Vietnam many GIs got rid of their underwear and 'hung loose' to get some ventilation.

Leeches, ticks and a host of tiny parasites present a very serious danger: it is vital to check every part of your and your mate's anatomy several times a day. Again, pay particular attention to your crotch. A Durex pro-

Tropical jungle is a hellhole of seen and unseen danger: noises travel surprisingly far, and few of them are familiar. Night falls with alarming suddenness, leaving you in a darkness as impenetrable as the undergrowth. It is a land of sickness and decay where clothing rots, weapons rust and wounds fester.

Dealing with Leeches

Leeches are a serious danger to your health in the jungle. You cannot avoid them attacking you, but it is vital to get them off as soon as possible. Leeches feed on your blood and produce a chemical that prevents your blood clotting and forming a scab over the wound. Leeches are not shy, so when checking your own or your mate's body for them remember to check between the buttocks as well as the testicles and obvious points like armpits and the backs of your knees.

You must NEVER remove a leech by pulling or brushing it off; if you do, it will fall apart, leaving its fangs still stuck in you. The result is a nasty wound that will go septic before you know it. Get leeches off with a burning cigarette end or by applying salt, then wash the area with clean water and cover it up with an antiseptic dressing or plaster.

vides good protection against ticks and other parasites; wearing one all day is certainly uncomfortable, but getting bitten down there is no fun either.

Stay alert for signs of heat exhaustion brought on as the high humidity saps your energy. The limbs begin to tingle, and although you feel as if you are going all out, your progress becomes painfully slow. Acting like advanced drunks, people coming down with heat exhaustion stagger, hallucinate, and talk with slurred words. Vision and hearing both fade out. If one of your team goes down with heat exhaustion, cool them down immediately. Dowsing them in a pool or a stream is one method. Administer salt tablets, but only when there is plenty of water, and do not let them smoke. Heat exhaustion is a killer.

Jungle travel

There are two kinds of jungle: they are known as primary and secondary. In primary jungles, enormous trees up to 200 feet high blot out the sunlight with their leaf canopy. Beneath it, you are shielded from hostile aerial observation – but, by the same token, rescue signals to friendly forces will also be obscured. Open river areas are the best sites for smoke and other visual signals. Undergrowth in primary jungle is usually sparse, so you can move across the terrain fairly swiftly as long as you have a compass or radio fix to keep you on course.

In military operations you're most likely to find yourself in secondary jungle. This is terrain that has been cleared for growing crops, usually by slash-and-burn techniques, then left to be reclaimed by the jungle. As a result, you will come up against a dense mixture of bushes, vines, undergrowth and creepers. These barriers are almost impassable unless you know the right way to overcome them.

Even if you have a compass bearing, do not attempt to move in a straight line through the tangle. You have to think and move like a jungle animal. Work your way round obstacles instead of trying to struggle through them. Seek the line of least resistance, remaining alert for dangers from animals (most probably snakes), plants, swamp, falling branches, and aware of your ultimate direction. Avoid, if possible, steep terrain; overgrown rocks are often very slippery and unstable. Move unhurriedly, twisting, ducking, and presenting a narrow, sideways target for clinging

Settling down for a bite and a rest. But take care: the tree above looks fine, but falling branches – 'dead-fall' – are one of the most common causes of death in the jungle.

vegetation. Do not tear free if you get snagged on thorns, but disengage carefully. Do not fight the jungle.

Eating and Sleeping

The jungle is rich with food. A soldier must be taught how to recognise a wide range of edible plants, how to obtain water in various ways, and how to get nourishment from everything from alligator tails to skinned frogs and dessicated earthworms. Practically everything in the jungle is edible – including you.

In the jungle you survive by thinking on your feet; you move carefully, always ready to react to circumstances. Each night you bivouac with equal care. We will be detailing how to build jungle shelters, how to protect yourself from insects, and other potential hazards such as ants, snakes and scorpions. And, when you get up in the morning, you turn inside-out and shake all your clothing to make sure it isn't harbouring any creature that could be waiting to inflict a painful and possibly lethal bite.

You need fires to dry out clothing, warm you up in the night, cook certain foods which are otherwise unpalatable or poisonous, and deter all manner of night creatures, from jaguars to mosquitoes. The jungle is full of wood, but often the outer surface of fallen or dead timber is waterlogged and rotten. Pare away the soft outer layers of rotten wood until you reach the hard heart-wood, which you can carve into slivers for starting fires. Palm-fibres from the base of palm-leaves make good tinder, as does the inside material of dry ant nests. Green turf, thrown on a fire, will produce thick smoke and at night may help keep the insects at bay – but your enemies on your track.

So many aspects of the jungle are threatening, from flash floods to the dreaded Amazonian candiru fish, which is reputed to swim up a stream of urine to enter the urethra, where it lodges by its dorsal spike. But forewarned is forearmed. If you are properly prepared for the jungle it will feed and shelter you. Future sections in this series will help prepare you for successful jungle survival.

GETTING IT WRONG:
the sting in the tail

I had been commanding a platoon in the jungle during the Borneo war for about five months and had completed several successful operations. The morale of the platoon was high. I thought I knew it all.

Then it happened: we had 'bashered'' up for the night after a day on patrol and the long 12-hour jungle night loomed ahead. Before it got completely and hopelessly dark – as only the jungle can – I realised I needed to answer the call of nature. I made my way outside the perimeter and stayed within sight of the sentry. This is standard procedure to avoid being caught with one's pants down, so to speak.

I adopted the necessary crouching position, then leapt into the air and let out a piercing scream that must have alerted every Indonesian for miles around. I had sat on a scorpion. I had failed to clear the ground as I had been taught, and as a result I suffered an incredibly painful bite in the nether regions. Soon, what had seemed at first to be an

amusing incident, and at worst an unfortunate one, rapidly ceased to be funny.

It was pitch dark. Helicopter evacuation was impossible. Movement at night in the jungle was operationally unacceptable, and I was now too ill to be moved. Moreover, we discovered that we had broken another cardinal rule: the platoon medical pack contained no antihistamine. There was no alternative but for me to sweat it out. The agony lasted all night as the poison worked its way through my system. Exactly how ill I was or how near to death I do not know.

This was a classic example of how overconfidence in the jungle can end in disaster. The jungle must be taken seriously: even defecation has its rules. Certainly the proper antidotes must be carried. Thereafter, I always ensured that the platoon medical bag was comprehensively stocked.

Lieutenant-Colonel Michael Dewar, RGJ

Jungle Warfare Kit

This is a basic jungle warfare kit. It will not stop you being very uncomfortable, but the clothing will reduce the effects of humidity and the attentions of the local insect population. The drugs will keep the most common tropical diseases at bay, and the kit should enable you to travel and shelter safely.

1 Combat suit
You will sweat constantly while in the jungle. The lightweight combat suit is specially baggy to stop it sticking to your skin and also to make it dry out quicker

2 Bush hat
Most troops prefer a simple cloth bush hat to the solar topees of years ago, but it is interesting that North Vietnamese soldiers wear a modified version of the French colonial pith helmet
3 Sweat band
Obvious perhaps, but an essential piece of kit
4 Jungle boots
Lightweight, canvas boots with holes in to let the water drain out
5 Paludrine anti-malaria tablets
Take four tablets a day to avoid malaria

6 Puritabs water-purifying tablets
Waterborne diseases are a serious menace in the jungle environment. Unclean water must never be used, not even to wash in or clean your teeth
7 Foot powder
Another essential, because your feet will be soaking wet most of the time. Wash your feet thoroughly every day, dry them carefully and let the air and the powder do their job
8 Insect repellent
Remember that some insects are after the salt in your sweat, others your blood; either way, they're a nuisance
9 Field dressing
Personal hygiene is critically important in the jungle; wounds must be cleaned and covered as soon as possible

10 Camouflage cream
White skin, made even more pallid by lack of sunlight on the jungle floor, will show up very easily unless camouflaged
11 Notebook
Should ideally be kept in a waterproof covering. In a survival situation this is important for recording all useful information, making sketch maps and keeping track of time
12 Compass
Make sure you know where this is at all times; in deep jungle there will be few reference points – not even the sun – and you could spend days wandering aimlessly in circles
13 Map
Maps of some jungle areas bear only the most coincidental resemblance to the actual lie of the land, and can be quickly out of date as the jungle reclaims farmland. Location is the worst problem; your spot might look like a hundred others

14 Upright torch
Useful because you can clip it to your webbing, leaving both hands free. The humidity will cause rust very quickly, so check it every day.
15 Machete
When clearing a path through dense tropical undergrowth, take your time and try to cut the vegetation so that it falls away from your path. Dry and oil the machete to keep rust at bay.
16 Ammunition pouch
Humidity is a big problem for ammunition, which will sweat and rust if not looked after. Lightly oil each round before putting it in the magazine; this will reduce the chance of a misfeed due to rusty ammo
17 and 18 Water bottles
It is important to carry extra supplies of clean water at all times – you need around 7 litres a day
19 Morphine
Even if operating with a group, you must carry your own supply of morphine in case of serious and painful injury. Tape easy-to-use syrettes of morphine to your ID discs

20 Knife
Use your machete for all the chopping jobs; the really sharp blade on your knife must be preserved.
21 Socks
Never go to sleep with wet socks on; dry them out whenever you can

Making Fire

Fire can be your best friend. It keeps you warm and dries your clothes; it cooks your food and purifies your water. But it can be your worst enemy, too. In enemy-held territory it can give away your position quicker than anything else. And a major burn is a dreadful wound, causing massive fluid loss and leaving you open to infection. This section of the survival course is devoted to fire: how to start it, control it and use in the most efficient way.

You have to bring three things together to make fire – fuel, heat and oxygen. Take away any one of these, and the fire goes out.

About a fifth of all the air around us is oxygen. All you have to do is make sure that there is free passage of air around – and especially up through – the fire.

Heat – the heat to start the fire – you have to provide. Friction in one form or another is the usual way, but you can use the rays of the sun, and perhaps even electricity, in its place.

You have to provide fuel in three quite different forms – **tinder**, to catch the spark; **kindling**, to set a flame; and the **fuel** itself, to keep the fire going.

Most fuel will not burn when it's wet. The water surrounds it and cuts off the air supply. Non-porous fuels like coal will burn when they are wet, however, and liquid fuels like oil, kerosene and petrol are completely unaffected by water.

Keep the fuel dry

But in most parts of the world it's wood and vegetable matter that you'll be burning, and this you must keep dry. Gathering and storing fuel for the fire is a very good example of how forward thinking pays dividends. But there is always something you can do to make a fire, even if you're shivering to death in a freezing rainstorm and the matches are soaked through.

Look for:

1 A sheltered place to build the fire.
2 Old, dead wood.
3 Kindling.
4 Tinder.

Take these tasks one at a time. Look for a rock overhang on the lee side of a hill or outcrop; or a low fallen branch, or a fallen tree. At this stage you're looking for protection for the fire, not shelter for yourself.

The difference between warm, dry comfort and freezing, wet misery is a little knowledge and skill and a handful of basic materials. So learn the skills and get that fire going as soon as you basha down for the night.

Making a simple fire and oven

1 Scrape a small pit of about 60×60×60 cm with an extra gap at one end so that you can insert your food for cooking. Line the bottom and sides with stones the size of your fist.

2 Gather your firemaking materials together: tinder to catch the spark, kindling to get the fire under way, and fuel to keep it going.

3 If it's a bright day focus the rays of the sun through a magnifying lens – perhaps a pair of glasses – and onto the tinder. Hold it steady and you'll soon get a flame.

4 If you've got a 'flint and steel', strike a few sparks onto the tinder. This thistledown burst into flames immediately, but lint or cotton fluff would work just as well.

5 Carefully add the kindling onto the tinder and work the fire up. If it doesn't respond a little blowing or fanning will give it more oxygen.

6 Having built the fire up, you can now bake your food in the oven below. Alternatively, and much more quickly, you can cook meat on an extra piece of tin held to one side of the fire.

Gathering fuel

Dead wood, as long as it's not actually lying in water, will usually have some dry material in it somewhere, but the best sources are dead timber that's still standing, and dead branches that are still attached to the tree. Look for the bark peeling off.

The main difference between kindling and fuel proper is its size. Remember, the kindling takes up the sparks and glowing embers from the tinder and turns it into flames that will ignite the fuel.

Small, bone-dry twigs are the best, but if necessary you can make 'firesticks' by shaving larger pieces with shallow cuts to feather them. Once again, this is a job much better done in advance.

Tinder must be dry. Absolutely, perfectly dry. You should have some

SOME NATURAL FIREMAKING MATERIALS

TINDER
Birch bark
Shredded inner bark from cedar, chestnut, red elm trees
Fine wood shavings
Dead grass, ferns, moss, fungi
Straw
Sawdust
Very fine pitch-wood scrapings
Dead evergreen needles
Rotted portions of dead logs or trees
Evergreen tree wood knots
Bird down (fine feathers)
Down seed heads
Fine, dried vegetable fibres
Spongy threads of dead puffball
Dead palm leaves

Skinlike membrane lining bamboo
Lint from pockets and seams
Charred cloth
Waxed paper
Outer bamboo shavings
Gunpowder
Cotton
Lint

KINDLING
Small twigs
Small strips of wood
Split wood
Heavy cardboard
Pieces of wood taken from inside larger pieces
Wood that has been soaked or doused in highly flammable

materials such as petrol, oil or wax
NB Must be completely dry!

FUEL
Dry standing wood and dry dead branches
Dry inside (heart) of fallen tree trunks and large branches
Green wood that is finely split
Dry grasses twisted into bunches
Peat dry enough to burn (may be found at the top of undercut banks)
Dried animal dung
Animal fats
Coal, oil shale or oil sand lying on the surface

Fire bows, saws and thongs

Fire Bow

Making a fire from the friction of wood upon wood really is a last-ditch alternative. The few aboriginal tribes that still make fire this way spend a very long time selecting exactly the right materials. Nevertheless, in the desert, where it's perfectly dry, it is possible to start a fire in this way.

You'll need:
1 A piece of green hardwood, about a metre long and 2½ cm in diameter
2 A piece of dry hardwood, 30 cm long and 1 cm in diameter.
3 A 5-cm hardwood cube, or a shell or a suitable stone
4 A piece of dry softwood, 2½ cm thick
5 A cord for the bow-string.

To make the fire bow:
1 Make the bow loosely using the cord and the long piece of hardwood.
2 Round off one end of the short piece of hardwood, and taper the other slightly.
3 Carve out the centre of the hardwood cube to fit the taper, or find a stone or shell of the right shape.

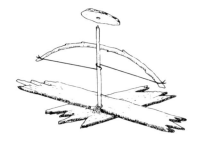

4 Make a depression in the softwood, close to one edge, and make a groove from it that leads to the edge.
5 Put some tinder next to the end of the groove.
6 Loop the bow-string round the drill, maintain pressure on the top with the cap, and work the bow backwards and forwards to create friction between the hardwood drill and the softwood baseboard. Wood dust will build up in the groove, and the end of the drill will become red-hot and ignite it.

Fire Saw

You'll need:
1 A piece of bamboo, 5-8 cm in diameter and ½ metre long
2 A forked stick, to anchor it into the ground.

To make the fire saw:
1 Split the bamboo lengthways.
2 Cut two notches in a straight line across the two exposed edges near to one end.
3 Brace the notched bamboo with the forked stick.
4 Fill the space between the notches with a handful of tinder.
5 Saw in the notches until the tinder ignites.

Fire Thongs

1 Make a thong (a strip or string of tough material) using rattan (a sort of tropical vine), leather or very tough cord.
2 Split a dry stick and hold the split open with a small wedge.
3 Run the thong through the split.
4 Place a small wad of tinder in the split.
5 Secure the stick with your foot and run the thong back and forth to create frictional heat. The tinder will eventually ignite.

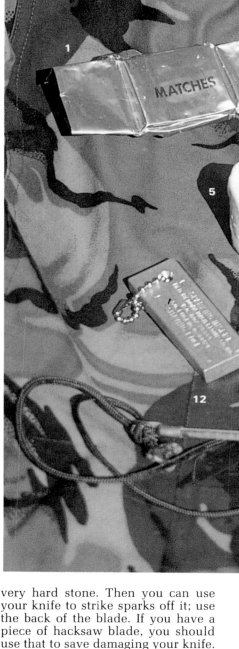

---

already, packed up securely in a water-tight box next to your skin. If not, you'll have to find some.

Don't look too far to start with: you won't need very much. Try the lining of your pockets and the seams of your clothes. The lint that collects there makes good tinder, except for wool. Dry bark, shredded into tiny pieces; dead grass, fern and moss; dead pine needles; downy seedheads from thistles and similar plants: all these make good tinder, as long as the material is dry.

The common factor is the size of the individual pieces or fibres. They must be tiny, so that as much of their substance as possible is exposed to the air and to the spark or flame.

The vital spark

If you don't have matches or a lighter that works, there are several alternative ways to start a fire.

If you have direct sunlight and a magnifying lens, you can use the glass to focus the sun's rays onto the tinder and start it burning that way. But this won't work at night in a rainstorm!

Flint and steel

Alternatively, you could use the 'flint and steel' method.

If you have a so-called 'metal match' (a metal strip with tiny flint chips embedded in it), then use that, scraping your knife blade along it to produce a shower of sparks.

Or look for a piece of flint or other very hard stone. Then you can use your knife to strike sparks off it; use the back of the blade. If you have a piece of hacksaw blade, you should use that to save damaging your knife.

Alternative technology

There are two other ways of making fire. The bow and drill and the fire saw both rely on friction between two pieces of wood. You have to make a small part of one of those pieces hot enough to set the tinder going. It is possible – but you'll only need to try it once to become fanatical about carrying matches with you everywhere you go!

If you have a vehicle you have another option – use the battery. Rip

If you've got this kit with you, you can light a fire under any conditions. You don't need all of it; a stove would make your life easier, but if you can't carry one you can make your own oven.

out some wire and attach a piece to each terminal. Touch the bare ends together and you'll get a spark.

If the vehicle is petrol driven, you can use a tiny amount of the fuel to help the process along, but remember that petrol in its liquid form doesn't burn. You can only set fire to it as a vapour. So, use less than a teaspoonful, soak some rag and make the spark into the air just above the surface. Diesel fuel doesn't work in this way — you need a good size flame to set it alight at all.

1 Matches
Service issue matches, found in survival packs, are books of paper matches weatherproofed by vacuum sealing in aluminium foil. The foil can also be used with tinder as fuel.
2 Folding stove
The service issue stove comes with a box of hexamine tablets, which can be used as fuel or broken up and used with tinder in firelighting.
3 Jelled alcohol stove
This is used mostly in the Arctic and by covert surveillance units and patrols in Northern Ireland, because of the absence of smoke and smells. The fuel can be topped up with inflammable jellies such as contact adhesive. The fire is put out by replacing the cap and therefore breaking the fire triangle by removing oxygen from the heat and fuel.
4 Zippo lighter
The Zippo is perhaps the best all-purpose lighter available, supposed to light first time in all weathers if it has fuel. When fuel runs out, other inflammable liquids can be used. Spare flints should be kept under the wadding of the lighter's fuel tank.
5 Tallow candle
Don't try to light your fire with a match; you could waste them all. Instead, light the candle in a sheltered spot and light your fire from it. Tallow is animal fat and in an emergency could provide food. In the absence of tallow, you could use joke birthday candles as these will usually relight if blown out by the wind.
6 Lifeboat matches
These are special long-burning waterproofed matches in a waterproof container. Contrary to accepted practice, it is not a good idea to split your matches into quarters or more as this can reduce their efficiency.
7 Potassium permanganate crystals
A useful addition to your survival kit as it can be used as an antiseptic, a gargle for throat infections, snow marker etc. For firelighting it should be combined with glycerine and sugar,

and will then spontaneously combust. Sugar will be found in your compo pack; glycerine is a constituent of antifreeze, and you could try using some from a vehicle.
8 Magnesium block
Scrape some slivers of magnesium off the block onto your tinder with your knife. Then use a section of hacksaw blade from your escape kit to ignite it by striking it off the flint on top of the magnesium block.
9 Ammunition
The powder contents of the cartridge can be used to help fire your tinder. You can also wedge a cloth in the cartridge once the ball or projectiles have been removed and chamber the round into your weapon. Aim at the tinder and fire. The cloth will be shot out smouldering.
10 Calcium carbide lighter
When water is added to calcium carbide it produces acetylene gas, which can be ignited with a spark.
11 Aluminium shavings
These can be mixed with tinder to help ignite and maintain the fire.
12 Flint and steel
A flint rod will produce sparks when steel (a piece of hacksaw blade) is drawn across it. The two should be kept together with a piece of nylon cord.
13 Chemical heaters
The contents of these can be mixed carefully with tinder to produce a fire. Other chemicals such as potassium chlorate and sugar can be ignited by sugar or using sulphuric acid from a car battery. Potassium chlorate is found in some weedkillers and also some throat lozenges.
14 Cotton wool
You can use the cotton wool absorbent layers of your combat dressing as tinder: open the dressing and cut through the lint at the back, allowing the dressing to remain sterile on its wound face so that it can still be used. Other tinder can be salvaged from pocket linings, old rope, fine wood shavings, dry bark, grasses or ferns, pine needles etc.

When you're making a fire under difficult conditions, you must start small and add to it very carefully. If you've been unable to find a site sheltered from the wind, then you must make a wind-break, although it may be simpler to dig a sloping trench and light the fire inside that.

If the ground is very wet, use stones as a base, but make sure that they're not porous. Wet, porous stones can explode: that will not only injure you, but also blow the fire all over the place.

Don't worry about making an elaborate fireplace at this stage. Get the fire alight first.

Hints for the firemaker

Fire is indeed a great comfort, but it can also be a great danger. If you're cold, wet or exhausted you may become careless and burn yourself, your shelter or your kit.

Plastic fuels
Plastic spoons, helmet visors and foam rubber will ignite from a burning match and will help in getting a fire going.

Beware firelight
If you are in enemy territory, watch that your fire does not betray your position. The light will reflect from surrounding trees and rocks.

Smoke signals
Smoke tends to go straight up in cold, calm weather, making a beacon to your position. In warmer weather smoke tends to hug the ground, making it less visible but betraying your position by its smell.

Careful cutting
Cut low tree branches for firewood rather than an entire tree. Fallen trees are easily spotted by enemy aircraft.

Smoke differences
The wood from coniferous trees (pine, larch, spruce etc) will give off more smoke than wood from deciduous (broadleaf) trees.

Other fuels
Dried moss, bundled grass or peat (old, dried-out reed beds) will make a productive slow-burning fuel.

Selecting and preparing the site

Think about the right place to build your fire:

1 Why do you need a fire – is it for warmth, to cook on or to dry off wet clothing? Do you need it close to your shelter?
2 Are you in hostile terrain? Do you have to be secretive?
3 How long are you going to be at your site? If it's for a long time, it's worth building a proper structure.
4 Select a site away from wind and in a position to reflect the heat in the direction you need it.
5 Build your fire near a good source of firemaking materials.

Reflectors and windbreaks

Construct a simple log wall on the side of the fire away from you and your shelter. This will reflect the heat, and provide a windbreak. And as a bonus it will dry out the next batch of logs for use.

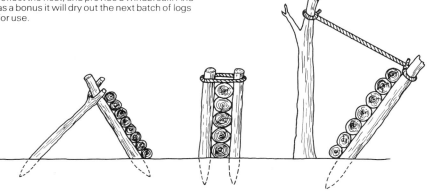

Laying a fire

The basic structure of a new fire is vital. Remember, the fire will need lots of air, so arrange your kindling in a cone around the tinder. Alternatively, leave the kindling against a larger log.

These survivors have built themselves a cosy set-up, with shelter, log fire and reflector all at close quarters. But you should watch the problems of smoke and the possibility of the shelter itself catching fire.

Make a nest of dry grass and the smallest twigs. If you can find a dry bird's or mouse's nest, so much the better. It will have down and fur mixed in with the grass, and probably some dry droppings too – all of them excellent tinder.

Put your tinder inside. Arrange dry kindling over it in the shape of a cone, or make a lean-to by pushing a green stick into the ground at an angle of about thirty degrees and build up the kindling along it to make a sort of tent.

Make sure that you've got all the materials you'll need to hand before attempting to light the fire – you may only get one chance, and at the beginning you'll have to work quickly, adding small amounts of kindling as the fire grows.

Keep the fire going

If you have a choice of different types of wood to use as fuel, use soft-wood – pine and spruce, for example – as the first load of fuel, but be careful of sparks. These woods contain resin and burn quickly. To keep the fire

The log cabin pile

This is a very good way of laying a fire. Plenty of air can circulate and it will not collapse until it's well away.

going, use hardwood such as oak or beech. They're much longer lasting.

You can use a mixture of green and dry wood to keep the fire going through the night, but don't just dump wood on it without thinking. Make sure that you keep a good stock of fuel close at hand, and arrange it so that the heat from the fire will help to dry the fuel out. Keep kindling at hand too, so that you can revive the fire quickly if it looks like dying out.

Improving the fire

How you improve the fire site depends on what you're going to use it for.

A fire that you use for smoking food, for instance, isn't much use for anything else. Its purpose is to produce

Cooking food

A small, slow-burning fire is the best for cooking. Raging naked flames will produce burned hands and scorched, inedible food.

The hobo stove

A simple stove made from an old tin or oildrum conserves heat and produces a stable, useful 'hotplate'.

A simple crane

Use a green wood pole with a forked notch to hold a container over a fire. Beware large naked flames: a burning pole will wreck your meal.

Underground fireplace

This is an old Red Indian arrangement. Make one or more vents on the upwind side of the fire for ventilation. It will reduce smoke and flame and the effects of high winds.

lots of smoke inside an enclosure. You won't be able to cook on it, and it won't give out much warmth.

You can cook on an open fire, but it's not too efficient: it's better to construct a stove of some sort. The simplest stove needs something like a five-gallon oil drum. Punch holes in one end and in a ring all around the side at the same end. Cut out a panel about two inches above that ring of holes. Punch a large hole in one side of the drum near the other end, to let the smoke out. Place the stove on a ring of stones to allow the air to circulate from underneath.

Now you can transfer some of your fire into the stove, stoke it through the cut-out panel and cook on top. It'll give off enough heat to keep you warm, too, and has the very positive benefit of not showing sparks and flames like an open fire does.

A rabbit becomes dinner on a spit. This fancy arrangement works OK as long as the fire isn't too strong and you're able to keep revolving the spit with the meal attached. You must cook wild food really thoroughly; a quick scorch on the outside and blood on the inside is a recipe for food poisoning or worse.

The fire pit

You can achieve much the same effect by digging a circular pit, and then another smaller one, slantwise, that meets it at the bottom. The slanting hole is for the air to circulate up through the fire, so dig it on the side of the prevailing wind.

If you dig it close to the trunk of a tree, the smoke will go up into the foliage and be dispersed, helping to disguise your position.

Making a Maori oven

This is a simple, efficient oven that can be made as big as you need, even to cook a whole deer. Once set up you can leave it to look after itself while you get on with other important things.

1 Dig a hole about 60 × 60 × 60 cm. Put very hot (red hot if possible) stones in the bottom. Cover with moss, ferns or other foliage. Make a second, smaller layer.

2 Wrap the portioned meat in foliage, making sure you don't use toxic plants, and place in the pit on top of the stones.

3 Place more foliage on top of the meat. Place an upright stick in the centre of the stove area and pile the excavated earth on top of the pit.

4 Withdraw the stick and pour about 2 pints of water into the pit. Steam will pour out, so cover with a large stone. After about two hours the meat will have been pressure-cooked and will fall from the bone.

You can make a fire more effective as a source of warmth by building a firewall across one or two sides, to reflect the heat back towards you.

Two in one

The simplest way is to drive four green-wood stakes into the ground in two pairs three or four inches apart, with three or four feet between them. Fill up the space with trimmed branches and trunks, but don't bind them together. That way you get a firewall and a stack of dry wood all in one!

You may have to build your fire in the wet – on snow, or in a swamp, for example. In the snow it's easiest to build a base out of layers of green wood. In swamp or marsh land, raise that platform up on four legs.

Don't bother to chop or even break up long pieces of wood for an open fire. Start at one end and feed the log in as it burns, or lay it across the fire and wait until it burns through, then turn the ends in.

Having gone through all the pain of getting your fire going, don't let it go out! Use well-dried hardwood during the day; it produces very little smoke. As the evening approaches, you may want to add green or damp fuel to produce smoke that will drive away insects.

Alternative fuels

If you have a vehicle, almost every part of it that isn't metal will burn.

Mix oil, petrol or diesel with sand in a pit and set fire to it. Rip out the upholstery and the trim and use for fuel.

The tyres will burn if you get them hot enough, but stay upwind of the smoke! Hydraulic fluid from the brake and clutch systems is highly flammable, and so is neat anti-freeze. All of this applies to aircraft as much as ground vehicles.

Animal droppings, if they are perfectly dry, are a very good source of fuel: easy to light, slow-burning and almost smokeless.

After a while, looking after your fire will become second nature to you. You'll sense changes in its moods, and be able to change its character to do different jobs.

Beware the unseen enem

Whatever the conditions in which you're trying to survive, you'll never see your worst enemies. They're the tiny botulism bacterium that thrives on rotting flesh; the poison molecule injected by a scorpion; the malaria passed on to you when a mosquito feeds on a tiny drop of your blood; the typhoid or cholera in the dirt on the feet of the fly that lands on your food; the bubonic plague carried by the fleas on the rat you ate yesterday. This section of the Survival Course shows you how to combat threats to your health. Some are just irritating or painful; some of them are fatal.

People survived to a ripe old age long before there was a chemist's shop in every High Street, and most of that time they lived at least partly off the land. They had to deal with the same kinds of pests and dangers that you'll meet in the wild. And, over the years, they discovered ways of treating everyday complaints. Most of those ways will be available to you, too.

Bites and stings

Insects are more likely to give you trouble than anything else you will meet in the wild, either from the poisons they produce themselves, or because of the diseases they carry and

The tsetse fly makes a meal of human blood. In return, he passes on sleeping sickness a disease that produces fever, wasting away and sluggishness. The tsetse is common throughout Africa and vast numbers are afflicted by it.

can transmit. Some people suffer more than others through being allergic to particular types of stings. If this is true for you, then carry the appropriate treatment kit on your body at all times. Not in your pack, because you may lose that or even have to abandon it, but actually on your body.

If you get a bite or a sting, don't scratch it; it may become infected as a result, and that infection may end up by killing you. In the tropics, especial-

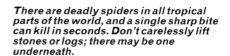

There are deadly spiders in all tropical parts of the world, and a single sharp bite can kill in seconds. Don't carelessly lift stones or logs; there may be one underneath.

ly, the slightest scratch can lead to blood poisoning and even gangrene if it becomes infected.

Check all over your body at least once a day to see that no insect has attached itself to you. If you find a tick, which can transmit a variety of diseases, cover it with grease, tree sap or something similar, to cut off its air supply. Then it will release its hold and you can remove it. Don't squeeze its body. Wash your hands and the area of the bite immediately.

If you're stung by a bee, wasp or hornet, remove the stinger and the venom sac, if it's attached, by scraping gently with a fingernail or knife blade. Don't squeeze the venom sac; you'll be squeezing more of the poison into the wound. Wash the whole area straight away.

Spiders, centipedes, scorpions and ants

These can all inflict a painful wound, and some may be fatal. In the case of spiders and scorpions, clean the wound completely, and try to suck the venom out by mouth or squeeze the wound. Then treat it like any other open wound.

In the Middle East, watch out for the Camel Spider in particular. This creature, which can be as big across as a small plate, is a meat eater. Its bite is a local anaesthetic, so you don't feel it eating away around the wound site. In Australia, the Funnel-Web Spider is said to be the most dangerous; its bite is almost always fatal.

Like spiders, scorpions can be anything from half an inch to six or eight inches long. Some are fatal, some only produce a painful wound. If you take any article of clothing off, examine it carefully for spiders and scorpions before you put it back on again.

Treat centipede and ant bites like wasp stings. Well-chewed tobacco, placed on the wound after you've cleaned it, will sometimes help to ease the pain.

If you can find out what the local people use against stings and bites, then you can copy them, but you should be very careful.

Open wounds

Normally, open wounds are dangerous because of tissue and fluid loss, and because of the shock to your system when they're inflicted.

Out in the middle of nowhere, with no proper medical kit, the greatest danger is from infection. Some infection is inevitable, but you can limit it and stop it spreading.

Clean the wound as soon as possible. That means:
1 Remove or cut clothing away from the wound site
2 Remove any obvious foreign bodies
3 Clean the area around the wound carefully

Disease is as big a killer in war as bullets. Millions upon millions died in this way in the jungles of Burma and China during World War II, and those diseases are just waiting out there for the next round. Personal hygiene is your number one priority.

Below and left: Not a welcome visitor, the tapeworm. You get these disgusting pests from eating undercooked meat. They attach themselves to your gut by the anchor arrangement shown left, whereupon they feast on your half-digested food. They grow to enormous size: the one below is about six metres long. Bits drop off the ends and migrate through your blood supply, lodging in inconvenient places such as your brain, where they start growing, with disastrous results.

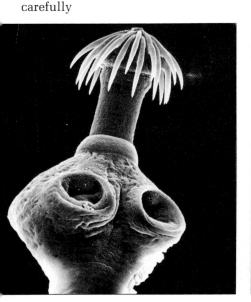

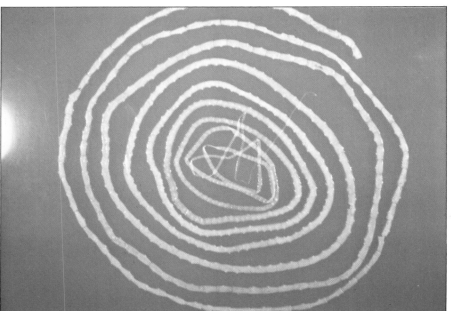

Clothes lice have infected fighting troops since warfare began. They live in the tight folds of clothes and sneak out from time to time to suck your blood. Classic ways of getting rid of them are to iron your seams with a hot iron or run a lighted candle along them, or to use insecticide powder. Personal cleanliness is the best way of avoiding them in the first place.

4 Flush out the wound, but don't scrub it

If you don't have a lot of fresh water, you can use fresh urine to flush out the wound. Don't keep urine. Fresh urine is sterile (so long as you don't have a bladder infection – if you do, it will hurt to urinate), but it soon becomes contaminated.

Don't apply undiluted iodine or mercurochrome from your first-aid kit to a wound – it will only do more damage. You can use it to sterilise surrounding areas, as long as you're very careful.

Don't try and sew the wound up, no matter how much it's gaping open, though you can try to bind it. In survival conditions, it's bound to become infected anyway. Keep it open so that pus and infected material can drain away. To clean the wound, use a warm compress, directly on to the wound, for half an hour at a time, three or four times a day.

If the wound closes, open it with something sterile. A few moments in a flame will sterilise a knife blade or a piece of broken glass. Don't wipe it when you take it out of the flame. Let the pus drain out and remove any accumulation of pus carefully, including any that has dried. Now dry the wound and dress it. And keep drinking as much water as you can. You must keep up this treatment until the wound starts to heal.

Skin infections

Boils, fungal infections and rashes rarely develop into a serious problem on their own, but they can if you scratch them and introduce infection from your fingers.

Apply a warm compress to a boil, to bring it to a head, then open it up with a sterile knife or needles. Clean out the pus thoroughly. Keep the site dry with a dressing, and check it from time to time.

Keep the skin clean and dry around a fungal infection. Don't scratch it, and don't use iodine or disinfectant to try and 'burn out' the infection – it doesn't work.

If you develop a heat rash, keep it clean and dry. If you have powder, then use it. Cold compresses may relieve the itching, but scratching won't.

Stomach bugs and parasites

The best way to deal with parasites is to avoid them. Don't go around barefoot. Don't eat raw meat or fish if

Below and left: These evil beasts live in your intestines and other sensitive tissues, drinking your bodily fluids and causing bilharzia, a widespread debilitating and deadly disease. You catch them by swimming in still tropical waters, where they burrow through your skin. The red threads in their stomachs are half-digested blood. Watch out for blood in your urine.

you can possibly avoid it, especially liver, because that's where most parasites gather in the body. Don't eat raw vegetables that might be contaminated with faeces used as fertiliser.

If you do become infected with a parasite of some sort (watch out for worms or parts of them in your faeces, and for a feeling of general tiredness), you can try one of the following remedies:

1 Drink two pints of salt water (do not repeat)

2 Eat one or two cigarettes' worth of tobacco. Repeat after 24 hours, but no sooner, if necessary

3 Drink two tablespoons of paraffin. Repeat after 24 hours, but no sooner, if necessary

4 Eat hot peppers as a regular part of your diet

Bear in mind that these remedies can be uncomfortable and may damage your intestine.

Diarrhoea is generally caused by drinking contaminated water or eating contaminated food. Be careful of melons, vegetable marrows and other plants that contain huge amounts of moisture. They take up contamination along with the water. It doesn't bother the plant, but it will bother you.

Try one of these remedies:

1 Take nothing but fluids for 24 hours

2 Drink one cup of extra-strong tea every 2 hours until the diarrhoea

The Maggot Treatment

As recently as the First World War, maggots were an accepted way of dealing with infected wounds. Before you decide to use them as a treatment, however, there are a couple of factors you should consider:

1 Maggots are the larvae of flies. To produce them, you have to let flies lay their eggs in the wound. Because flies carry all sorts of other infections around with them, you run the risk of complicating the situation further.

2 Maggots will eat healthy tissue just as happily as infected tissue.

Even so, if you have a severe case of infection and no antibiotics, you should consider maggot treatment if the wound shows no signs of healing on its own. This is how you go about it:

1 Expose the wound to flies for one day, then cover it up and check it regularly.

2 When the maggots appear, keep the wound covered, but keep checking on its progress.

3 When the maggots have eaten their way through the infected flesh, remove them. Increased pain and bright, fresh blood in the wound indicate that the maggots are into healthy flesh.

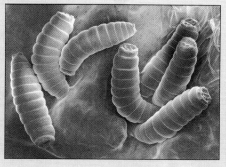

Maggots feast on dead flesh. They say that wounds cleaned by maggots heal very well indeed.

4 Flush the wound several times with fresh urine.

5 Check the wound every four hours for several days, to make sure that no maggots remain.

6 Bandage the wound and treat it normally.

stops. It's the tannin in the tea that does the job. If you don't have tea, boil up the inner bark of a hardwood tree (one with broad leaves) for two hours or more. It will smell and taste quite awful.

3 Make up a paste with clean water and ground-up chalk, charcoal or dried bone. Take two tablespoonsful every two hours. If you have oranges, lemons or other citrus fruits, add the white pith, or the squeezed-out flesh of an apple, to the mixture.

Drink lots of liquids after the attack has passed, to replace the body fluids you've lost in the meantime.

Malaria kills more people than any other disease. Mosquitoes feed by sucking your blood, but at the same time they squirt anticoagulants into your bloodstream along with the malaria parasite. These creatures then take up residence in your blood cells, where they multiply and burst the cell walls. Moral: keep taking the tablets.

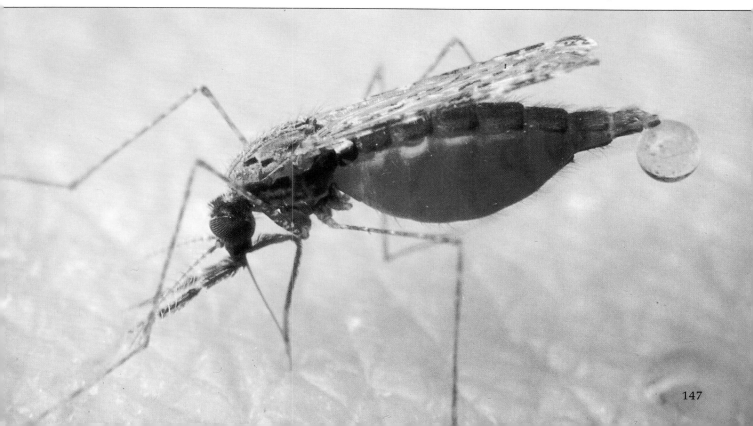

CHAPTER SIX

THE INNER SOLDIER

There were the times when troops were not fed by their leaders, the common soldier was left to fend and forage for himself and since they were comparatively brutalized soldiery, usually in a foreign country, the local population had a very bad time. Their homes were ransacked and anything of food value was simply stolen along with all edible livestock. The means to feed hungry troops is now very sophisticated, and has moved forward considerably since those brutal times, but the same problem exists in that large bodies of men have to be supplied with sufficient food to keep them fighting fit.

We introduce this SURVIVAL chapter with an article about the kind of sustenance the soldier is supplied with in the field, in a form that is nutritious enough to keep him fit, but which can be prepared easily and quickly. Elaborate meals, as far as possible, will naturally be available when the action quietens down. But the British Army ration is very adequate and although not exactly *nouvelle cuisine* in appearance, has been described as giving as little as possible for as much as possible. The army ratpack has as many calories and is much cheaper. This subject is important for keeping a soldier alert and able to withstand stress. Not least important to the soldier is the unavoidable subject of what happens to the residue of the food at the other end of its journey. A mention is made here.

The absolute necessity for water to support life has already been stressed and in this chapter we discuss the ways it is located. In our normal, civilized, home lives we expect to turn a tap in order to obtain perfectly drinkable water. But there are still many parts of the world, including places on the Continent, that do not have a clean, piped water supply,

let alone taps. To many people the available water will be that found naturally and unless, like the local population, you have developed a life-long immunity from the bugs it contains one sip will be enough to give you a dose of the dreaded 'Montezuma's Revenge' (or the local equivalent) and it is well known to be so severe in its effects as to turn your insides to liquid for days on end and reduce you to a limp, lifeless and useless object. A soldier must assume that all local natural water contains harmful bacteria and should always be purified before drinking. It is an important subject, which forms the third article. The ways that water can be purified and made drinkable form the subject of the following article here.

Next, some real Stone Age advice. Not about knocking people over the head and dragging them off to the nearest cave, but about tools. That early period in man's development was so called because it was the time when he had learned to make weapons and tools from stones, usually flint. This material, basically silica in one of its forms, fractures into very sharp edges when properly struck (the word is 'knapped'). If there is a supply of flints where you are you have the raw material for making axes, knives, saws, arrowheads – if you know how.

Two articles are necessary to cover the touchy matter of the soldier's survival knife. Like all weapons, knives are only dangerous in the wrong hands, but they can legitimately be employed in the right hands at the right time. A survival knife is an essential piece of equipment and there is a good range of models from which the serious purchaser can make his selection, some better than others. We offer the reader who needs to know some good and sensible advice.

Today's soldier has food airlifted even in remote areas, but still needs his personal ration pack.

Scoff that Ratpack!

The current British army ration pack (ratpack) is thought by many armies to be the best in the world, and when compared to others this appears to be the case.

There are about four different menus commonly available in the GS (General Service) range, and in theory you should be issued a different pack each day to provide variety: in reality you often get the same one for days.

Meals and sundries

Each pack contains a main meal, a breakfast and a snack, hot drinks – enough coffee and tea to make about three pints, and beef stock – and sundries such as a can opener, toilet paper, chewing gum, salt and matches. The meals are in tins, soups are in sachets, and biscuits are in green foil wrappers.

Distribute the rations

The pack weighs about 2 kg and is issued with a solid fuel hexamine cooker or the new petro-jelly cooker. The rations are in a cardboard box; you take everything out and distribute it among your personal equipment. One side of the box has a range card printed on it, which you tear off and keep until you need it. Apart from wondering what's in your ration pack, your main preoccupation will be how to cook your meal.

There are three basic methods of cooking your tinned rations:

1 The least popular method is to open the tin and tip the contents into your mess tin and heat it. It's after the meal that your problems begin – trying to clean the mess tin, which you never have the time or enough water to do.

2 A cleaner method is to pierce the lid of the tin and place it half-submerged in boiling water for 10 minutes. This is slow, and uses a good deal of fuel and water, but is the most commonly-used method of cooking and is the one described in the cooking instructions found in the pack.

3 The third method is to make a shallow dent in the side of the tin and place it on the stove. When the dent bulges out or resumes its normal shape, remove the tin. Holding it away from you, pierce it with the tin opener and release the pressure, then open the tin and eat the contents.

The advantage of this method is that if you are attacked while cooking you just put the tin in your pocket or pack (be careful, it will be hot) and continue to cook it whenever you have the time. Also, unlike the first two methods it produces no steam or cooking smells.

24-hour Ratpacks

The individual 24-hour pack is the most expensive way to feed a soldier, and is only used where fresh rations or larger composite ration packs cannot be used. Where possible, fresh rations should be issued to supplement the pack. It provides a balanced diet, if you do not end up with menu A chicken curry for several weeks. The quality is excellent and has enough calories and vitamins to keep you going on all but the most arduous tasks over a long period. The ration is issued in the box shown, with hexamine and cooker separate.

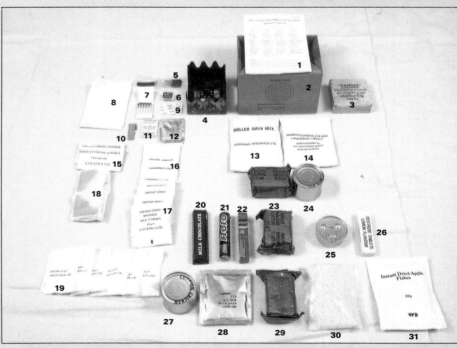

1 Menu sheet	**16** Orange powder
2 Ration box with range card	**17** Powdered milk
3 Hexamine cooking blocks	**18** Tea bags
	19 Sugar
4 Hexamine cooking stove	**20** Chocolate bar
5 Waterproof matches	**21** Chocolate covered caramels
6 Chewing gum	**22** Boiled sweets
7 Matches	**23** Biscuits brown
8 Toilet paper	**24** Bacon grill
9 Salt	**25** Meat spread
10 Tin opener	**26** Dextrose tablets
11 Water purifying tablets	**27** Curried chicken
12 Beef stock	**28** Packet soup
13 Rolled oats porridge mix	**29** Fruit biscuits
14 Hot chocolate drink	**30** Rice
15 Coffee powder	**31** Dried apple flakes

DGOS FORM 494
(Revised 1984)

MENU SHEET AND COOKING INSTRUCTIONS
24-HOUR RATION GS

The content of each pack differ and a different pack should be issued each day.

MENU 'A'	MENU 'B'	MENU 'C'	MENU 'D'
BREAKFAST	**BREAKFAST**	**BREAKFAST**	**BREAKFAST**
Porridge	Porridge	Porridge	Porridge
Bacon Grill	Baconburger	Bacon Grill	Baconburger
Biscuits Brown	Biscuits Brown	Biscuits Brown	Biscuits Brown
Chocolate Drink	Chocolate Drink	Chocolate Drink	Chocolate Drink
SNACK	**SNACK**	**SNACK**	**SNACK**
Biscuits Brown	Biscuits Brown	Biscuits Brown	Biscuits Brown
Ham Spread	Beef Spread	Chicken Spread	Chicken & Bacon Spread
Chocolate Full Cream	Chocolate Full Cream	Chocolate Full Cream	Chocolate Full Cream
Spangles	Boiled Sweets	Confectionery Bar	Spangles
Chocolate Covered	Chocolate Covered	Chocolate Covered	Chocolate Covered
Caramel	Caramel	Caramel	Caramel
Dextrose Tablets	Dextrose Tablets	Dextrose Tablets	Dextrose Tablets
(Lemon)	(Orange)	(Lemon)	(Orange)
MAIN MEAL	**MAIN MEAL**	**MAIN MEAL**	**MAIN MEAL**
Biscuit Fruit Filled	Biscuit Fruit Filled	Biscuit Fruit Filled	Biscuit Fruit Filled
Instant Soup	Instant Soup	Instant Soup	Instant Soup
Chicken Curry	Steak & Kidney	Steak & Onion	Minced Steak
Pre-cooked Rice	Pudding	Casserole	Mixed Vegetables
Apple Flakes	Spaghetti in Tomato	Beans in Tomato Sauce	Mixed Fruit Pudding
	Sauce	Fruit Salad	
	Apple & Apricot Flakes		

DRINKS
Instant Skimmed Milk, Sugar, Tea, Coffee, Beef Stock Drink and Orange Lemon Powder.

SUNDRIES
Chewing Gum, Toilet Paper, Salt, Book Matches, Waterproof Matches, Can Opener, Water Purification Tablets and Menu Sheet.

Note: Contents may vary from printed menu sheets, depending on items available at time of packing.

COOKING INSTRUCTIONS

ROLLED OATS FOR PORRIDGE (Oats containing milk already mixed)
All Menus. Add mixture to a little cold water and make a paste, add a little more water, add a pinch of salt, bring to boil, simmer and stir for 4-5 minutes. Add sugar to taste.

BACON GRILL
Slice to the thickness of bacon rashers. Fry on a low heat until golden brown. Can also be eaten cold.

BACON BURGERS
Use fat in can for frying. Fry on a low heat until golden brown. Can be sliced in two for quick cooking. Can also be eaten cold if sliced thinly.

INSTANT SOUP
Put contents of one sachet into a mug. Add ½ pint boiling water and stir well. The variety will depend on availability at time of packing.

TO HEAT CANS
The can should be pierced twice on the lid and placed in water so that the can is half submerged. Boil for 10 minutes.

PRE-COOKED RICE
Place water in small mess tin up to bottom rivet and bring to boil. Add rice and a pinch of salt, bring back to boil, simmer for 5 minutes. Allow to stand for 2 minutes to absorb water.

APPLE FLAKES/APPLE AND APRICOT FLAKES
Pour boiling water over flakes in sachet and leave for 2 minutes to absorb the water. The flakes are then ready to eat.

DRINKS
There are sufficient beverage ingredients to make three pints of Tea, two pints of Coffee, one pint of Drinking Chocolate, one or two pints Orange/Lemon Drink and ½ pint Beef Stock Drink.

WATER PURIFICATION TABLETS
For Drinking Water. Add one water purification tablet to each litre (1¾ pints) of water. Leave for 10 minutes before use.

WINDPROOF/WATERPROOF MATCHES
The matches should be retained for lighting the hexamine blocks under adverse weather conditions.

NOTE: The smaller section of a mess tin filled to centre of lower rivet, equals one pint.

The major problem with composite rations is weight: it is physically impossible to carry more than a week's supply of rat packs. Resupply in most tactical environments is at best difficult, and it may be better to go hungry than risk being compromised by resupply. Here an observation post on the Belize/Guatemala border is resupplied by air: the only way that makes sense in primary jungle.

Tactical Cooking

1 Never cook for one. One buddy should cook the other buddy's food to save time and effort and so that only one lot of kit is unpacked and used.

2 Be prepared to eat on the move. Break the menu down into various meals, and stow them where you can get to them without taking kit off.

3 If you are going to cook in a tactical situation place your sentries at the limit of the smell *or* noise, whichever is the furthest. If you have to eat your rations cold, beware: morale nose-dives on too much cold compo.

3 Hexamine stoves have a very pungent and distinctive odour. The bluet involves less risk of compromise, but make sure you use it on half power as it can be noisy.

5 Watch out: even when cold, the issue curried chicken can be detected by the educated nose at 40-50 metres.

6 Cook unopened tins slowly.

7 Do not add the coffee or tea to the water and then boil it; boil the water first, remove from the heat, and then add the coffee. This cuts down on smell.

8 Cooking within a unit should be staggered. Cook in pairs; those cooking should still watch their arcs, weapons at the ready.

9 Make sure that you only take out of your kit what you need immediately. You may have to bug out at speed, so as soon as you use anything put it away.

10 If you can, burn all rubbish. Top and tail the tins and flatten them first. Burning sterilises them and gets rid of any particles of food, so there is less trouble from flies and ants, then pack all the gash in airtight containers.

11 In an NBC environment many food sources will be contaminated, so only use tinned food.

Soups and snacks

The soup mixes should be prepared by adding the water to the powder while cold and then heating it: otherwise it gets very lumpy and unpleasant.

With the apple and apricot flakes, you just pour boiling water into the foil sachet and stir it. They are then ready to eat.

The plain biscuits, or 'Biscuits AB' as they are called, are not popular, but are an important part of the ration: they are a good, quick snack, and quite filling. You also get a small can of spread to put on them, though it rarely tastes anything like described in the menu. The biscuits can be smashed in the packet and then added to boiling water to make a form of porridge, as can the pack's oatmeal block, which most soldiers eat cold.

In the pack there is a good selection of chocolates and sweets which

The ration for the buddy-buddy system: the two-man 24-hour pack. Ideally you should only have one set of cooking and washing and shaving kit between you and your oppo so that you can maximise your ammunition load.

double as unofficial currency; it's common for people to swap packets of Rolos for a tin of baconburgers or whatever.

The sweets are also important because while on operations such as ambushes and OPs you are not allowed to cook. The tube of dextrose tablets is always a good source of quick energy (ideal for bringing exhausted recruits back to life).

Favourite fruit

Obviously, some items are more popular than others. The chicken curry has a varied reputation for obvious reasons, as does the baconburger. A universally-loved item is the

fruit salad 'Menu C', which is always jealously guarded.

You should only have one item unpacked and cooking at any one time and should use only one hexamine block at a time.

Cooking equipment

Mess tins are by no means ideal for heating water, although the introduction of mess tin lids has made them more efficient. One of the best vessels for heating water is the old 44 pattern mug; with care and a little practice it can be drunk from whilst hot by wrapping a piece of silver paper or tape over the rim on the side before you drink.

New mug

Another development in this area has been the 85 pattern mug, which is a metal version of the plastic '58' mug and fits on the top of the water bottle.

A very important aspect of field cooking is the concealment of cookers. If you have to cook at night, you must keep stoves concealed. This is

Points to remember

1 If you boil tins in your mess tin, the water will be contaminated by zinc, so do not use the water for brews.

2 Hexamine gives off poisonous fumes, which can be a hazard in enclosed spaces such as a shelter bay of a trench.

3 Keep eating. Under training, and certainly in war, you will reach a level of exhaustion where eating becomes very hard work. But you must try, or you will very rapidly become a casualty. The easiest way to eat the pack, if you are desperate, is to empty the entire contents into a plastic bag – tins, soups, brew kit, biscuits, the lot – then crush and mix together with 1½ pints of water. Put the bag inside your combat jacket, and the contents will heat up as you move. Then on a short halt you can just grab a handful.

4 Do not put rations in ammo pouches.

5 Do not throw away parts of the menu just because you do not like them, except in a long-term ambush where cooking is not allowed and when defecation may be a problem. In an OP, make sure you eat the Biscuits, brown; they make your faeces easier to bag or wrap in Clingfilm.

6 Never put off until tomorrow what you can do today. Constipation can make you a casualty just as effectively as a bullet. Never go for a 'shovel recce' on your own; always get your buddy to cover you and dig it in and cam it up when you have finished.

Top left: The cook-in-the-mug method. Blacken the outside and add some insulating tape to the rim.

Left: Buddy-buddy cooking, heating the sealed tins. Dried peas, Oxo cubes and onions are useful additions.

Below: The petroleum jelly, hexamine and bluet cookers. Each have advantages and disadvantages, so try them out: you may find that you need different cookers for different types of operation.

doubly important in cold conditions, where steam is visible over great distances during the day.

Conceal your cooker

At night and under normal conditions, any cooker should be buried so that no light is visible. If you are using only one hexamine block the hole only needs to be 15-20 cm deep. If you need to put the fire out in a hurry, remove the mess tin or mug and dump the earth on top of the block.

Added flavour

Many soldiers add curry powder and spices to enhance the flavour of the rations and to provide variety, which after a week of menu 'A' may be essential. The one danger of curry powder is the smell: it may give you away in a tactical situation.

The Search for Water

Water is a basic human need. There is no adequate substitute, and without it you cannot live more than a few days. Within the human body water acts as a stabilizer; it helps to maintain warmth in cold environments, and is vital to staying cool in hot environments. It is also part of the body's mechanism for distributing food and removing waste. As soon as you are cut off from a source of fresh water, you begin to dehydrate.

The rate at which you dehydrate depends on a number of factors: the amount of water your body already contains, the clothing you are wearing, the local temperature, how hard you are working, whether you are in shade or sunlight, whether you are smoking and whether you are calm or nervous.

If you allow dehydration to continue, there will come a point when you can no longer search for water. Your first priority is to minimise further dehydration and, having done this, you must find water. (If you are stranded in a desert with little chance of finding water, stay still to prevent further dehydration, and make efforts to signal for rescue.)

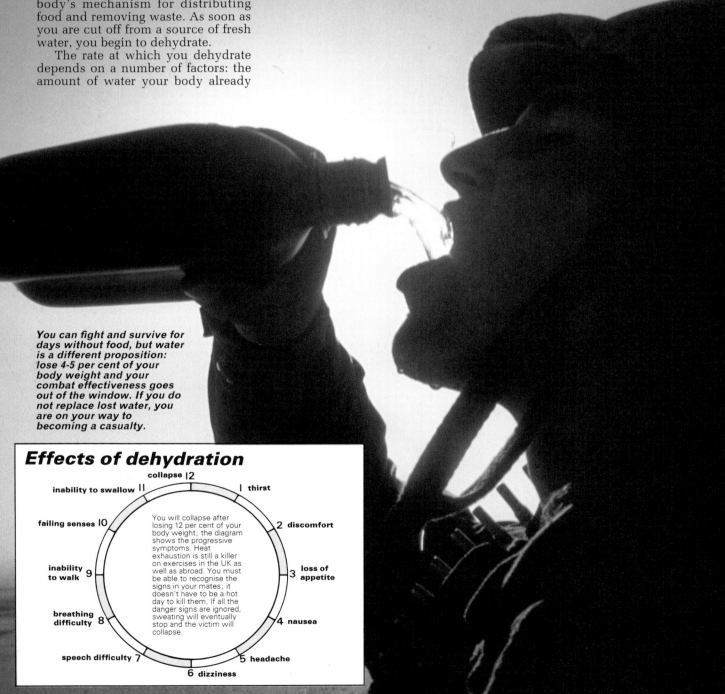

You can fight and survive for days without food, but water is a different proposition: lose 4-5 per cent of your body weight and your combat effectiveness goes out of the window. If you do not replace lost water, you are on your way to becoming a casualty.

Effects of dehydration

collapse 12

inability to swallow 11

failing senses 10

inability to walk 9

breathing difficulty 8

speech difficulty 7

6 dizziness

5 headache

4 nausea

3 loss of appetite

2 discomfort

1 thirst

You will collapse after losing 12 per cent of your body weight; the diagram shows the progressive symptoms. Heat exhaustion is still a killer on exercises in the UK as well as abroad. You must be able to recognise the signs in your mates; it doesn't have to be a hot day to kill them. If all the danger signs are ignored, sweating will eventually stop and the victim will collapse.

Finding water

You do not have to be in a desert to have difficulty finding water. Forests often offer such poor visibility that, although surrounded by water-loving trees, you cannot spot readily-available surface water. (In combat conditions, however, you may have to deliberately avoid obvious sources of water, for fear of ambush.)

So how do you go about finding water? The first thing you do is to remember the following points:

1 Water runs downhill, so make for lower country.
2 Where there is water, there is usually an abundance of lush vegetation. If possible, learn to recognise the moisture-loving plants in the area. If this vegetation is wilted or dead, it probably indicates chemical pollution.
3 Animals need water too. Observe the habits of the local wildlife; it may lead you to a source of water.
4 Grain- and seed-eating birds need water, so observe them too.
5 Listen for frogs croaking: they live in water.
6 Cliffs often have seepages of water at their base, so look carefully.

Sources of water (assuming no equipment)

Familiarise yourself with the various sources of water and their relative merits.

1 Dew

Dew is one of the most reliable sources of water for the survivor. It can be collected soon after it has started to form until it evaporates in the morning sunlight. Improvise a mop from an absorbent article of

Water can often be found in the hollows of trees, but is usually tainted with tannin from the bark. If you expect rain, empty the hollow out, wait until it fills up and then boil the new water.

clothing. Drag this through long grass or use it to wipe the condensed moisture from shrubs and rocks. If you do not have a convenient mop, finely teased, non-poisonous inner barks or grasses can be used. When the mop is saturated, wring out the water into a container. Although labour-intensive, this is a very effective way to collect water.

Dew itself is a pure source of water, but when you wipe it off vegetation and rocks you also wipe off bacteria and perhaps parasites. It is therefore best to boil this water before consumption.

2 Rain and snow

Rainwater is usually the safest source of water in the wilderness. If it rains, make sure you gather as much as you can. But remember the water is

Most soldiers take water for granted. In British forces, steps are being taken to recognise water as an important factor by forming trained water 'recce' teams and introducing strict controls – for instance, not being allowed to drink without permission.

Iranian prisoners receive a drink from an Iraqi recce unit atop a BRDM-2. In a protracted campaign, shortage of water may well be a reason for not taking prisoners.

only as pure as your method of collection: if you are in doubt, boil it before consumption. Snow, if it is clean, is probably pure. The major problem with snow is melting it: a time-consuming and labour-intensive process, as you require eight to 10 containers of snow to produce one container of water.

3 Ice

Ice is not pure and should always be boiled before consumption, but is far more economical as a source of water than snow. Icicles are often found hanging from trees and rocks, so may provide you with a ready source of water. Those hanging from trees may be slightly stained brown by the tannin in the bark, but unless they

are very heavily stained they will be safe to drink after boiling.

4 Puddles and hidden water

Rainwater is often found trapped in depressions in rocks, called kettles, and in puddles. While such water may smell foul and be stagnant, it only needs filtering and boiling to make it drinkable.

Rainwater can also often be found trapped in hollows in trees. Unfortunately, this is often so badly polluted with tannin that it is undrinkable. However, if you expect rain you can bale these hollows out and let them fill with fresh rainwater; as long as you use the water before it too becomes tannin-stained, you have a handy water tank. Always boil this water before drinking it, and only use water found in non-poisonous trees.

Note: Tannin-stained water, although undrinkable, can be boiled to make a very effective antiseptic: unlike syn-

Tree ice
Remember, you will need to boil it. On a chemical battlefield, however, this would be useless.

Birch sap
A North American Indian technique is to tap off the sap as shown, with a collecting barrel attached to the tap. Be careful that you do not completely break the tree's ring of bark when doing this several times.

Mud pool (above)
Not instantly recognisable as a source of water; but if you filter and boil it you can drink it.

Stagnant water (left)
This can also provide drinking water and in many situations this will be the only type of water available.

thetic antiseptics, tannin actually pro-
motes healing. You can also dilute it to
a mild tea and drink it to ease diarrhoea.

5 Drinkable saps

For short-term relief of thirst, you
may be able to tap the sap of certain
trees. The sap of maple, birch and
sycamore can be tapped during the
early spring (sycamore will produce
sap from spring to autumn, depending
on local conditions). Sap is thirst-
quenching but it contains sugar,
which if taken in sufficient quantity
will hasten dehydration; in fact, the
woodland North American Indians
still boil maple and birch sap to produce sugar.

Only mature trees should be
tapped, and the sap drunk while fresh,
as it will ferment if stored. Some
plants can also be used to provide
water.

6 Springs and seepages

Springs are often regarded as foolproof sources of drinking water, but
unfortunately this is not true: spring
water should always be boiled before
drinking. Very often, springs are
covered with soil and appear as
patches of saturated ground supporting lush plant growth. To obtain water
from these areas, dig an Indian Well.

7 Ponds

These are principally a feature of
farmland, and are therefore a potential
source of water for the evading soldier. Such water should always be
considered suspect, as at the very
least there will be fluke infestation.
Keep contact with this water to a minimum, and if used as a source of drinking water, filter and thoroughly boil it
before drinking.

8 Streams, rivers and lakes

Streams are often a tempting source
of water, but care should be taken as
they are very often polluted by decay-
ing carcasses of animals that have
drowned or become caught in boggy
ground. In alpine regions, the clear,
ice-cold glacial meltwaters carry an
invisible hazard: sediment – rock
powder scoured from living rock by
the awesome power of the glacier. If
this is not filtered out, you may get
digestive problems.

The further water travels from its
source, the more pollutants it picks
up. In an age where chemicals are an
integral part of farming and land management, rivers and lakes should be
avoided as sources of water.

Indian Well

The Indian Well is an easily prepared and efficient method of collecting reasonably good water.
Selection of the ground is all-important and the water produced requires filtering and boiling.
Also, it takes some time to produce clear water, and quality is dependent on soil type. In
practice, watch out for sources of contamination, boil very carefully, and add Steritabs.

*Choose an area of saturated ground. If in
a tactical environment, don't pick a place
that can be easily spotted.*

*If you haven't a bowl for baling out (see
following two pages), cupped
hands will do.*

*This is good enough to use; the water
seeping into the well has a filtering
effect. The water will get cleaner the
longer you spend baling out.*

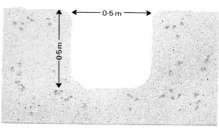

1 Dig a hole about half a metre deep and half a
metre wide. Water will begin to seep into the
hole.

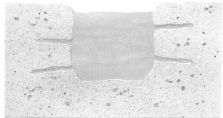

2 You can push a stick into the sides of the
well to increase seepage of water into the well.

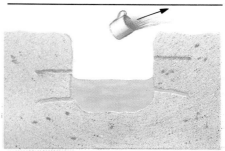

3 Bale out this water carefully so that you do
not stir up the sediment at the bottom of the
hole. Repeat this process until the seeping
water is fairly clear.

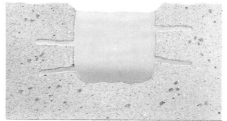

4 After some time, the water at the top of the
well will be clear enough to collect. Be careful
not to disturb the muddy layer that usually lurks
at the bottom.

157

Purifying Water

Now you've found a source of water. Is it safe to drink? The answer seems obvious — assume the water is dirty and purify it. But dehydration is causing you to be uncharacteristically impatient and irritable. You are tired, hungry, lonely and somewhat frightened. Your hands and shins are covered in the scratches you sustained searching what seemed like every patch of vegetation in the last 100 miles. And but for the incessant biting of the mosquitoes you would fall asleep.

You are faced with water that will need filtering and boiling before it is safe to drink, but you have no container and no fire. Surely one little sip won't hurt?

The hazard of polluted water

Without the support of modern medicine to fall back on, wilderness survival is all about maintaining good health. The human body is an amazing machine, but it is finely tuned: it only takes one drop of contaminated water to make you ill.

Of the many waterborne problems you may develop, the most common is diarrhoea. In a survival situation, diarrhoea may prove fatal. It causes dehydration and makes hygiene very difficult, increasing the risk of further unpleasant infections, and destroys the will to live.

To make your water safe, you will need three things:

1 Fire
2 A container
3 A filter

As a fire will also warm you, drive away the mosquitoes and boost your morale, it is usually best to start this first. Hopefully you will have practised your firelighting skill, as this is a bad time to learn!

Improvised water containers

Improvised water containers fall into three categories:
1 Kettles: containers that can be used directly over flames
2 Cauldrons: cannot be used directly over flames, but can be used for rock boiling
3 Storage: containers that are solely for carrying or storing safe water

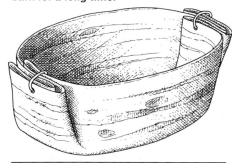

Above, right and below: Cherry or birch bark bowls can be made by simple folding, and improved by stitching; the more robust version is shown here stitched and with a wooden rim. You will have to soak the bark for a long time.

Kettles

Kettles can be made from flammable materials because the water contained within them prevents their burning. The secret is not to allow the flames to reach beyond the water level.

1 Bamboo

In some tropical regions, bamboo can be found with stems large enough to be turned into kettles. Many other containers can also be improvised from bamboo, and sometimes fresh drinking water can be found trapped in the stems.

2 Birch or cherry bark

The woodland Indians of North America routinely made kettles from birch bark while on their travels. Only the outer bark is used. It should be carefully removed from an unblemished section of the trunk, and can be made pliable by either soaking or gently warming by the fire. The brown inside of the bark is the most durable side, and is used to form the outside of containers which are simply made by folding.

Cauldrons

Cauldrons are made from materials that will hold water but are not suitable for direct heating; put heated rocks into the water to boil it.

If your local soil is clay or clay-like enough to contain muddy water, a ground cauldron can be made. Dig a bowl-shaped depression in the ground and smooth the inside. Form a raised rim at the top, to help prevent humus falling into the cauldron.

Make the cauldron one third larger than the amount of water you intend to boil. This will allow for the water displaced by the heated rocks. To prevent sediment muddying your water, you will need to line the pit. For this you can use either some material, (for example, a T-shirt) or large non-poisonous leaves such as dock or burdock. Take great care to ensure that the lining fits snugly.

The water purified in this type of cauldron will always be a little muddy, but if you leave it to settle you can skim clear water off of the top.

Natural cauldrons
1 Rocks and trees

Water can often be found in depressions in rocks, and the hollows in trees, and these can be turned into ready-made cauldrons. Again, allow for the displacement of the heated rocks by choosing a depression large enough. If possible, it is best to scrape any slime out of these depressions prior to their use. This is especially important when using tree hollows. Remember, never rock boil in a poisonous tree.

2 Skin

If you are able to catch an animal of the size of a rabbit upwards, you will have secured meat as well as two containers good enough to stew it in: if you are careful with the skinning and gutting, both the skin and the stomach can be used as cauldrons.

To use the skin you can leave the fur on or take it off, as you please. To use the stomach it is best turned inside out. You have a choice when making

Bowl burning

Wooden bowls and containers have been used for centuries and are well within your capabilities to produce. The method is called 'burn and scrape'. First, select a piece of wood of the right thickness. Remember the hardwoods are by nature a lot harder to work, but the product is more durable. Softer dead woods are usually easier.

1 Select a few choice embers from your fire and place them in the centre of the log. Hold them in place with a twig and blow through a tube if possible, perhaps a reed straw. The embers will flare and char the wood.

2 Once a sufficient area has been charred, remove the embers and scrape out the charred wood with a knife or sharp stone. Do not burn too fast or the wood might crack.

3 Repeat the process. It becomes easier as the hole gets deeper at each stage, so you don't need to hold the embers in place. Don't blow too hard – just steadily enough to keep the embers going.

4 The vital ingredient is patience; this method does take time, but you will have a lasting piece of equipment. The bowl on the left is made from a knot in the trunk of the tree.

your skin cauldron. You can line a pit with it, securing it around the rim by stakes, or you can suspend it from a tripod.

3 Wooden bowls

Bowls and containers can be carved out of wood. While not as quickly constructed as the previous methods, wooden bowls are well within the capabilities of a survivor. If carefully made, they are portable and very durable.

The best method of producing a wooden bowl is to 'burn and scrape'. To achieve this, make a small depression in the centre of your bowl-to-be and place a couple of glowing coals in this depression. By then blowing on the coals, ideally through a reed straw, you can use them to char the surrounding wood.

When you have charred a patch of wood, scrape it away using a sharp stone, and begin the process again. It does not take long to form a reasonable sized bowl.

Storage containers

The manufacture of storage containers is a long-term prospect. They can be made from the materials discussed above, and also from clay pottery and tightly-woven basketry.

Filtering

Having secured a container in which to boil your water, you now need a filter to remove the particles of dirt suspended in the water.

Improvised filter

The simplest filter that can be improvised uses a pair of ordinary trousers. Simply turn them inside out, placing one leg inside the other, and tie the leg off at the bottom. Soak the material before use: this helps tighten the weave, making the filter more efficient. Suspend the filter so that you can easily fill it, with the container positioned underneath to collect the clean water that drips out. Such filters can be improved by filling them with charcoal (not ash, which would produce a strong lye solution).

Rock boiling

Rock boiling is an easy and effective way to purify water. The rocks must be of a manageable size and weight, and thoroughly dry. (Rocks from stream beds and damp places contain moisture which, when heated, expands, causing the rock to explode. Also, glass-like rocks such as flint and obsidian should be avoided.)

Heat the rocks in your fire, and when hot transfer them to your container with some improvised tongs. Tap off any ash before dropping them in the water.

Do not wait to use these skills until you have to. Practice is essential to success.

NB When practising, only gather bark from dead trees.

Purifying water by boiling

After filtering to make water safe to drink, you need to boil it. This can be done without fireproof containers in the following way, by using heated rocks. You need a fire; several thick, reasonably straight branches cut to length for the stand and cross braces; some green wood for fire tongs; and an animal skin, fresh or cured (if fresh, make sure you get all the fat off). Rabbit skins are too small – you really need large hare size and above for a worthwhile set-up.

1 Once you have got a decent fire going, build a platform of sticks on the fire, two layers at 90° to each other, to put the rocks on. While these are heating up you can put the finishing touches to the stand.

2 Pour your filtered water into the skin. Do not overfill it, or you will lose precious water when you add the rocks. When the rocks have heated up, pick them up using green twigs.

3 Carefully put the rocks into the water. Note that the feet of the animal are left on the skin as they make useful anchor points.

A simple water filter

If you are going to be operating in an area for some time, this sort of filter will save you a good deal of time: if there is no risk of discovery, you can leave it set up and on the go while you carry on with other tasks.

A spare pair of lightweight issue trousers or, even better, combat trousers with the liners in, make excellent filters because of their dense weave. Soak them thoroughly before you start. A vast improvement is the addition of charcoal: for a small filter you can use spare S6 respirator canisters tied to the bottom of the bag (they contain animated charcoal). Make sure you are not going to need them for their original purpose as they are useless when wet!

charcoal

double thickness of material

filtered water (filtrate)

4 Continue adding rocks until the water boils. You can repeat the process by replacing 'used rocks' back on the fire.

5 This is also a good method for cooking without containers: you can make soups or stews by putting the ingredients into the water with the hot rocks.

6 The stand and skin container set up. Disaster can occur if you try to pour your filtered water in too quickly. Push your hand into the skin to form a bowl and pour the water in slowly; this will allow the skin to expand and take the water.

Flint Tools for Survival

If you're stranded in the wilderness without equipment, you will have to struggle to obtain your most basic needs. But our ancestors faced these difficulties every day. To learn to cope without equipment, you must lay aside your Space Age gadgets and learn the distant skills of the Stone Age. A major step forward that divides our way of life from that of ancestors is our ability to use one resource: metal. We have learned to use it with such skill that we have even been able to leave the planet. In the process we have also become totally dependent upon metal, for it provides our basic needs; in taming nature, we have tamed ourselves.

The biggest mistake you can make when learning survival skills is to assume that you will have a knife or similar metal tool. Your aim should be to become totally self reliant, and the first major step in this direction is to find some cutting tools. Nature provides a variety of materials: the most popular is stone, as it is commonly available, easily worked, gives a very sharp edge, and is durable. Other materials include seashells, wood, antler and bone.

Working stone

Different types of rock need to be worked in different ways. Your first task is to study the unfamiliar stone, and try to 'get a feel for it'. Experiment with the following stone working techniques until you feel you know how to tackle it.

1 Pecking

Pecking is a slow method of shaping stone, used mainly on rocks with a heavy granular character, such as **granite**. You tap the rock with a hard or sharp-edged stone, such as **flint**, to gradually wear away the rock to the desired shape. Axes made in this way are sharpened by abrading.

2 Abrading

Another slow method of working stone, abrading is normally used for shaping rock that is soft enough for this process, but hard enough to take a sharp edge, such as **slate**. It is also used to sharpen and re-touch the edges of harder stone axes. The process involves rubbing with a coarse-grained abrading stone, such as **sandstone**. The process can be aided by the addition of sand and water.

3 Sawing

Some of the harder rocks, such as **nephrite**, make very good edged tools but are difficult to work. They are often best sawn to size using a suitably-shaped 'saw stone' plus sand and water: often **sandstone** again, which you may have to abrade before use. It is not always necessary to saw completely through a rock; two deep saw cuts that almost meet will often cause a fracture line when the stone is struck with a hammer.

4 Knapping

Knapping is the technique employed when working glass-like rocks, and involves the controlled

Pecking a stone hammer head for the hammer shaft
The groove made in the stone is for the hammer shaft, which is bound on with cord or strips of hide soaked in water which set solidly as they dry out. The result is a robust and useful tool.

Slate filleting knife
The slate blade is produced by abrading and is sandwiched between two pieces of wood so that the knife fits into the palm of the hand.

Abrading stones
You should look for a rough, granular, hard sandstone, which is usually easy to break into usable pieces. It is possible to build up a selection of stones from very coarse grain to fine grain, rather like different grades of sandpaper.

Abrading slate
This is used to sharpen hard, granular stone axe heads. In this case a softer stone such as slate can be abraded to produce extremely sharp but less durable cutting tools.

striking of the rock (the 'core') to remove flakes. This is the most complicated stoneworking technique, but once you've mastered it it's the quickest and most versatile method.

The key factor is the 'Conchoidal' (mussel-like) fracture. Any rock that easily produces this type of fracture can be knapped. Carefully remove the flakes and form the core into an axe. By further knapping and flaking the cores can be fashioned into knives, saws, arrow heads and many other useful tools.

How to knap flint

Flint is the most common stone that can be knapped, although not all flint is suitable. Ideally it should be freshly quarried, but this is almost certainly not going to happen in a survival situation, and you will have to make do with surface flints.

A rough test of workability is to tap the flint with a pebble: a clear ring is a good indication, whereas a dull sound will mean a flint that will fracture unpredictably.

Tools

To work flint you will need some tools: hammers and pressure flakers. Improvise a hammer from tough, non-brittle stones of varying sizes and, if available, from antler. The size and weight will depend on the size of the raw material.

Pressure flakers are made from antler tines or similarly-shaped stones. You will also need a protective pad, ideally of rawhide or buckskin, although bark might also be used.

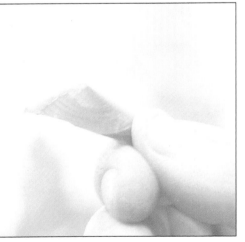

'Conchoidal' fracture
This is the test for whether a rock will 'knapp', i.e. allow you to sculpt its shape by controlled blows with another rock. A rock which does not 'knapp' either refuses to break up or disintegrates in a random pattern.

The flint tool kit

The Mesolithic hunters who roamed early Britain relied solely on flint for their tools. Their basic tool kit enabled them to make their hunting gear from wood, bone and antler as well as simplifying the task of tanning hides. It is just such a tool kit that the survivor will need.

Key to photo:
1 Hand axe
2 Axe head
This is made from a core as described overleaf, and is sharpened by flaking when necessary.
3 Knife
Almost any suitably-shaped flake is a ready-made knife. To make it more comfortable to hold, the reverse edge can be dulled by pressure flaking.
4 Saw
A saw can be made from a flint flake by pressure-flaking. Very fine teeth are the secret: between 8 and 12 per centimetre. This type of saw is excellent for bone and antler working.
5, 6, 7 Scrappers
Scrappers are simply re-touched flint flakes, purpose-made for whatever job you have in hand.
8, 9, 10, 11, 12 Arrowheads
These are crude, but they work effectively. They are fine flint flakes shaped by pressure flaking.

Although these tools may appear primitive, they are very effective and easy to produce. With practice you will be able to make more advanced tools. Remember that your practice will produce a pile of chippings that are very difficult to distinguish from ancient chippings, so dispose of them carefully; the survival skills shown here come straight from the Stone Age because we have been able to piece together the information from archaeological remains. It would be a pity to hinder further useful discoveries.

A selection of hard hammers
These are crude hammers used to achieve a rough shape, referred to as hard hammers because they are stone rather than bone or wood. It is useful to have a selection of different weighted hammers for different tasks

Flint Knapping

Tools and theory

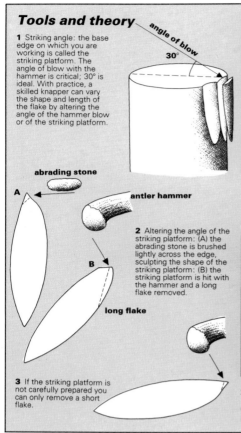

1 Striking angle: the base edge on which you are working is called the striking platform. The angle of blow with the hammer is critical; 30° is ideal. With practice, a skilled knapper can vary the shape and length of the flake by altering the angle of the hammer blow or of the striking platform.

angle of blow

30°

abrading stone

A

antler hammer

B

2 Altering the angle of the striking platform: (A) the abrading stone is brushed lightly across the edge, sculpting the shape of the striking platform: (B) the striking platform is hit with the hammer and a long flake removed.

long flake

3 If the striking platform is not carefully prepared you can only remove a short flake.

A selection of flint working tools
Finer work is done with soft hammers of boxwood or antler. The abrading stones and antler points at the bottom are for pecking and abrading and the buckskin pad is for working on.

Antler billets or hammers
These are used for finer work after using the crude stone hammers. The angle of the blow is more easily predicted and controlled.

Start with the hard stone hammers; use a skin to protect your knees. The first task is to strike off the odd nodules to get a rough shape.

By striking off the nodules, you should also create a number of striking platforms.

Remove all the white outer surface (cortex) from the core by careful flaking.

Stone Age societies

Even today there are people that rely totally on stone tools, in New Guinea and the Amazon basin, for example; both of them far harsher environments that you are likely to encounter. The most basic survival resource of all – how to make your own tools – is more important than collecting kit, which you may not have with you when you need it most.

Right: The start point for manufacturing flint core tools. Flints come in awkward shapes, so think carefully what you want to make before you start.

Manufacturing flint core tools

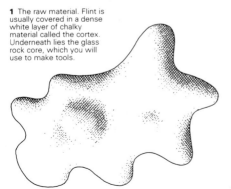

1 The raw material. Flint is usually covered in a dense white layer of chalky material called the cortex. Underneath lies the glass rock core, which you will use to make tools.

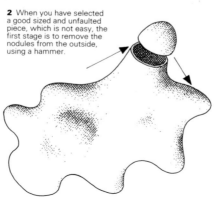

2 When you have selected a good sized and unfaulted piece, which is not easy, the first stage is to remove the nodules from the outside, using a hammer.

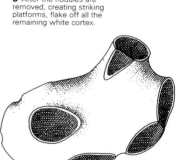

3 After the nodules are removed, creating striking platforms, flake off all the remaining white cortex.

Flaking continues to shape the core.
Watch out for faults in the flint and be careful not to crack the whole thing!

Move on to soft hammers for the fine, detailed work. These are made from antler or boxwood.

The finished product: a usable flint axe head for use in a survival situation. With time it can be refined into a more sophisticated tool.

4 Further flaking gradually sculpts the flint into the shape you require. It is vital to work with patience; one over-enthusiastic strike at the end could ruin all your work.

5 With skill and patience you can continue to flake a piece of flint until you produce a more specialised implement such as a spearpoint.

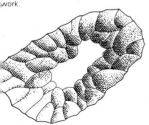

Shaping

The first task is to tidy your flint nodule into a convenient shape and to remove as much of the white outer surface – the cortex – as this acts as a shock absorber and will spoil your hammer blows.

1 Create a striking platform on the stone you are working; the easiest way is to strike off a convenient projection.

2 Begin to strike off flakes: strike the platform about half a centimetre from the edge, at about 30 degrees, and follow through. You should find that a flake has detached.

3 To continue, simply carry on around the core until as much cortex as possible has been removed.

To make core tools such as axes you carry on flaking in this way, with the aim of producing an almond-shaped core. As the core becomes thinner you should use progressively lighter hammers, if possible switching to an antler hammer.

As you become more proficient, you will be able to fashion flint in this way very rapidly. But remember, a good knapper spends more time studying the flint than striking it.

Flake tools

In the process of making your core tool you will have produced a large quantity of flakes, and many of these can be turned into other tools such as arrow heads by pressure flaking. In this method, small flakes are removed from the larger flake by applying pressure with an antler tine to the edge. This increases control, allowing more precision and finer tools.

Pressure flakers

When you produce a tool with a large piece of flint, for example an axe head, you produce a large number of small flakes. Do not throw them away, because they can serve as the raw material for arrow heads and some of them are already usable as crude knives. Fine tools such as arrowheads can be made by patient pressure flaking.

1 The pressure flakers: these are antler points sawn from antlers shed by deer.

2 Press in with the tip of the antler against the edge of the flint to remove a tiny chip.

3 Continue the process along the whole edge of the flint to shape and sharpen. This arrowhead is nearly finished.

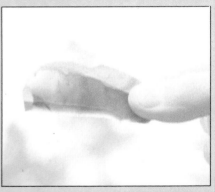

4 This is a flint saw produced by pressure flaking. Note the number of tiny teeth. This can be used to saw bone or wood into further types of tool.

Alternatives to Stone

The only 'gadget' you can be certain to have with you in the wilderness is your ability and training: a fundamental part of this training is learning to use natural resources. Stone is a first-class resource material but it does have its drawbacks: its very nature makes it unsuitable for a variety of uses and it may take too long to work compared to other readily-available materials. The primary use for stone is as tools that can be used to work the softer resource materials such as wood, bone, antler and seashell.

Of the softer resource materials, wood is the most abundant and easily

Above: The skull of a hind Sika deer as it was found in close woodland, indicating a treasure trove of useful tools. Note the patches of matted grey hair left intact by scavengers.

Below: Bones of a young Sika stag. Killed by a poacher's crossbow bolt rather than natural causes, the skeleton has been scattered by small scavenging animals.

Nature's own harvest (and road traffic!) often provides a plentiful source of wild animal bone. In farming country this can be matched by domestic sources, especially in winter.

worked. Different woods possess different qualities, and although they require no special working techniques there are a variety of ways to alter these characteristics to your advantage.

Bone

The second most abundant of the softer resources is bone: a very useful material, and easy to find. Where there is game, there is bone. To obtain bone, you will not have to hunt: in the course of time, nature pulls her dark blanket over the old, sick and stranded animals, beasts of carrion remove the flesh, and small creatures pick the bones clean.

Having been bleached by the sun the bones stand out against the earth, almost asking to be found. An hour of searching should produce what you are looking for. Good areas to search are boggy ground where deer sometimes become stranded. The very corpse that may be threatening your water supply can provide you with many useful bones!

As bone ages, its characteristics change. When 'green' (fresh), it is tough, non-brittle, waxy, slippery and can be difficult to work. It also contains fresh marrow. As the bone ages, it loses its waxy appearance, hardens and becomes more brittle. The marrow shrinks inside, leaving the bone tubular in cross-section. It also becomes more easy to work.

Although not as hard as stone, bone is a very hard material with a reputation for blunting the finest hunting knives. Even if you are lucky enough to possess a knife you would be wise to use stone to work the bone.

The way in which you work the bone will depend on what you are aiming to produce. The secret of bone working is to use great care and patience; rushing will cause breakages.

1 Smashing

This is the easiest and crudest way to work bone: you smash it into fragments using a suitable hammer. You have very little control over the end product, the aim being to reduce the bone in the hope you will produce a suitably sized and shaped fragment that can be used either as it is or by further shaping.

2 Sawing and striking

More control can be exercised by sawing (using a stone saw) or scoring the bone where you intend it to break, and then striking it with a hammer or snapping it. Producing very little waste, this is both the easiest and most economical method of bone working.

Having broken open the bone, you will now need to consider blanking out the tools you are intending to

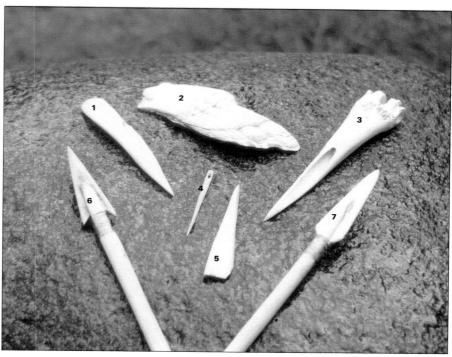

A selection of bone and shell tools:
1. A bone awl
2. A shell knife
3. A large bone awl made from shinbone
4. A bone needle
5. A bone boring tool
6. An antler arrow head
7. A bone arrow head

make. The easiest way of doing this is to score and snap the bone. However, for the long, thin blanks you need for tools such as needles and fishing barbs, there is rarely enough purchase to snap the blank manually. The answer may be to simply saw out the blank you are aiming for, although a quicker method is wedge splitting.

3 Wedge splitting

To produce long, thin blanks, score the break line. The deeper the score the better. Then place a chisel-like wedge in the score line: try to use as wide a wedge as possible. Strike the wedge with a suitable hammer. Your blank should fracture neatly along the score line.

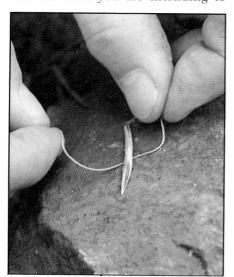

This bone fish-hook was made from a rabbit rib by snapping and abrading to produce sharp points. The line is attached in the middle and bait moulded or threaded onto it.

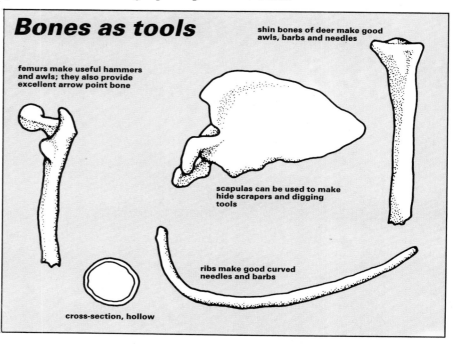

Bones as tools

shin bones of deer make good awls, barbs and needles

femurs make useful hammers and awls; they also provide excellent arrow point bone

scapulas can be used to make hide scrapers and digging tools

ribs make good curved needles and barbs

cross-section, hollow

When you have produced blanks of various shapes and sizes, you need to fashion them into the finished arte-fact. On the whole, bone is too hard to be whittled (although you can soak it to soften it), so you have to resort to slower methods.

4 Scraping

If you are able to improvise a scrap-ing tool, ideally from a flint flake, this is a quick and effective way to shape bone.

5 Abrading

This is probably the most common way of finishing bone tools. Simply rub the bone against coarse grained stones, ideally grit or sandstone. By varying the grain of the rock and using water with the finest-grained abrading stone, you will be able to create a very fine finish and some surprisingly sharp edges and points.

You may also need to be able to per-forate the bone, as in the eye of a needle. This can be done by drilling with a stone drill, or more usually by incising a groove in each side of the blank until they meet in the middle.

Antler

Similar to but not the same as bone, antler is much harder to come by. Many species of deer shed their antlers annually, usually during the first few weeks of April, and at this time of year antler can usually be found; at other times you will be very lucky to find it as they are rich in minerals and are eaten by a variety of creatures.

Antler is harder, stronger and much less brittle than bone, and is not hol-low although it contains a marrow. When you first handle it you may be forgiven for thinking it is weaker than it actually is. Most of the techniques used to work bone can be used to work antler, excepting the methods that rely upon the brittle nature of bone.

The greatest difficulty you will meet when working antler is to remove the tines. Sawing and striking will work, but this is very slow. To overcome this problem, use your fire.

The easiest way to cut the antler into sections, is to hold a glowing ember from your fire (using impro-vised tongs) on the point at which you want to cut the antler, and blow on the ember, ideally using a reed straw. The smell will be revolting but you will soon have burned far enough to cleanly snap the antler.

Seashell

This is another very useful resource material, obviously commonly found on the coast; but you may be able to

WORKING BONE

Smashing
As you would expect, a simple, fast but haphazard way of producing a variety of very crude tools. Not recommended as you waste a good deal of bone.

Sawing
For those with more patience, sawing with a flint saw round the piece you want to knock off and then hitting it allows you to control the fractures.

Scoring and halving (1)
Once you have sectioned the bone, you can halve it by scoring with a sharp flint chip and then bashing with a hammer. It should fracture down the score lines.

Scoring and halving (2)
After halving the section, you can score and saw out 'blanks' of the tools that you want to make and then further score and snap the bone into shape.

Antler scraper
This is ideal for scraping the fat off a hide. Stretch and dry the skin and thin by scraping, in order to make a buckskin garment.

find seashell well inland, especially on sandy soils, where there was once a coastline many centuries before.

Sharp but brittle

Seashell is very hard and it makes good projectile points and cutting edges, but is not suitable for chisel-like work as it is too brittle. To work seashell you can score and snap it to form blanks; you may even be able to pressure-flake it in the same way you would a flint arrow head. But by far the best way is to abrade it on rock.

Antler

Antler scraping
Antler can be worked by scraping to produce a wide range of tools. Antler is harder, stronger and much less brittle than bone. The item depicted is a fishing spear point.

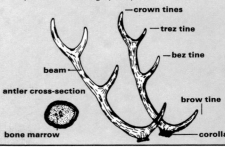

crown tines
trez tine
bez tine
beam
antler cross-section
brow tine
bone marrow
corolla

Sectioning (1)
Sawing and striking is used to section longer bones such as the femur. Knock the ends off and make a variety of long, sharp tools from the hollow section in the middle.

Sectioning (2)
Make sure you saw all the way round the ends to a depth of at least two millimetres, as this ensures a clean fracture. A good stone hammer and a solid surface are required.

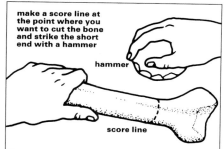

Sectioning (Diagram)
The bone should fracture along the saw line with one well-aimed blow. Take your time when sawing, as haste might mean wasting a possibly limited supply of bone.

Wedgesplitting
If you have scored out the shape you want but cannot snap it, a wedge-shaped slice of flint placed in the score line and tapped with an antler hammer should do the job.

Scraping
You can use a knife or a flint flake to tune up the shape. How fast this method is depends on the age and condition of the bone (new bone is almost impossible to scrape).

Abrading
Slightly slower than scraping and dependent upon a suitable hard sandstone or gritstone being available, you simply rub the bone 'blank' on the stone to wear it into shape.

Sea shells

Sea shells (1)
Sea shells are fragile but can be incredibly sharp when freshly broken. They make good arrow points and other cutting edges, but are very easily blunted.

Sea shells (2)
Abrading is probably the best way of shaping shell tools. With care, it may be possible to pressure-flake them like flint, or scrape them into shape with a knife or flint chip.

Hunting with *Spears*

On your foraging excursions, you have spotted signs of large mammals. If you can catch one you will provide yourself with a large amount of meat that can be preserved and stored, as well as useful skin and bone. But how do you catch the animal? Of the many hunting techniques at your disposal, the age-old method of spear hunting is a practical answer. Spears are easy to make, easy to learn how to use, and allow you to hunt while on the move.

In fact, spears are so effective that early man, hunting in bands, was able to catch animals as big as mammoths. In areas where there are large carnivores that pose a serious threat to your survival (obviously best avoided), a spear is about the most effective deterrent you can carry with you, as these predators will almost certainly have encountered horns and antlers and have therefore learned to respect long, sharp points. There are even native American tales of grizzly bears backing away from spears, but don't count on it!

Simple spears

The quickest and simplest spear you can make is the 'self spear'. In its crudest form, this is simply a straight piece of hard, natured wood with a sharpened point. You can vastly improve it by fire hardening the point and fashioning it into a leaf-shaped blade. But the self spear is a primitive and brutal weapon and a skilled survivor should make every effort to kill as cleanly as possible, reducing the suffering of his prey to the absolute minimum.

An effective spear must have a sharp cutting edge that is wide enough to cause maximum bleeding, but not so wide that it prevents the spear penetrating to the vital organs. So the most important part of a spear is the point. As a survivor, you can never be certain of precisely what raw materials you will have to hand, so the broader your knowledge of spear design the better.

Basically, spears fall into one or both of two categories: **thrusting spears** and **throwing spears**. As the

Above: A Mesolithic Atlatl point. On the hardwood fore-shaft is pressure-flaked flint, gummed into position. The barbs fix the weapon in the wound as well as providing a vicious edge.

Target area
A spear kills by causing loss of blood. It must be thrust or thrown into the chest cavity, and should ideally penetrate deep enough to damage heart and lungs.

Below: In the 'stalking thrusting position', the spear is carried at the ready. You should not need to make any rearward movement in the short, powerful stabbing thrust.

Spear heads

Fire-hardened boxwood spearhead. The shape is a compromise between a wide leaf to produce maximum damage, and a thin point to permit maximum penetration.

Magdalenian antler point spear. The point can be bound onto the shaft simply by splitting the shaft and binding the head in with rawhide.

Slate spearhead. This is produced by abrading the slate can be mounted on the shaft by cutting out or drilling out a centre section and binding with rawhide.

Flint-flake thrusting spearhead. Crude but very effective; the flakes are gummed into position to provide a durable and extremely sharp cutting edge.

Large flint Atlatl point. This is quite capable of cutting through the ribcage of a deer.

North American Indian spearpoint. Bound with buckskin, this has a flint head with a pressure-flaked edge.

name suggests, thrusting spears are used at very close range so the spear point can be broad, as the impact force is guaranteed to be great. Throwing spears, on the other hand, are used at a distance: they need to be light so that they can fly fast, and the point needs to allow penetration as the impact force of a throwing spear can vary greatly. Throwing spear points are also often barbed.

Choosing your spear

The design you choose should be tailored to meet your circumstances, and with a specific prey in mind. Obviously you will be limited in raw materials. If you have difficulty finding a suitable spear shaft, consider using a lighter material — reed, bamboo or elder — with a short, hard wood foreshaft.

The length of the spear is also important. Where dangerous animals are concerned, you will obviously need a long spear, but if you are in an area of scrub bush you may find a long spear too unwieldy. Try to achieve the right balance of factors. Lastly, make sure you are happy with its feel and heft.

Hunting with spears

To hunt with spears you need to be as close to your prey as possible. You can do this only by careful stalking and attention to camouflage and de-scenting.

1 Hunting with thrusting spears

These are used from 'Lying up positions' beside frequently-used animal runs. As the animal passes by, you thrust the spear into it. The best hiding place is in a tree above the run, as large game rarely looks up.

An added bonus in such a hiding place is that you can drop on your prey, imparting the full force of your body weight to your spear.

The disadvantage of this hunting method is that it is static; you may spend many fruitless hours waiting to pounce with no luck.

2 Hunting with throwing spears

Success comes more from stalking than from throwing, and a good stalker should be able to get within touching distance of most prey. If necessary, though, a throwing spear can be used over some distance.

Throwing a spear is not like throwing a javelin. Having stalked to within a few metres of your prey, you cannot risk a 'run up' or a large movement of your throwing arm, 'pulling back' before the throw. You should launch the spear before your prey detects any movement at all. Try at all times to remain hidden; if your first shot

The ambush
This is a real test of your skills, but is a valid method of killing larger game. When you leap down on the quarry, use both hands and your downward momentum to drive the spear between its shoulderblades. Look carefully at the centre of the photograph on the right and you will see the hunter in position.

misses, you may be allowed a second chance.

Throwing your spear
Having stalked close to your quarry, very slowly draw your throwing arm back like a coiled spring. Do not draw it back beyond your shoulder; to do so means that you will have to turn your body. Instead use the resistance of your shoulder as the buffer from which all your throwing force is gen-

Below: Don't throw a spear like a sporting javelin; hurl it like a dart in one powerful movement and follow through.

Animal tracks
Game tends to travel on well-used tracks. This is what you should be looking for when choosing your ambush site.

erated. If you feel it will help, raise your free hand as an aiming aid.

When you are ready, cast the spear like a dart in one explosive movement. Follow the movement through and be still. Do not chase after the wounded animal but remain hidden, until the prey is lying down, then swiftly put the injured animal to

sleep. This is the theory, but even for experts things do not always go so smoothly; whatever happens, remain calm.

Improving spears

The weight and size of a spear is proportionate to the force of propulsion. In survival terms, this means that the faster the spear flies the lighter and shorter it can be. To make a spear fly faster requires more propulsive force.

Arm extensions

You can make a light spear travel very fast by using a spear thrower, known to the Aztecs as an Atlatl and by the Australian Aborigine as a Woomera. In simple terms this is an extension to the arm, allowing greater leverage. It comprises an arm of wood from between 45 cm to one metre or so in length, with at the far end a peg which locates in a depression at the tail end of the spear. It is operated with a free arm and a flicking wrist action.

Spear throwers greatly increase the range and velocity of the spear. To make it more accurate the spear can be flighted like an arrow.

The Atlatl
The longer your arm, the harder and farther you can throw a spear. The Atlatl (above) can extend your reach considerably; it is not a device to master overnight, but with patience and practice it will greatly increase your hunting ability. This is an Atlatl in the ready-to-throw position.

Right: The Atlatl and the similar Australian aboriginal Woomera are simple wooden arms with a notch at one end used for launching light throwing spears. They can be up to a metre in length.

Throwing the Atlatl
Using an Atlatl can give a light throwing spear all the penetrating power of a much heavier weapon. The spear is projected at great speed from the device by a practised flick of the thrower's wrist. Follow the throw through and then remain still. Remember that you do not chase after wounded prey.

Choosing Your Survival Knife

The Al-Mar Sere 6 is a beautifully crafted knife, but a little too light for heavy chopping and cleaving.

A civilian stranded after a disaster such as a shipwreck or a plane crash will not have chosen a survival knife. He will have to make do with whatever he's got with him – perhaps a piece of sharpened fuselage, or at best a Swiss Army Knife. But soldiers and adventurers operating in remote regions of the world will almost certainly have a knife with them at all times, and they will have made a choice.

The wrong choice could be fatal, as a knife is literally a lifeline in the wilderness, upon which you must be able to rely completely. It's too late to find out your knife is not strong enough when you are trying to cut yourself free from a capsized white water raft heading for a waterfall!

Survival knife?

When choosing your knife, find a reputable dealer with a large range of quality knives. Often the best shops stock custom knifemaker ranges.

Do not limit your choice of knife to those described as 'Survival Knives'; there are many hunting knives eminently suited to survival use. Try also to be practical. There are many beautiful knives for sale, well made and by top-class manufacturers; but they are not all practical for the specialised use you will be demanding.

You must always carry your knife with you; you never know when you'll need it. This means that your knife must be a convenient size to be

carried without becoming a drag, and must also be capable of carrying out all those basic camp chores such as opening tins, hammering tent pegs, cutting string and so on. And if you become stranded or have to go to ground it will have to do the job of a small axe as well, so it must be strong. Generally speaking, a fixed blade is the better option as it is stronger and more rugged, but most professionals carry two knives: a large fixed blade and a small folding blade.

What metal?

There are really only two basic choices: carbon steel or stainless steel.

Traditionally, soldiers have purchased their own knives to take into battle. Note the Gerber Mark 2, excellent as a fighting knife but of limited use in survival.

Carbon steel will rust (generally speaking) unless cared for, whereas stainless steel should not. It is widely recognised that carbon steel takes a keener edge than stainless, although in some modern aircraft and cutlery, stainless steels are challenging this traditional concept. Stainless steel should hold its edge longer than carbon steel, but is in many cases harder to sharpen.

In most cases, stainless steel would be the best choice. Take the advice of a reputable dealer, as there are many varieties in use, in many cases alloyed with other metals such as vanadium, molybdenum and chromium to change their qualities. In general, avoid divers' knives (unless made by a reputable manufacturer), as the steel is usually very poor.

When you are finding out about the type of steel used, try also to find out about the temper. If a knife is under-tempered it will be strong but will not take an edge; if it is over-tempered, it could shatter in use. There is a tendency for manufacturers to over-temper blades!

Size, weight and balance

The wise traveller tries to reduce the weight of his pack, but when travelling far off the beaten track don't try to economise on the weight of your knife. You need a knife with a weighty blade, as this reduces the force you need to apply and allows more control and efficiency. But if you choose a blade that is too heavy, it will cause fatigue in your fingers, wrist and arm, and this can lead to dangerous accidents.

The length and weight of your knife are critical factors, but no real formula exists to help you choose. In jungles, machetes and long, light knives are the norm, but for more general use these are really too long. As a rough guide, don't choose a knife that is more than two and a half times the length of your hand, and no less than one and a half times long.

Leverage principle

To illustrate the principle, imagine that you are striking a nail into a piece of wood with a one-metre steel bar. If you want to achieve the same result with a bar 50 centimetres long, you must either use a lot more force or a heavier bar. The shorter, heavier bar is more controllable as it exerts less leverage on the wrist, and can be used in more confined space. The same is true of knife lengths.

Once you have chosen the length and weight of your blade, try to decide where the point of balance lies. Ideally it should be just in front of the guard.

The parts of a survival knife

In war, there is no room for the amateur. You must have the right knife for the job and be skilled in its use: you won't have time to start thinking about it if you're on the brink of a war zone.

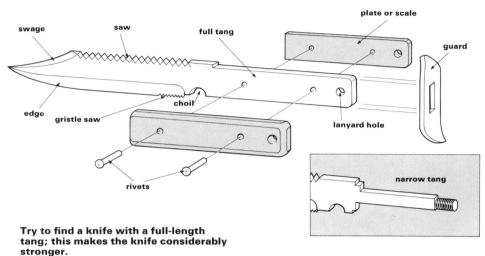

Try to find a knife with a full-length tang; this makes the knife considerably stronger.

This means that the knife is slightly blade-heavy, yet easily controlled by adjusting your grip.

If the point of balance is too far forward it will cause muscle strain, which makes the knife slip from your grasp. The more common fault is that the knife is too handle-heavy. Excess weight in the grip is a burden, as it does not contribute to the blade's cutting ability.

Features and fittings

The most important fitting to your knife is the grip; probably the commonest fault in most survival knives is the way by which the grip is attached. The part of the blade that goes to make up the handle is called the 'tang'.

This American pilot in Vietnam is sporting a .357 Magnum revolver and US issue aircrew survival knife, while the SEAL carries a Gerber fighting knife.

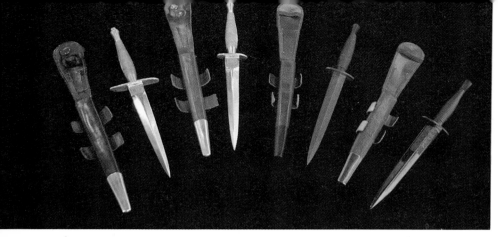

This is **Wilkinson Sword's** range of Commando daggers, from the original Sykes-Fairburn to the later production model. These are fighting knives and have very little survival application. Double-edged weapons cannot be used for skinning or fine cutting as the finger cannot be placed on the back of the blade for control, and they are too light for chopping or cleaving. You are better off with a survival knife that has a variety of functions.

The Cold Steel Tanto
A very strong knife with a very comfortable grip and designed to incorporate Western and Oriental ideas, this is a good fighting knife but again has limited chopping capability.

The Robert Parrish knife
A 20-cm survival and combat knife, this is a good all-rounder although it does not have a full tang. It has a hollow handle for survival kit.

The Jimmy Lile Sly 2 (top) and the **Rambo** (below)
As seen in the movies: good quality, but a little too large for fine cutting. Both have hollow handles and a thong eye in the butt.

The Survival Aids Explora survival knife
This features a survival kit, sharping stone, wirecutters, compass, a screwdriver tip and removable handguard and, of course, saw-back blade.

The Tekna Wilderness Edge
This features a survival kit stored in the sheath, a Tekna torch in the handle, a honing stone and flint, and a 15-cm blade.

The Eikhorn survival knife
This well-made German knife with a bowie type blade with thumb rest and hollow handle, again suffers from not really being heavy enough.

In many knives, this narrows at the join of the guard and grip. This is an inherent weakness, at the point of greatest strain. The ideal attachment is what is called 'full tang', where the blade remains the width of the grip throughout.

Hollow handles often mean that the tang not only narrows but shortens as well. While not all hollow handles are weak, take great care in your choice.

The guard is an important feature of any survival knife. Its purpose is to prevent your fingers slipping forward onto the sharp edge while using the knife. Remember: even the smallest cut can fester and prove fatal under survival conditions.

The point of your knife is another important feature. It needs to be sharp, and strong enough to pry with. It is an advantage if it falls below the horizontal mid-line of your knife: this is a 'true drop point', and prevents the point snagging the flesh of an animal's stomach wall during skinning and gutting.

Saws and hollow handles

Saws are a regular feature of survival knives. Do not expect them to saw through wood. They will, however, cut grooves in wood and cut ropes, making them a useful additional feature although not essential.

Gristle saws are sometimes found in front of the guard. These again are a useful additional feature that will find many uses.

Hollow handles are designed to accommodate useful survival tools such as fishing lines or firelighting

*An East German border guard photographs the West German border guards, equipped with an **AKM** and an interesting stiletto dagger that looks remarkably like a Sykes-Fairburn.*

Machetes
Great for jungle work, but of limited use for anything else. The kukri (right) is a good cleavering and cutting knife, but is no good for fine cutting or hammering.

Army issue: Golok and SLR bayonet
The Golok is a popular survival knife, and can be improved by regrinding the edge and shortening the grip. The SLR bayonet is useless as a survival knife.

aids, and as long as they do not weaken the grip are an excellent addition.

Sheaths

Sheaths are an important feature of any knife. As well as protecting the knife, they must be strong enough to protect you from injury if you fall on the encased blade. Good-quality leather sheaths are almost as good as the very strong scabbards being made from modern plastics, but beware of cheap leather. If you find a good knife that has a poor sheath you may be able

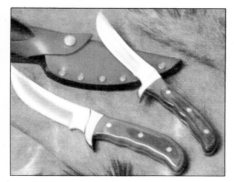

The Buck Kalinga and Akonua
These are top quality presentation knives, ideal for skinning and cutting but too light for cleaving.

A US Army Ranger poses complete with hatchet. Try to select a knife that will do the job of a knife and hatchet; your personal kit will be heavy enough without duplication.

The Buck M9 bayonet
On issue to the US Army for use with the M16 A2, this is well thought out and well produced, falling somewhere between a knife and a bayonet.

The Buckmaster
Seen as *the* survival knife for some time, it has a hollow handle and detachable anchor pins. It can be used in conjunction with rope as a grappling hook for climbing walls etc!

The Buck Hunter and Ranger
These are excellent-quality lock blades for fine cutting. This is the only additional type of knife you should consider carrying in addition to your survival knife.

to have a better sheath made for it.

The method of carrying the sheath is entirely up to you, and you may want to make some modifications. You may also consider taping additional survival gear to the outside of your scabbard, as long as you don't end up looking like a Christmas tree.

Having carefully selected your knife, work it in, personalise it, practise using it and, above all, look after it. Your life may one day depend on it.

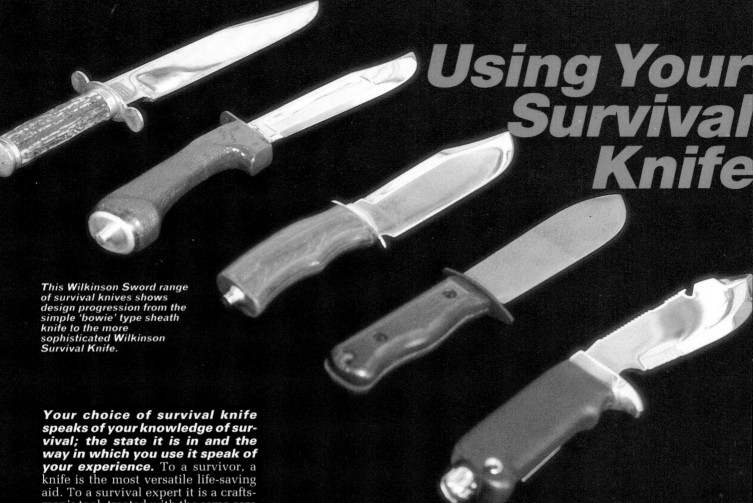

Using Your Survival Knife

This Wilkinson Sword range of survival knives shows design progression from the simple 'bowie' type sheath knife to the more sophisticated Wilkinson Survival Knife.

Your choice of survival knife speaks of your knowledge of survival; the state it is in and the way in which you use it speak of your experience. To a survivor, a knife is the most versatile life-saving aid. To a survival expert it is a craftsman's tool, treated with the same care and attention as a master carpenter's chisels. It is not toyed with; it remains in its sheath until it is needed, and is then used with great dexterity and ease for a multitude of tasks before being returned to its resting place.

The grip

The grip is the best place to begin your personalisation. It is an essential feature of your knife, and must allow for exact and secure control of the blade in many differing uses and environments.

1 If a grip is too large you will not be able to hold onto it for heavy cutting.

2 If a grip is too small you will have to clench it tightly for heavy cutting; this is very tiring and dangerous. Blisters and severe hand cramps can result.

3 If a grip is too long it may pull out from your hand.

4 If a grip is too short you will not be able to hold onto the knife correctly, which may be dangerous.

As a general rule, it is better to have a grip that is slightly too big, as it is less tiring to use than a too-small grip – and when your hand tires you will have accidents. A large grip is easier to hold when wearing gloves. Your grip should be easy to hold in a variety of different ways, with no sharp edges or protuberances that will impede its use. It should be the correct shape in cross section, which is a blunt oval shape.

Improving the shape

1 If your grip is too round you may be able to build it up using Gaffa tape or nylon webbing and a strong resin. Very often round grips are all-metal: these are best covered, as metal is a 'non-friendly' material, hot in the desert, dangerously freezing in the Arctic and always hard. Remember that whatever you use as a grip covering must be resilient to a variety of temperatures and environmental conditions.

2 If your grip is too square you may (if the grip material is soft or man-made) be able to file or sand it to the correct shape. This is preferable to covering because the performance of the grip will not be impaired by changing climates.

3 If your grip is of bone it may feel as though it is more comfortable when gripped as for hammering. In this case there is usually little that can be done other than replacing the grip entirely.

Grip cross-sections

Altering the grip may seem a drastic thing to do, but once the knife fits your hand, there will be a vast improvement in its effectiveness as it will take less effort to use.

The best shape for the grip.

Too square: this will need reducing.

Too round: this will need to be built up.

Antler handles are not suitable: substitute a better-shaped grip.

Common uses for your knife

Slashing
Grip the knife as far back as possible. Use long, sweeping motions with a straight arm.

Chopping
Grip the knife further forward, with your cutting action more from the elbow than the shoulder.

Hammering
Use the flat of the blade, keeping the edge aimed away from your body.

Stake pointing
Hold the grip even further forward and, using mainly wrist action, cut away from you.

Rasping
If your knife has a saw back, you can set it into a log and work bone on it.

Draw knife
Fit a makeshift split stick-handle to the point end of your knife.

Sawing
Sawing is not designed to cut through wood but is mainly for grooving wood and cutting ropes. Cut on the draw stroke.

Splitting
This is an important operation. Strike the blade through the work piece with a wooden baton (not stone or metal).

Whittling
Control is the name of the game. If you can lever with the thumb of your free hand, on the back of the blade, do so. Otherwise take your time with many small, shallow cuts.

Parallel honing

Once you have a professional edge, make sure you do not destroy it while honing. A common failing is to tilt the edge too sharply; this gradually blunts the knife. These cross-sections of the blade show the right and wrong methods, and the results of each.

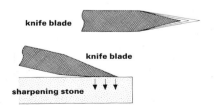

knife blade

knife blade

sharpening stone

WRONG: Pressure is greatest near the edge.

Sharpening with too much pressure on the edge of the blade progressively changes the cutting angle, blunting the knife. The only remedy is to have the whole edge re-ground: an expensive business. In the field, the knife will become blunter and more difficult to sharpen.

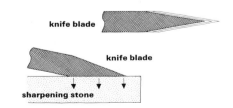

knife blade

knife blade

sharpening stone

RIGHT: Pressure is exerted at a shallower angle.

Maintaining the pressure in the correct way retains the cutting edge. Patience is the essential ingredient: remember that a blunt knife is not just an inefficient tool, but is also dangerous.

The blade

Having set up the grip, give your knife a 'road test': there should be an immediate and definite improvement in its performance. But the blade is where the major transformation will occur. You will have to alter the angle of the edge, to improve its cutting ability, which in most cases means a long session of filing. Avoid using a high-speed grinding wheel, unless you are very expert in its use, and back-street knife sharpeners, as the risk of the blade overheating and losing its temper is high.

To help you, some of the better established knife manufacturers will supply a knife with a 'professional edge', but only on request. Once the edge has been altered you should

Rockwell testing

When the knife is ready to be finished it is carefully tested to check that is has been correctly tempered. The steel of the blade is indented with a diamond tool at a set pressure. The softer the steel, the deeper and wider the dent made by the tool. A reading of this indentation is taken: in the case of the steel used for the Wilkinson Sword Survival Knife, a reading of 54-55 Rockwell C is correct. 52 would be too soft, reducing the edge retention, and 57 would be too hard, causing brittleness.

The master grinder shapes the edge on a rotating whetstone. The stone is 1½ metres in diameter, so the grinder sits astride it on a saddle-like seat.

The master polisher puts a mirror finish on the blade: a slow and patient task. He uses a series of buffers, from coarse to super-fine.

A master craftsman applies the 'professional edge': this is supplied only on request.

Above: The display on the Rockwell testing machine clearly shows the diamond dent punched in the blade.

Right: The master grinder puts an edge on the knife.

never have to re-grind the edge, because you will now 'parallel sharpen.'

Sharpening

To sharpen your knife you will need a stone. The best type of stone is still a natural stone such as a Washita or Soft Arkansas stone, although there is much to be said for the strength of a diamond whetstone for field use.

At home base you should have a large stone. This makes sharpening an easy task, using six long strokes on the left of the blade, six on the right, and six alternately.

In the field you will need a small pocket stone, or failing this a suitable local stone or large pebble. Hold the knife steady and move the stone: the opposite to home sharpening.

Whenever you sharpen your blade, maintain an even pressure across the full width of the edge. If you place too much pressure on the edge itself you will not be sharpening parallel to the edge angle you originally laboured to achieve, but will be gradually blunting the knife.

Honing

Having sharpened your knife, a really razor-like edge can be achieved by lightly honing with a ceramic rod. Use this before all major cutting to help maintain the edge.

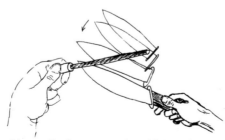

Above: Honing a razor edge with a steel or ceramic rod, use ten light strokes alternatively on each side of the edge. As each stroke nears the point the angle of the blade should become less acute.

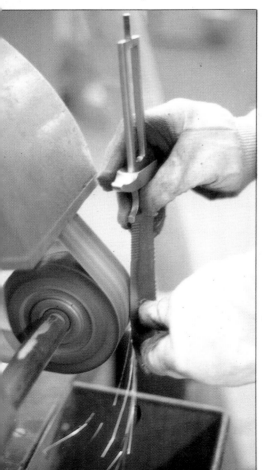

Left: Polishing as part of producing a professional edge, definitely a worthwhile investment if you are serious about your knife.

Profession use

In the hands of a professional a survival knife takes on jobs that seem impossible. This is because he has learned to use the correct cutting techniques and angles. Experience and practice will be your best guide here, although the most basic principles are:

1 Safety first.
2 Cut with the grain in your favour.
3 Always follow through.
4 Use smooth, steady cuts, the fewer the better.

Making other tools

A professional's knife is a tool to make other tools. Wherever possible he avoids any use of the knife which may result in its damage or loss. If a root needs to be dug up, make a digging stick; if a spear point is needed, whittle one.

Safety first

1 When you carry your knife, carry a first aid kit.
2 Plan every cut before you make it.
3 Keep all limbs away from the arc of your cut.
4 *Always* cut away from the body.
5 Be aware of what is going on around you.
6 Replace the knife in its scabbard immediately after use.
7 Never lend your knife; you may never see it again.

IMPORTANT

The privilege of owning a survival knife is one that all survival students must uphold and defend. Be professional in your approach and use of your knife, and be seen to be professional.

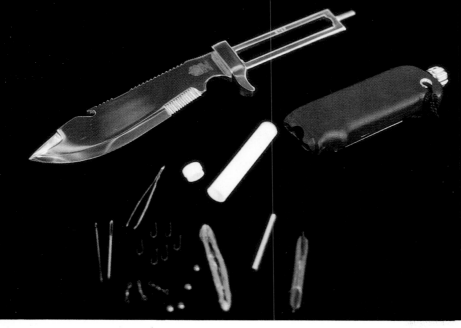

The Wilkinson Sword Survival Knife and contents. It is designed to cope with a very wide range of tasks, from very fine skinning to heavy chopping and hammering. The aim is a single comprehensive survival tool from which you are never separated. The deer below was grallocked (gutted), skinned and butchered using only this knife.

Preparing a deer

Gutting, skinning and halving usually requires two knives and a saw. If you can achieve this with one knife, you've got a good survival knife.

1 Cut off the head as close to the base of the skull as possible by cutting through to the bone and chopping through it.

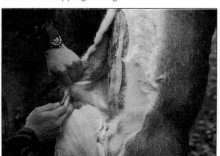

2 Start at the base of the sternum and pull the skin away as you cut. Leave as little flesh or fat on the skin as possible.

3 The skin comes off quite easily and you should be able to use your hands for most of it.

4 Cut round the windpipe, separating it from the flesh of the neck.

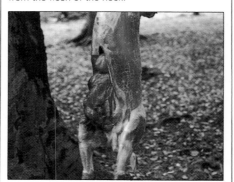

5 Start at the sternum and cut carefully down to the pelvis. Push your hands up on each side, cut round the diaphragm and grasp the windpipe or the heart and lungs and pull down.

6 Heart and lungs and all the guts should come out in one piece. You will need to cleaver through the pelvic basin.

7 Halving Your knife must be heavy enough for cleavering through bone to butcher, extract marrow and split the skull

Trapping Animals for Food

Meat is the most nourishing food for man, and is certainly the most satisfying for the fugitive who is surviving for any length of time in the wild. Collecting and eating grubs may be an easier option than trapping larger animals, but you have to get through a lot of worms and caterpillars to beat a decent rabbit or duck. Here we describe how to set about catching whatever you find.

The first thing to know is that all animals are edible (but not necessary the whole of the beast). The second thing is that they're nearly all very difficult to catch and you'll have to use all your skills to be successful; and that means understanding the animal's way of life.

Daily habits

They're usually fairly regular in their habits, using the same paths and trails, drinking at the same places on the river bank and from pools, sleeping in the same sheltered places. They also have a timetable, and stick to it; if an animal went to a certain place to drink at dawn this morning, there's a very good chance that it will do the same again tomorrow. Spend time looking for signs of animals.

If there's a lot of animal activity going on, find a hiding place and stay in it until you recognise the local wildlife patterns. It will make trap-

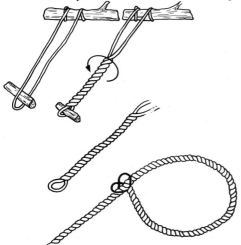

A simple wire snare
The simplest snare of all is just a running noose, but you can improve on that by making it out of a pair of wires twisted together. The two loops of single wire that make the 'slip knot' will lock into the twists and stop the animal getting away.

Small animals make their homes in all sorts of unlikely places. Sheets of old corrugated iron like this one will often be home to a family of mice – but snakes find it comfortable here too, so lift the edge with a knife or a piece of wood – not with your hand.

ping or hunting them a great deal easier. All you've got going for you is your intelligence; they've lived there all their lives!

Unless you have an accurate weapon, such as a rifle, shotgun or cross-bow, hunting will be a lot less likely to provide you with dinner than trapping. In a hostile environment, where there are enemy forces or natives, hunting is almost certain to be impossible anyway, but let's look at some of the basic skills you'll need to hunt game in the wild.

Always assume that any small animals in the area will be wary and quick to run away. If they spot you, hear you or smell you (remember that their sense of smell may be a thousand times better than yours), they will either go to ground or disappear off into the distance. Seeing them before they become aware of you greatly increases your chances of catching them.

They often use the same pathways and drinking places, and make perma-

Setting a Snare

A snare has two essential parts – the wire noose and the stick to anchor it into the ground. This is how to put it to use.

2. A branch of a Christmas tree is ideal for the peg of a snare. Trim off both ends.

3. Cut a slit in one end to take the string tail.

1. The snare itself is just a running noose of wire with a tail of strong string.

4. Pass the tail through the slot, make two turns around the stalk and tie it off.

5. Anchor the stick into the ground so that the snare is a hand's breadth above the ground.

6. Set your snare along tracks and paths used by animals. This track has been beaten down by rabbits and is an ideal spot.

nent homes. Look for their signs – tracks, paths in grass, faeces, dens, feeding places – and use that intelligence to help you set up a plan to catch them.

Camouflage and approach

Remember, the fieldcraft that makes you a good foot-soldier can also make you a good hunter. Always obey the rules of camouflage and approach. Never silhouette yourself against the skyline, even in woodland. Always move upwind or across wind. Approach streams, rivers and waterholes very carefully, especially around dawn and dusk. Find cover and get into it, and wait for the animals.

And stay still! Fidgetting may cost you a meal – and that may end up costing you your life.

A pole to catch squirrels

Take a pole, fix some wire snares to it and lean it up against a tree where you've seen squirrels. It may seem too simple to be true, but these inquisitive creatures are quite likely to get caught up before too long.

Siting traps

You can't just put a trap anywhere and expect it to work. Careful siting is the most important part of trapping. The mouths of burrows are good places, but you must be sure to disguise or obliterate your scent.

Deadfalls

The figure-four deadfall is simple to make and surprisingly sensitive. The props should be as thin as you can make them, the fall itself as heavy as possible. The one shown here is relatively small, but you can make larger ones too, to stun larger animals.

Cut two sticks of roughly equal length, and trim and notch them as shown. Sharpen one end of each stick, one to go into the ground and the other to take the bait.

Cut and notch a third, longer stick to form the third side of the triangle.

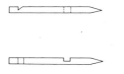

Pay careful attention to the notches. Cut them too shallow and they won't hold for very long.

You may find it frustrating, trying to set the trap up. But remember, the harder it is to get it to stay together, the more sensitive it will be in use.

Larger game, even if it sees you, may not take flight straight away. Stop and keep still until it loses interest, and then approach in a wide zig-zag. In hills and mountains, always try to get above the animal you're stalking.

Best target areas

If you are shooting game, the best targets are the head, neck and the spine just behind the shoulder. Take your time, and make the first shot count – because you're not likely to get a second chance. If you hit and wound the animal and it runs off, follow the blood trail. A badly wounded creature won't have the strength to run far. Give it the chance to go to ground before following it up. Approach slowly and then make the kill. Don't waste ammunition if you can finish it off by clubbing it.

Hunting, however, should take second place to making and setting traps. Traps are much more likely to provide you with a lasting supply of meat. Simple ones are very easy to make and set: the simplest of all is a snare – a slip noose firmly pegged into the ground or anchored to a rock or tree. Make them from wire if it's available, or use plastic fishing line, string or even line made up from natural fibres.

These snares are especially effective when you set them at the entrance to burrows and dens. Set them in trees to catch squirrels, or make a 'squirrel pole': an eight- to 12-ft pole with perhaps half-a-dozen snares around it, leaned up against a tree used by squirrels. It may sound too easy, but squirrels are inquisitive creatures and will often investigate something new just for the fun of it.

You're not likely to be able to kill anything larger than a rabbit or a small cat with a wire snare, though you may slow down larger animals so that you have a better chance of clubbing them to death.

Looking for signs

Trapping, even more than hunting, depends on how well you can read the signs. There is no point in placing a trap just anywhere hoping that an animal will stumble into it by chance! Entrances to burrows and tunnels are the best place. Look for signs that they are occupied – fresh droppings, signs of feeding and movement in and out.

Unless you're using wire for the snare, which may stand up on its own, you will have to make a stand to hold the noose open. Two twigs, one each side of the mouth of the burrow or the path will do, with another one perhaps placed across the top to support the trap.

Human scent

Don't forget to cover your scent, both on the snare itself and on the surrounding ground: soaking the snare in a stream after you've made it and before setting it is one way. Or you can rub it with cold ashes, or disguise your own scent with something stronger – urine from the bladder of a dead animal, for example. Animals are usually attracted to urine from their own kind.

Improved noose

You can improve on the simple noose, and make it more difficult for the animal to escape from the trap, by inter-twining two lengths of wire. Use the two strands that are left at the end to make up a double running loop. These two loops will naturally catch in the twists of the wire that makes the body of the line and noose, and will make it much more difficult for the animal to wriggle out of the noose.

You can always let predators do your hunting for you. Watch until you can work out their pattern of activity, then wait for them to make a kill. If you rush them you'll often cause them to drop their prey.

Hanging snares

Hanging snares are a more secure way of holding on to the animal that you've caught. They use the creature's own weight to keep it from wriggling out of the noose. Apart from the wire noose itself, to make a hanging snare you need a sapling close to the run you've chosen, and a forked stick, or one bent over into a hoop.

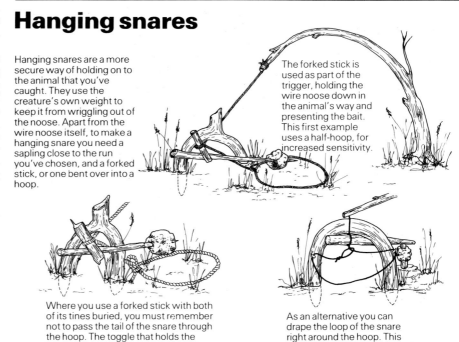

The forked stick is used as part of the trigger, holding the wire noose down in the animal's way and presenting the bait. This first example uses a half-hoop, for increased sensitivity.

Where you use a forked stick with both of its tines buried, you must remember not to pass the tail of the snare through the hoop. The toggle that holds the baited trigger is caught in a loop of the tail, not knotted.

As an alternative you can drape the loop of the snare right around the hoop. This gets the noose off the ground without needing extra sticks.

Skinning a Rabbit

All furry animals have to be skinned before you can cook them. Here's how to deal with small creatures such as rabbits or squirrels.

1. Lay the animal down on its back, spread all four legs wide, and cut from the anus up to the breastbone, taking care not to rupture the intestine.

2. Cut the skin through around all four paws at the first joint. Remove the guts, starting from the throat and working downwards. Do not eat these innards.

3. Now you can peel the skin off. You may find it necessary to remove the tail first.

4. Take the skin off in one piece. A firm grip and a quick pull are all that is needed.

5. The last thing to do is to remove the head. Keep the skin for making clothing.

You can even scare off large animals this way – cats and bears, for instance. Building a fire when you've frightened them off will often make them stay away long enough for them to forget you've robbed them of their meal. But unless you're well armed, don't be too ready to take on these large predators yourself.

Obvious targets

Don't go around chasing squirrels while ignoring more obvious targets such as cows, sheep and other domestic animals – including cats and dogs. They're all food, and often they're just standing around waiting to become somebody's meal – it may as well be yours. Bats and mice make good eating, but do not eat any of their innards, and immediately discard their heads, skin, feet and tails.

Experienced infantrymen are familiar with ways of cooking and preserving meat and fish and – more important for health reasons – ways of spotting the tell-tale signs that flesh is inedible as a result of decay, and what to do if you do eat it! Remember, survival is to do with common sense and intelligence – not with taking chances.

Treadle-spring snare

For really large game you need a bigger noose, but to keep it in the most effective position you will have to make up the much more complex treadle-spring snare.

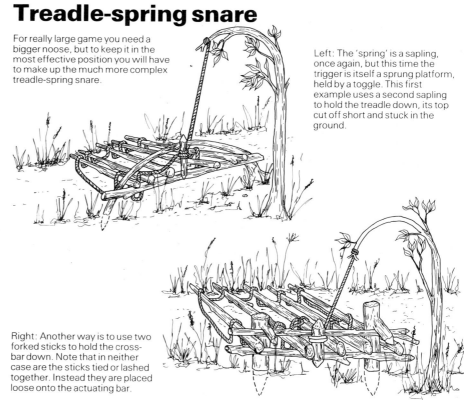

Left: The 'spring' is a sapling, once again, but this time the trigger is itself a sprung platform, held by a toggle. This first example uses a second sapling to hold the treadle down, its top cut off short and stuck in the ground.

Right: Another way is to use two forked sticks to hold the cross-bar down. Note that in neither case are the sticks tied or lashed together. Instead they are placed loose onto the actuating bar.

INDEX

Afghanistan 15
Agent Orange 36
ALICE (All-Purpose Lightweight
    Individual Carrying
    Equipment 52, 53
alligators 112-13
ammo pouches 62, 63
ammunition 67
  carrying 53, 66, 70
animals:
  hunting with spears 170-3
  preparing for cooking 181, 185
  trapping 182-5
antiseptics, natural 156-7
antler tools 168
ants 144-5
Arctic 118
  navigation in 130-1
  surviving 124-7
  travel in 128-31
Argentinians 46, 49
armour, body 8-9, 10, 12-19
Armourshield clothing 17-18
avalanches 129

basha 122-3
battle equipment 59, 60-7
bayonets: carrying 53-4
beds 122-3
Beirut 99
belt kit 19
belt order 52-3
  SAS 67, 95
Bergens 54, 55
  contents 68-71
bilharzia 146
Biological, Chemical and
    Toxinal agents 32, 34-5
biological contamination 34,
    36-7
bites 144
Bligh, William 8
blizzards 130
Blood Chit 76
body armour 8-9, 10, 12-19
bogs 117
bomb-disposal teams 9, 12
bombs: protection from 12
bone tools 166-9
booby traps 13
boot liners 50
boots 9, 46, 48, 50-1
  as hiding place 95
  improvised 51
  inner soles 50
bowl: burning 159
building: burning, escape
    from 30-1
bulletproof accessories 12
bullets:
  shock from 14-15
  types 18
burns 136
bush combat 54

camouflage 9
  personal 10, 20-3
  of vehicles 10, 24-7
capture 72, 75, 77
caves: for cover 93
cayman 112-13

centipedes 113, 144-5
chainmail 8
checkpoints: passing 101
chemical contamination 36, 37
chemical weapons 34, 35
Chernobyl 43-4
civilians: help from 75-6, 103-4
clothing 8-9, 12-19
  carrying 55, 68
  for cold 124, 125
  on fire 31
  in jungle 132
  protection against
    contaminants 32
codes 85
cold diuresis 126
colour: in camouflage 22-3
combat jackets:
  packing 56-7
  types 56
communication: as POW 84-5
communications harness 18
compasses 54, 96
Complete Equipment Fighting
    Order (CEFO) 59, 60-3
Complete Equipment Marching
    Order (CEMO) 46, 59, 68-71
concealment 20
  on move 24
  of position 24-6, 26
condoms:
  concealing 96
  uses 97, 132-3
constipation 127
contaminants 32, 34-7
contaminated zones:
  marking 34, 44-5
cookers: concealing 152-3
cooking:
  on fire 142-3
  tinned rations 150-3
cordons: passing 101
crocodiles 112-13

deadfalls 184
deer: preparing 181
dehydration 126, 154, 155, 158
dew: as water source 155
diarrhoea 147, 157, 158
diseases 144-7
  as contaminants 36-7
disguise: for evader 93
distance: judging in Arctic 131
distress signals 77
dogs 72, 106-9
  combating 109
  evading 106-9
  immobilising 109
'E and E' kit 72, 90, 94-7
enemy positions: searching 12
entrenching tool 54
escape 9, 72, 86-9
  equipment 94-7
  from fire 30
escape committee 88-9
evasion:
  of dogs 106-9
  equipment 94-7
  in jungle 102-5
  long-term 75, 90-3
  short-term 74, 90, 91

urban 98-101
  exercises: equipment for 60-3
Explosive Ordnance Device suit
    (EOD) 12

face: camouflaging 22
Falklands War 8, 9, 46, 49, 56,
    60, 64, 127
feet:
  armour for 15
  care of 48
field dressings 55
fire 10
  caused by water 28
  dangers of 140
  fighting 28-31
  importance 118
  keeping alight 141
  laying 141
  lighting 138-9
  making 118, 134, 136-43
  reflectors 141
  rescue:
    from blazing building 30-1
    from blazing vehicle 28-9
  site 141
  surviving 28-31
fire extinguishers 29
fire fighting 10
fire pit 142-3
fire retardant fabric 15, 17
fireman's lift 31
first-aid kit 55
flak jackets 8-9, 12-14
flash floods 117
flint: knapping 163, 164
flint tools 162-5
flotation devices 116
flying jackets 15
food 148, 150-3
  after nuclear attack 41
  carrying 54-5
  for evader 91-2
  foraging raid for 92-3
  hunting animals for 170-3
  in jungle 134
  trapping animals for 182-5
footprints 51
footwear 46, 48-51
foraging raid 92-3
frogs 110, 113
frostbite 118, 125-6, 126
fuels 137-8, 143

gangrene 125, 126
gas 34
gasmasks 34
Geneva Convention 72, 78, 80
Gore-Tex 48-50
grenades 12
  action against 13
  carrying 53
Gulf War 13, 17, 37

hammock 122-3
heat exhaustion 133
heat rash 146
helmets:
  ballistic 10, 13, 17, 18
  camouflaging 22
  importance of 12

'tin-hat' 8
houses: hiding in 98, 99
hunting, with spears 170-3
hygiene 127, 132
hypothermia 126, 131

ice:
  crossing 131
  use for water 156
illness 144-7
immersion foot 126
Indian well 157
Individual Protection
    Equipment (IPE) 34-5, 36-7
infra-red reflection 20, 25
insects 113, 144
Integrated Personal Protection
    System (IPPS) 9, 17-19
interrogation 72, 78-81
Iranian Embassy Siege 19
Israelis 15

jackets:
  armoured vest 17, 18
  combat 56-7
  flak 8-9, 12-14
Japanese 72, 77
jungle:
  dangers 72, 118
  evasion in 102-5
  kit 54, 134-5
  surviving in 132-5
  travel in 133-4
jungle rot 132

kidney pouches 62-3
knives: carrying 53
knives, survival 148
  blade 179-80
  choosing 174-7
  grip 178
  honing 179, 180
  professional edge 180
  Rockwell testing 180
  safety 180
  sharpening 180
  using 178-81

lakes: as water source 157
leeches 132
lice 127, 146
lizards 111-12
load carrying 52-71

maggot treatment 147
malaria 118, 147
man-lift 31
Maori oven 143
maps:
  carrying 54, 57
  for escape 96
marching: equipment 59, 68-71
medical kit 70-1
  field dressings 55
  first aid kit 55
microphone: in respirator 18
missiles, nuclear 40
Morse code 85
mosquitoes 118, 147
mud: as source of water 156
mugs 152

muskeg 117

navigation: in Arctic 130-1
NBC clothing 32, 34-5, 36-7, 53, 62
neck: protection for 14
newts 113
Nomex fabric 15, 17
Northern Ireland 8-9, 12
nuclear contamination 35-6
nuclear explosions 35-6
  decontamination 41, 43, 45
  effects 38-40, 44
  personal protective
    measures 39, 41
  surviving blast 44
  types 39, 40
Nuclear Immediate Action
  Drill 40
nuclear power stations 44
nuclear strikes 32
  surviving 38-45
nuclear weapons 9
  means of delivery 43
  range 40

ovens 137, 143

parachute tent 121-2
parasites 132, 146-7
paratroopers 46, 52
Personal Load Carrying
  Equipment (PLCE) 58, 61
poncho roll 62
poncho shelter 120-1
ponds: as water source 157
prisoners:
  escape 86-9
  interrogation 78-81
  killing 91
  life as 82-5
  searching and handling 76-7
  signalling to aircraft 89
private soldier: kit 56

quagmires 117
quicksands 116, 117

rabbit: skinning 185
radar 9
radiation 35-6, 42
  decontamination 41, 43, 45
  detecting 43
  marking areas 44-5
  measuring 43
  sickness symptoms 39
radio 67
  building 89
  effect of nuclear explosion
    on 38

rafts 115, 117
rain: use for water 155-6
rapids 116
rations 148
  carrying 68
  cooking 150-3
ratpack 148, 150-3
Red Army 46
Red Cross/Red Crescent 78
rescue:
  by air 76-7
  of POWs 89
resistance groups 76
respirator haversack 63
respirators 18, 34, 35, 42, 43
  carrying 53
rifles:
  camouflaging 23
  cleaning kit 71
  customising 66
rivers:
  crossing 91, 114-17
  as water source 157

rocket launcher 13
Royal Marines 60

salamanders 113
sap, drinkable 156, 157
SAS 98
  belt order 67, 95
saws: on knives 176
scopes 66
scorpions 112, 113, 134, 144-5
SCUD missiles 41
searching enemy position 12
seashell tools 168
section commander: kit 57
shape: camouflaging 20
sheaths: for knives 177
shelter 118
  carrying 68
  in jungle 134
  natural 123
  site 120
  for survival 96
  types 120-3
shield 19
shine: camouflaging 20-1
shooting: for food 184
sign language 84-5
signals: to aircraft 89
silhouette: camouflaging 21
skin infectionss 146
skinning animal 185
skis 128
sleeping bags:
  making 127
  packing 68
sleeping sickness 144
smell: camouflaging 22, 25
smoke 30,31
snakebite 110-11, 112
snakes 110-11, 112
snares 182, 183, 184, 185
snow:
  dangers of 128
  use for water 155-6
snow blindness 126, 127
snowshoes 128
  improvising 130
socks 48
sound: reducing 22, 25
Soviets 15
  nuclear weapons 15
spear throwers 173
spears:
  heads 171
  hunting with 170-3
  killing with 170
  making 170-1
  throwing 171-2
  thrusting 170, 171
Special Forces 9, 10
  personal protection 16-19
spiders 112, 113, 144, 144-5
spontaneous combustion 28
spring water 157
stings 144
stomach bugs 146-7
stone: working 162-5
Stone Age societies 164
stone tools 162-5
stoves 142
streams: as water source 157
sunburn 126-7
surrender 77

tannin: as antiseptic 156-7
tap codes 85
tapeworm 118, 145
tarantulas 113
terrorists 78
thermal imaging 20, 25, 26
ticks 132, 144
tools:
  antler 168
  bone 166-9

flint 162-5
  making 148
  seashell 168-9
  wood 166
torches 54
torture 66
toxins 34, 37
trapping animals 182-5
travel:
  in Arctic 128-31
  in jungle 133-4
trench foot 48, 126, 127
trenches: in nuclear attack 39
tropics 118

unit: rejoining 75
urban areas: camouflage in 23
urban areas: evasion 98-101
urine:
  in dehydration 126
  use on wounds 146

vagrant: evasion as 99
vehicle:
  burning: rescue from 28-9
  camouflaging 24-7
vest, armoured 17, 18
Vietnam War 12, 15, 36, 76, 88

washing 127
water:
  body's requirements 118
  boiling 160-1

carrying 54, 70
for drinking 148
filtering 160
finding 154-7
heating 152
improvising containers
  for 158-60
in jungle 103
polluted 158
purifying 158-61
water bottle pouch 62
waterproof clothing 55
weapons: making 148
webbing 9, 46, 52-3, 58-9, 68
  assembling 59
  contents 61-3
well, Indian 157
whiteout 130
wind chill effect 125
windbreaks 141
women: showing respect
  for 104
wood tools 166
wounded:
  carrying 30, 31
  rescuing 77
  treatment after nuclear
    attack 41
wounds:
  maggot treatment 147
  open 145-6

zips 12

188